PRIMARY MATHEMATICS

Challenging Word Problems

Yan Kow Cheong

Published by Marshall Cavendish Education
Times Centre, 1 New Industrial Road, Singapore 536196
Customer Service Hotline: (65) 6213 9688
US Office Tel: (+1-914) 332 8888 | Fax: (+1-914) 332 8882
E-mail: cs@mceducation.com
Website: www.mceducation.com

First published 2010
New edition 2014
Reprinted 2014, 2015, 2017, 2018, 2019, 2020

Primary Mathematics (Common Core Edition) Challenging Word Problems 4
ISBN 978-981-01-8974-7

Printed in Singapore

We would like to acknowledge contributions by:

Primary Mathematics (Common Core Edition) Challenging Word Problems
Jennifer Kempe (Curriculum Advisor from Singapore Math Inc.®)

Preface

PRIMARY MATHEMATICS Common Core Edition Challenging Word Problems provides graded exercises for students of mixed abilities and challenging questions for better math students. This series is written to supplement Singapore's **Primary Mathematics** textbooks (Common Core Edition) distributed by Singapore Math Inc.® for use in the USA.

Adopting a topical approach in which mathematical concepts and skills are taught and reinforced, the **Challenging Word Problems** series serves to improve students' problem-solving skills and enhance their mathematical reasoning.

Each book in the series features the following:

- **Worked Examples** for each topic show common methods of solution used in the Primary Mathematics textbooks;
- **Practice Questions** allow students to apply and practice questions similar to the ones discussed in the Worked Examples and in the Primary Mathematics textbooks;
- **Challenging Problems** provide opportunities for more capable students to solve higher-order word problems and further develop their problem-solving skills;
- **Review Questions** allow students to test their understanding of the concepts discussed in earlier topics and in the Primary Mathematics textbooks;
- **Answers** allow teachers or students to check their answers to all practice exercises and challenging problems;
- **Worked solutions** provide commonly used methods of solving non-routine questions, while encouraging creative or intuitive ones as well.

A student's guide to using the **Challenging Word Problems** series effectively.

1. Read each question given in the Worked Example. Try to solve it before reading the solution.

2. If your solution is similar to the one given in the Worked Example, well done. If you have used a different method, yet have arrived at the same answer, great—you now have at least two methods of solving this question.

3. If your answer is different, look at your work again and figure out where you may have gone wrong.

4. If you have understood all the worked examples, proceed to the Practice Questions; then check your answers with the ones at the back of the book. Should you get stuck at any question, don't panic; go through it again. If you still find difficulty in solving the question, seek help from your friend or teacher.

5. If you have understood and solved all the Practice Questions, you are now ready to try the Challenging Problems. Do them on your own first. Seek help only if you need some hints or clarification.

6. Try to come up with similar questions and challenge your friends to solve them. For a given question, discuss some possible solutions that you may have used in arriving at the answer.

Contents

1 Whole Numbers

Worked Example 1

The sum of all the digits of a 4-digit number is 16. The digit in the ones place is equal to the digit in the thousands place. The digit in the thousands place is twice the digit in the hundreds place. What are the possible numbers?

Let's tabulate the possible combinations.

Note: The digit in the hundreds place must be less than 5 as the digit in the thousands place cannot be more than 9.

The digit in the hundreds place cannot be less than 2 as the tens will then have a 2-digit number which is not possible.

Ones	4	6	8
Tens	6	1	0
Hundreds	2	3	4
Thousands	4	6	8
Possible Answer	✓	✓	✗

□ □ □ □

thousands digit (first box) · units digit (last box)

There are 2 possible numbers.
The numbers are **4,264** and **6,316**.

Note: The ones digit is also known as the units digit.

Worked Example 2

Find the
(a) factors of 120,
(b) factors of 210, and
(c) highest common factor of 120 and 210.

(a) 120 = 1 × 120
= 2 × 60
= 3 × 40
= 4 × 30
= 5 × 24
= 6 × 20
= 8 × 15
= 10 × 12

Make a systematic list to avoid missing out any factor.

The factors of 120 are **1**, **2**, **3**, **4**, **5**, **6**, **8**, **10**, **12**, **15**, **20**, **24**, **30**, **40**, **60**, and **120**.

(b) 210 = 1 × 210
= 2 × 105
= 3 × 70
= 5 × 42
= 6 × 35
= 7 × 30
= 10 × 21
= 14 × 15

The factors of 210 are **1**, **2**, **3**, **5**, **6**, **7**, **10**, **14**, **15**, **21**, **30**, **35**, **42**, **70**, **105**, and **210**.

(c) The common factors of 120 and 210 are 1, 2, 3, 5, 6, 10, 15, and 30.

Among the 8 common factors, the highest common factor of 120 and 210 is **30**.

Note: Every whole number greater than 1 has at least two factors: The number 1 and the number itself.

Worked Example 3

There are fewer than 100 chairs in a seminar room. All the chairs may be arranged in equal rows of 8 or 11. How many chairs are there in the seminar room?

Multiples of 8: 8, 16, 24, 32, 40, 48, 56, 64, 72, 80, (88), 96
Multiples of 11: 11, 22, 33, 44, 55, 66, 77, (88), 99

The common multiple is 88.

There are **88** chairs in the seminar room.

Think!
What is the next largest number of chairs in the room, which can still be arranged in equal rows of 8 or 11?

Practice Questions

Answer all questions. Show your work and write your statements clearly.

1. Using each of the digits 5, 7, 8, and 0 only once, find
   (a) the smallest 4-digit number that can be formed,
   (b) the greatest 4-digit number that can be formed.

   Hint: No numbers can begin with a zero.

   Extension:
   (i) What is the smallest 4-digit odd number that can be formed?
   (ii) What is the greatest 4-digit odd number that can be formed?

2. Using each of the digits only once, find
   (a) the smallest 5-digit number that can be formed,
   (b) the greatest 5-digit number that can be formed.

   4 7 9 0 2

   Extension: What are the smallest and greatest 5-digit even and odd numbers?

3. Using each of the digits 3, 4, 7, and 0 only once, find
   (a) the greatest 4-digit odd number that can be formed,
   (b) the smallest 4-digit even number that can be formed.

4. Round the following numbers to the nearest 100.
   (a) 23,476 (b) 75,747 (c) 49,050 (d) 50,453

5. Round the following numbers to the nearest 1,000.
   (a) 18,987 (b) 120,456 (c) 486,502 (d) 199,990

6. What is the common factor of 39 and 54 that is greater than 1?

7. What is the difference between the sum of the first 2 multiples of 9 and the 3rd multiple of 6?

8. What is the sum of the first 3 multiples of 4 and the first 4 multiples of 3?

9. What is the smallest whole number that is divisible by 4, 8, and 11?

10. P is a number. After multiplying it by 7 and adding 4 to the answer, the result is the 13th multiple of 3. What is P?

11. This year, Isaac's age is between 30 and 60 years and is a multiple of 6. Next year, his age will be a multiple of 7. How old is he now?

12. I am thinking of a number from 40 to 60. When it is divided by 5, it leaves a remainder of 3. When it is divided by 4, it leaves a remainder of 1. What number am I thinking of?

Worked Example 1

Thirty blue buttons and forty-five yellow buttons need to be placed in bags so that each bag has the same number of buttons. What is the greatest possible number of bags needed?

Buttons	Possible numbers of bags needed
30 blue	1, 2, 3, 5, 6, 10, (15)
45 yellow	1, 3, 5, 9, (15)

The greatest possible number of bags needed is **15**.

Worked Example 2

Mrs. Oliver has a number of tarts. If she gives 3 or 4 tarts to each child, there will be 1 tart left over each time. If she gives 5 tarts to each child, she will have no tarts left over. What is the smallest number of tarts that Mrs. Oliver could have?

The number of tarts must be a multiple of 5 that leaves a remainder of 1 when divided by 3 or 4.

Multiple of 5	5	10	15	20	25
Remainder when divided by 3	2	1	0	2	1
Remainder when divided by 4	1	2	3	0	1

The smallest number of tarts that Mrs. Oliver could have is **25**.

Answer all questions. Show your work and write your statements clearly.

1. Mrs. Holmes's monthly expense is $38,100 when rounded to the nearest $100. Find her
   (a) greatest possible monthly expense,
   (b) smallest possible monthly expense.

2. Twelve sandwiches need to be arranged on plates so that each plate has the same number of sandwiches. What are the possible numbers of plates needed?

3. Thirty red pens, forty-five blue pens and seventy-five black pens need to be placed in boxes so that each box has each color pen and each box has the same assortment of pens.
   (a) What are the possible numbers of boxes needed?

Pens	Possible numbers of boxes needed
Red	
Blue	
Black	

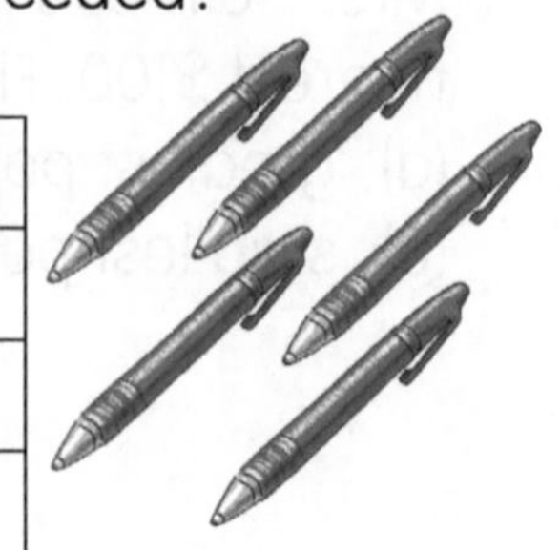

   (b) What is the greatest possible number of boxes needed?

   Hint: See Worked Example 1.

4. Every group of 10 students shared a big plate of fried noodles and every group of 8 students shared a big plate of salad. If a total of 9 plates of fried noodles and salad were used, how many students were there?

   Hint: The total number of students does not leave any remainders when divided by 10 and 8.

5. Study the diagram below by observing the numbers in each group. Describe your observations about each group.

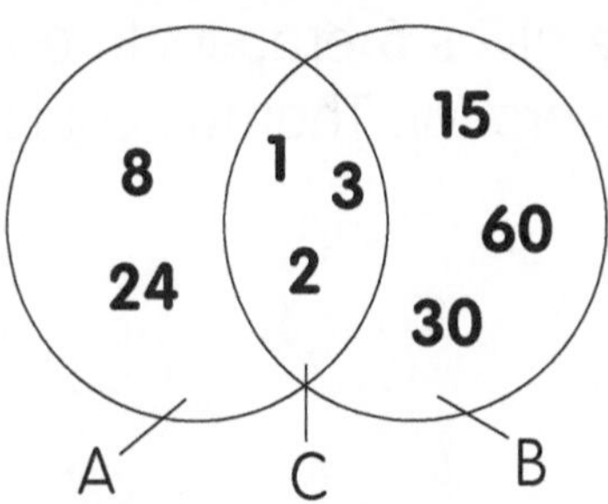

(a) Which group contains some factors of 96?
(b) Which group contains some factors of 60?
(c) Which group would the number 6 go into?

6. A rectangular piece of wood of length 175 cm, width 150 cm, and height 75 cm, is cut exactly into a number of identical cubes. How many cubes of the greatest possible size can be cut from the piece of wood?

Hint: The length of the sides of the cube must divide the length, the width, and the height exactly—it must be a factor of all three dimensions.

7. Mr. Thomas has some erasers. When he gives 4 erasers or 5 erasers to each student, he has 2 erasers left. There are no erasers left when he gives 6 erasers to each student. What is the least number of erasers Mr. Thomas could have?

8. Some of Mr. Edward's students want to buy him a gift. If each of them pays $2, they will be short of $4 for the gift. If each of them pays $3, there will be an extra $3. How much does the gift cost?

9. Students were selected from a school's fourth grade classes to take part in a science contest and a spelling contest. From one class, 9 students were selected for the science contest and 3 for the spelling contest. For each of the remaining classes, 4 students were selected for the science contest and 6 for the spelling contest. The number of students who were selected to take part in both contests is the same. What is the smallest possible number of fourth grade classes?

10. A group of foreign students visited the Smithsonian Museum. Some students took taxis and 3 students took a subway from their hotel. Each taxi carried 4 students. On the way back, 8 students took the subway while the rest took taxis. Each taxi carried 3 students. The number of taxis and the number of students were the same for both trips. How many students and how many taxis were there for each trip?

11. A whole number greater than 11 gives the same non-zero remainder when divided by 3, 5, 7, or 11. What is the smallest value of this whole number?

Hint: The numbers 3, 5, 7, and 11 each have only two factors.

12. List all the 4-digit numbers which can be formed from the digits below. Each digit can only be used once. How many such numbers are there?

6	2	9	0

Hint: Make a systematic list.

2 The Four Operations of Whole Numbers

Worked Example 1

Joe has $960. If Rick had another $240, he would have twice as much money as Joe. How much less money does Joe have than Rick?

Method 1

$960

Joe

?

Rick

$240

1 unit ⟶ $960
2 units ⟶ 2 × $960 = $1,920
$1,920 – $240 = $1,680
Rick has $1,680.
$1,680 – $960 = $720
Joe has **$720** less than Rick.

Method 2

$960

Joe

?

Rick

$240

From the model,
$960 – $240 = $720
Joe has **$720** less than Rick.

Worked Example 2

I am thinking of two numbers. Their sum is 1,544 and their difference is 152. What are the two numbers?

Method 1

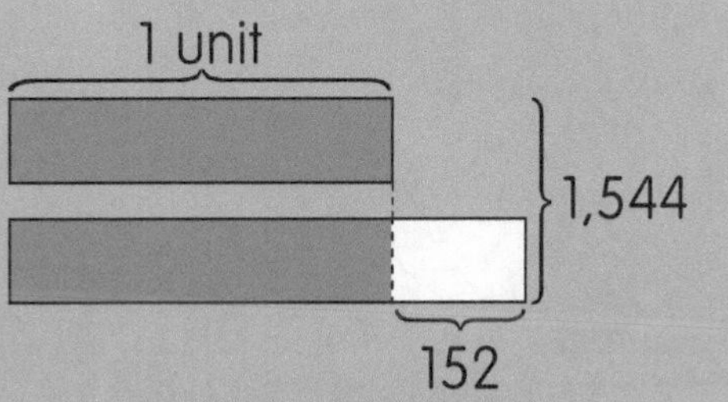

2 units ⟶ 1,544 – 152 = 1,392
1 unit ⟶ 1,392 ÷ 2 = 696

The smaller number is **696**.

696 + 152 = 848 or 1,544 – 696 = 848
The greater number is **848**.

Method 2

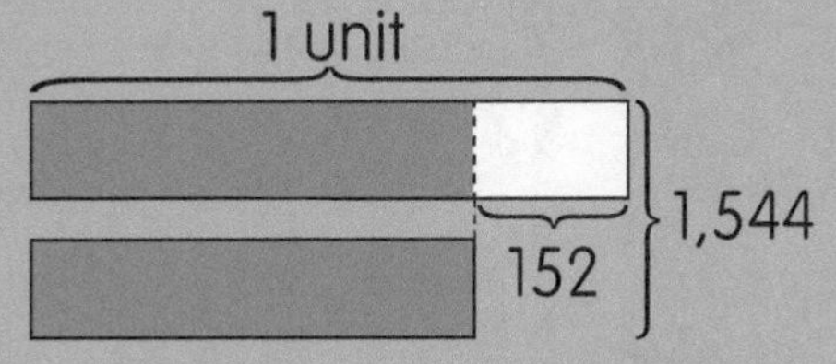

2 units ⟶ 1,544 + 152 = 1,696
1 unit ⟶ 1,696 ÷ 2 = 848

The greater number is **848**.

848 – 152 = 696 or 1,544 – 848 = 696

The smaller number is **696**.

Worked Example 3

Bob, Jean, and Paul have a total of 5,590 stickers. Paul has twice as many stickers as Bob. Bob has 3 times as many stickers as Jean. How many stickers does each one have?

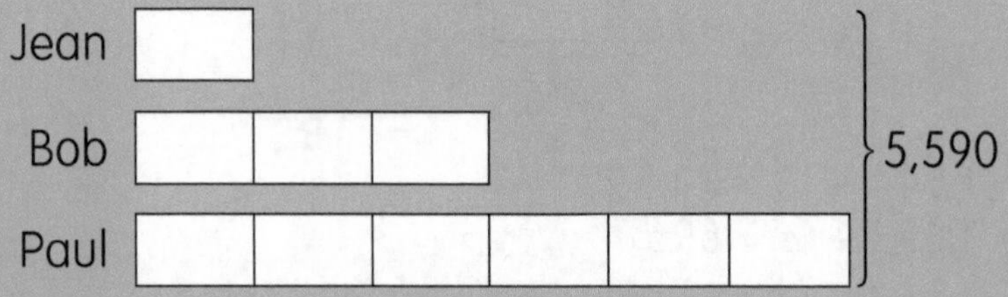

10 units ⟶ 5,590
1 unit ⟶ $5,590 \div 10 = 559$
3 units ⟶ $3 \times 559 = 1,677$
6 units ⟶ $6 \times 559 = 3,354$
or $2 \times 1,677 = 3,354$

Drawing a model helps us to see things better.

Jean has **559** stickers.
Bob has **1,677** stickers.
Paul has **3,354** stickers.

Check:
$559 + 1,677 + 3,354 = 5,590$

Practice Questions

Answer all questions. Show your work and write your statements clearly.

1. It is reported that there are 873 thousands native speakers of Mandarin Chinese and 178 thousands who speak it as a second language. How many speakers of Mandarin Chinese are there?

2. Peter has 438 cards. If Pam had another 379 more cards, she would have twice as many cards as Peter. How many cards does Pam have?

   Hint: See Worked Example 1.

3. The sum of two numbers is 1,200. Their difference is 214. What are the two numbers?

   Hint: See Worked Example 2. Solve this in more than one way.

4. Four apples and seven lemons cost $47. Each apple costs $2 less than a lemon. What is the cost of three lemons?

5. Vince and Zac collected a total of 952 stickers. Vince collected 3 times as many stickers as Zac. Jason collected half as many stickers as Zac. How many stickers did each person collect?

   Hint: Use a model drawing. See Worked Example 3.

6. Tripods have 3 legs; bipods have 2 legs. Some tripods and bipods have 15 legs altogether. What are the possible numbers of tripods and bipods?

   Hint: Use guess and check.

7. Wendy and Carol each bought the same laptop at the same price. In addition, Wendy bought a flash drive and Carol bought an infrared mouse. The flash drive cost $60. Find the cost of the infrared mouse if Carol spent $1,810 and Wendy spent $1,840.

8. A street vendor sells burgers for $3 each in the morning. The price drops to $2.50 each in the afternoon. On Sunday, the vendor made $120 in the morning. In the afternoon he sold twice as many burgers. How much money did he make on Sunday?

   Hint: How many burgers were sold in the morning?

9. String P is 3 times as long as string Q. String R is 3 m longer than half the total length of strings P and Q. If the total length of all three strings is 5,400 cm, what is the length of string R?

10. A farmer had twice as many cows as sheep. After he had sold 375 cows and another 12 cows died, he had half as many cows as sheep left. How many cows remained?

Challenging Problems

Worked Example 1

Phil had 3 times as much money as Anne. After Phil gave $285 to Anne, he had twice as much money as she did. How much money did Phil have at first?

Method 1

Before

Phil

Anne

1 unit

After

$285 $285

Phil

Anne

$285

1 unit ⟶ 3 × $285 = $855
3 units ⟶ 3 × $855 = $2,565
Phil had **$2,565** at first.

Method 2

Before After

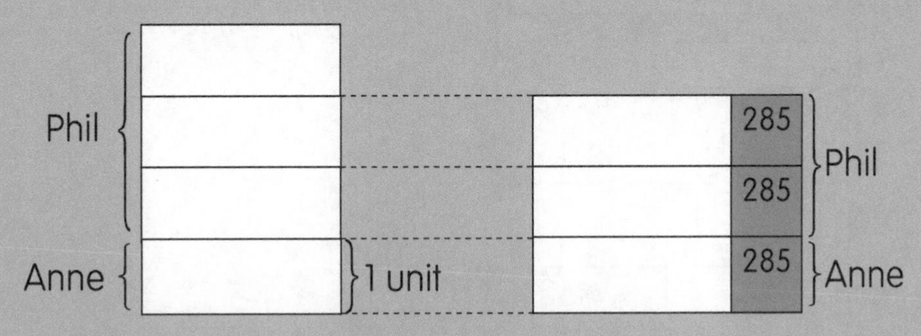

From the model,
1 unit ⟶ 3 × 285 = 855
3 units ⟶ 3 × 855 = 2,565
Phil had **$2,565** at first.

Worked Example 2

There were twice as many women as men in a hall. After 350 women left and 450 men entered, there were 3 times as many men as women. If 1,000 adults remained, how many adults were there in the hall at first?

Method 1

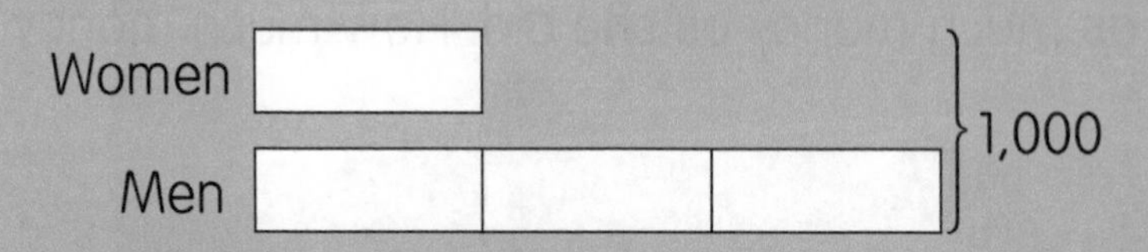

4 units ⟶ 1,000
1 unit ⟶ $1{,}000 \div 4 = 250$
3 units ⟶ $3 \times 250 = 750$

$750 - 450 = 300$
There were 300 men at first.
$250 + 350 = 600$
There were 600 women at first.
$300 + 600 = 900$

There were **900** adults in the hall at first.

Method 2

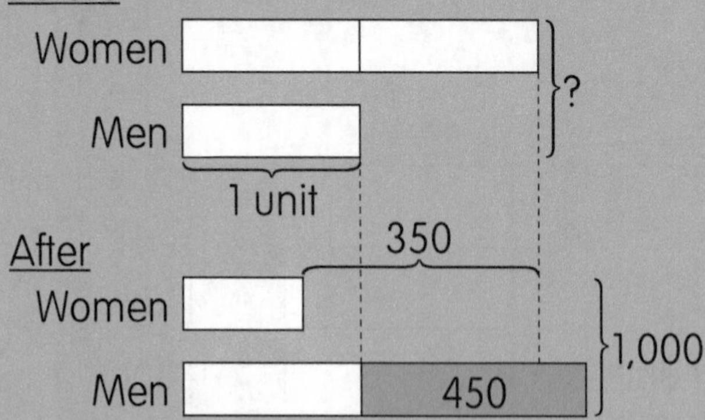

From the model,
3 units ⟶ $1{,}000 + 350 - 450 = 900$
There were **900** adults in the hall at first.

Extension: Think of two other methods of solving this question.

Answer all questions. Show your work and write your statements clearly.

1. There were 3 times as many boys as girls in a sports hall. After 75 boys left and 25 girls entered, there were 2 times as many girls as boys. If 90 children remained, how many children were in the sports hall at first?

   Hint: See Worked Example 2.

2. The sum of three whole numbers is the same as their product. What are the numbers?

   Hint: Use guess and check.

3. The product of two whole numbers is 10,000. Neither contains a zero. What are the two numbers?

   Hint: Think of multiples of 10.

4. Belinda is 7 years older than her brother. Three years ago, their total age was 43 years. What will be Belinda's age in 12 years' time?

5. Peter and Lillian spent a total of $78. Lillian and Adam spent a total of $124. Adam spent 3 times as much as Peter.
   (a) How much more did Adam spend than Peter?
   (b) How much did Lillian spend?

6. A tall glass can hold 750 cm^3 of water. A bottle can hold twice as much water as the glass. A jug can hold four times as much water as the bottle. What is the total capacity of 3 such bottles and 4 such jugs?

7. Tom had $190 and Jane had $60. After each of them received an equal amount of money from their father, Tom had twice as much money as Jane. How much did their father give each of them?

8. An adult ticket cost $10 and a child ticket cost $7. Mr. Sullivan bought 13 tickets for $106. How many child tickets did he buy?

9. There were twice as many cows as goats on a farm. All the cows and goats have a total of 108 legs. How many cows were there?

10. There are 3 times as many chickens as goats on a farm. All the chickens and goats have a total of 2,400 legs. How many more chickens than goats are there?

3 Mental Calculation

Worked Example 1

Perform the following mentally.
(a) $348 + 55 - 48$
(b) $2,072 - 998 - 997$
(c) $563 + 456 - 99 - 256$

(a) $348 + 55 - 48$
$= 348 - 48 + 55$
$= 300 + 55$
$=$ **355**

(b) $2,072 - 998 - 997$
$= 2,072 - 1,000 + 2 - 1,000 + 3$
$= 2,072 - 2,000 + 5$
$= 72 + 5$
$=$ **77**

(c) $563 + 456 - 99 - 256$
$= 463 + 100 - 99 + 456 - 256$
$= 463 + 1 + 200$
$=$ **664**

or

$563 + 456 - 99 - 256$
$= 563 - 100 + 1 + 456 - 256$
$= 463 + 1 + 200$
$=$ **664**

Worked Example 2

Perform the following mentally.
(a) 8×99
(b) 47×299
(c) $25 \times 32 \times 125$

(a) $8 \times 99 = 100$ groups of $8 - 1$ group of 8
$= 100 \times 8 - 1 \times 8$
$= 800 - 8$
$= \mathbf{792}$

or

$8 \times 99 = 8$ groups of $90 + 8$ groups of 9
$= 8 \times 90 + 8 \times 9$
$= 720 + 72$
$= \mathbf{792}$

(b) $47 \times 299 = 47 \times 300 - 47 \times 1$
$= 47 \times 3 \times 100 - 47$
$= 141 \times 100 - 47$
$= 14{,}100 - 47$
$= \mathbf{14{,}053}$

$47 \times 3 = 40 \times 3 + 7 \times 3$
$= 120 + 21$
$= 141$

(c) $25 \times 32 \times 125 = 25 \times 4 \times 8 \times 125$
$= 25 \times 4 \times 4 \times 2 \times 25 \times 5$
$= 25 \times 4 \times 25 \times 4 \times 2 \times 5$
$= 100 \times 100 \times 10$
$= \mathbf{100{,}000}$

Practice Questions

Answer all questions. Show your work and write your statements clearly.

1. 556 + 67 – 56

Try evaluating each expression in as many ways as possible.

2. 255 + 364 + 145 + 636

Be a "mental calculator."

3. 752 + 62 + 38 – 252

4. 604 + 1,796

5. 60×99

6. 36×199

7. $25 \times 16 \times 125$

8. $125 \times 5 \times 32$

9. $24 \times 25 \times 125$

10. $4 \times 125 \times 25 \times 8$

Challenging Problems

Worked Example 1

Perform each of the following mentally.

(a) $45 \times 36 + 55 \times 36$

(b) $58 \times 12 + 21 \times 24$

(a) $45 \times 36 + 55 \times 36$
$= 100 \times 36$
$= \mathbf{3,600}$

45 groups of 36
+ 55 groups of 36
= 100 groups of 36

(b) $58 \times 12 + 21 \times 24$
$= 58 \times 12 + 21 \times 2 \times 12$
$= 58 \times 12 + 42 \times 12$
$= (58 + 42) \times 12$
$= 100 \times 12$
$= \mathbf{1,200}$

or

$58 \times 12 + 21 \times 24$
$= 29 \times 2 \times 12 + 21 \times 24$
$= 29 \times 24 + 21 \times 24$
$= (29 + 21) \times 24$
$= 50 \times 24$
$= 50 \times 2 \times 12$
$= 100 \times 12$
$= \mathbf{1,200}$

I prefer groups of 24 to 12.

Worked Example 2

Perform the following mentally.

(a) $49 + 499 + 4{,}999$

(b) $100 - 99 + 98 - 97 + \cdots + 4 - 3 + 2 - 1$

(a) $49 + 499 + 4{,}999$

$= 50 - 1 + 500 - 1 + 5{,}000 - 1$

$= 5{,}550 - 3$

$= \mathbf{5{,}547}$

(b) $\underbrace{100 - 99}_{1} + \underbrace{98 - 97}_{1} + \cdots + \underbrace{4 - 3}_{1} + \underbrace{2 - 1}_{1}$

$100 - 99 + 98 - 97 + \cdots + 4 - 3 + 2 - 1$

$= \dfrac{100}{2} \times 1$

$= 50 \times 1$

$= \mathbf{50}$

There are $\dfrac{100}{2} = 50$ pairs, each with a value of 1.

Extension: What is the value of $1 + 2 + 3 + \cdots + 98 + 99 + 100$?

Answer all questions. Show your work and write your statements clearly.

1. $98 + 999 \times 98$

2. $56 \times 77 + 56 \times 23$

3. $74 \times 13 + 13 \times 26$

4. $23 \times 1{,}562 - 23 \times 562$

5. $65 \times 3{,}142 - 2{,}142 \times 65$

6. $3{,}568 \times 14 - 2{,}568 \times 14$

7. $62 \times 36 + 76 \times 18$

8. $(2 + 4 + 6 + \cdots + 2{,}012) - (1 + 3 + 5 + \cdots + 2{,}011)$

9. $1 - 2 + 3 - 4 + 5 - 6 + \ldots + 2{,}009 - 2{,}010 + 2{,}011$

10. Mona learned a method to multiply two numbers. She demonstrated the method to her cousin, using the following two examples.

Example 1: 13×12

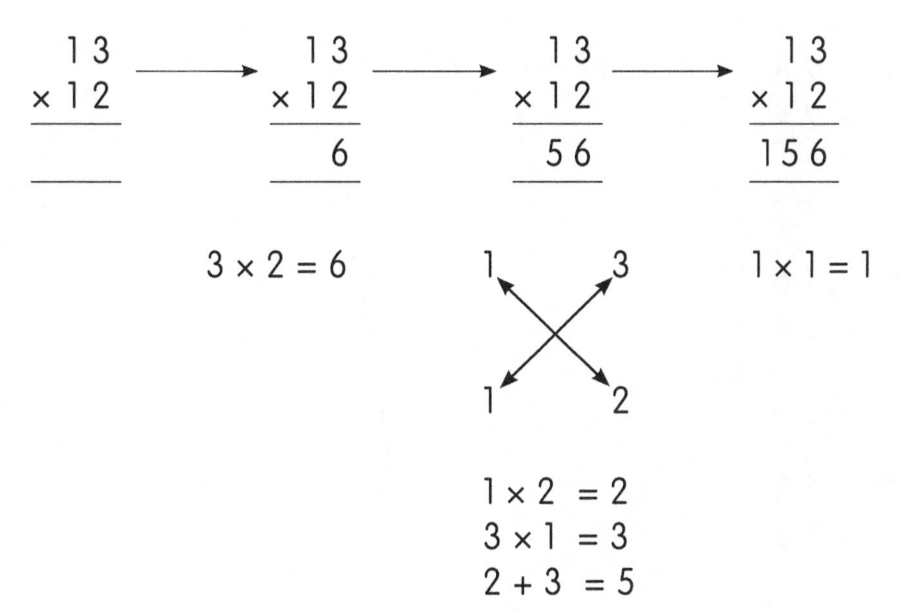

Example 2: 24 × 53

$$\begin{array}{r} 24 \\ \times 53 \\ \hline \\ \hline \end{array} \longrightarrow \begin{array}{r} 24 \\ \times 53 \\ \hline 2 \\ \hline \end{array} \longrightarrow \begin{array}{r} 24 \\ \times 53 \\ \hline 72 \\ \hline \end{array} \longrightarrow \begin{array}{r} 24 \\ \times 53 \\ \hline 1272 \\ \hline \end{array}$$

4 × 3 = (1)2

2 × 3 = 6
4 × 5 = 20
→ 1 + 6 + 20 = (2)7

2 × 5 = 10
→ 2 + 10 = 12

Apply the method to each of the multiplications below.

(a)
$$\begin{array}{r} 14 \\ \times 11 \\ \hline \\ \hline \end{array}$$

(b)
$$\begin{array}{r} 28 \\ \times 24 \\ \hline \\ \hline \end{array}$$

(c)
$$\begin{array}{r} 16 \\ \times 34 \\ \hline \\ \hline \end{array}$$

(d)
$$\begin{array}{r} 53 \\ \times 35 \\ \hline \\ \hline \end{array}$$

4 Operations on Fractions

Worked Example 1

Mrs. Jees ordered a cake for the family. She ate $\frac{1}{8}$ of it and her two sons ate $\frac{1}{4}$ of it. What fraction of the cake was left?

Method 1

$\frac{1}{4} + \frac{1}{8} = \frac{2}{8} + \frac{1}{8} = \frac{3}{8}$

Mrs. Jees and her two sons ate $\frac{3}{8}$ of the cake.

$1 - \frac{3}{8} = \frac{8}{8} - \frac{3}{8} = \frac{5}{8}$

$\mathbf{\frac{5}{8}}$ of the cake was left.

Method 2

$$1 - \frac{1}{8} - \frac{1}{4} = \frac{8}{8} - \frac{1}{8} - \frac{2}{8}$$
$$= \frac{7}{8} - \frac{2}{8}$$
$$= \frac{5}{8}$$

$\mathbf{\frac{5}{8}}$ of the cake was left.

Method 3

$\frac{1}{4} = \frac{1 \times 2}{4 \times 2} = \frac{2}{8}$

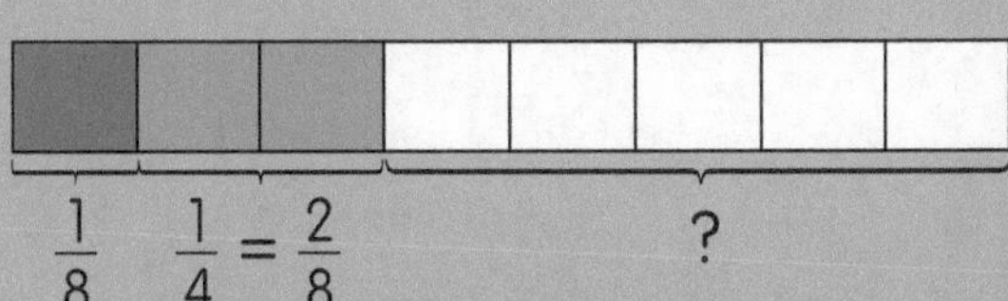

From the model, $\mathbf{\frac{5}{8}}$ of the cake was left.

Worked Example 2

Melvin gave $\frac{7}{12}$ of his stamps to his cousin. He gave $\frac{1}{3}$ fewer stamps to his neighbor. What fraction of his stamps did Melvin give away?

Method 1

$$\frac{7}{12} - \frac{1}{3} = \frac{7}{12} - \frac{4}{12} = \frac{3}{12}$$

Melvin gave $\frac{3}{12}$ of his stamps to his neighbor.

$$\frac{7}{12} + \frac{3}{12} = \frac{10}{12} = \frac{5}{6}$$

Melvin gave away $\mathbf{\frac{5}{6}}$ of his stamps.

Method 2

Melvin: bar of length $\frac{7}{12}$

Neighbor: bar $\frac{1}{3}$ shorter

Total: ?

$$\frac{7}{12} + \frac{7}{12} - \frac{1}{3} = \frac{7}{12} + \frac{7}{12} - \frac{4}{12}$$

$$= \frac{7+7-4}{12}$$

$$= \frac{10}{12}$$

$$= \frac{2 \times 5}{2 \times 6}$$

$$= \frac{5}{6}$$

Melvin gave away $\mathbf{\frac{5}{6}}$ of his stamps.

Worked Example 3

James ate $\frac{2}{5}$ of a cake and Lisa ate $\frac{1}{10}$ more cake than he did. What fraction of the cake remained?

Method 1

$\frac{2}{5} + \frac{1}{10} = \frac{4}{10} + \frac{1}{10} = \frac{5}{10}$

Lisa ate $\frac{5}{10}$ of the cake.

$\frac{2}{5} + \frac{5}{10} = \frac{4}{10} + \frac{5}{10} = \frac{9}{10}$

James and Lisa ate $\frac{9}{10}$ of the cake.

$1 - \frac{9}{10} = \frac{1}{10}$

$\mathbf{\frac{1}{10}}$ of the cake remained.

Method 2

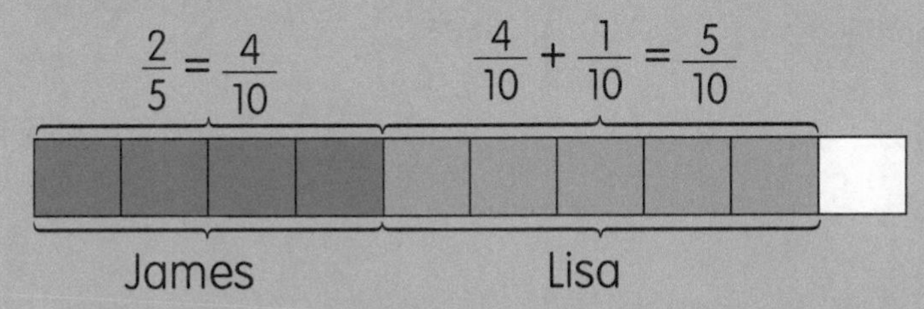

From the model, $\mathbf{\frac{1}{10}}$ of the cake remained.

Worked Example 4

There are 45 students in a class. $\frac{5}{9}$ of them do not wear glasses. How many students wear glasses?

Method 1

$1 - \frac{5}{9} = \frac{4}{9}$

$\frac{4}{9}$ of the students wear glasses.

$\frac{4}{\cancel{9}} \times \cancel{45}^{5} = 4 \times 5$

$= 20$

20 students wear glasses.

Method 2

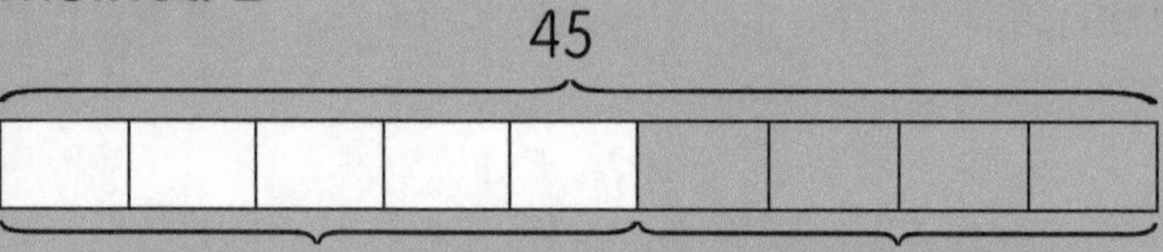

From the model,

9 parts $\longrightarrow$ 45

1 part $\longrightarrow$ $45 \div 9 = 5$

4 parts $\longrightarrow$ $4 \times 5 = 20$

20 students wear glasses.

Worked Example 5

(a) If $\frac{3}{5}$ of a number is 12, what is the number?

(b) If $\frac{4}{3}$ of a number is 20, what is the number?

(a)

12

Number

3 units ⟶ 12
1 unit ⟶ $12 \div 3 = 4$
5 units ⟶ $5 \times 4 = 20$

The number is **20**.

Check
$\frac{3}{\cancel{5}} \times \overset{4}{\cancel{20}} = 3 \times 4 = 12$

(b)

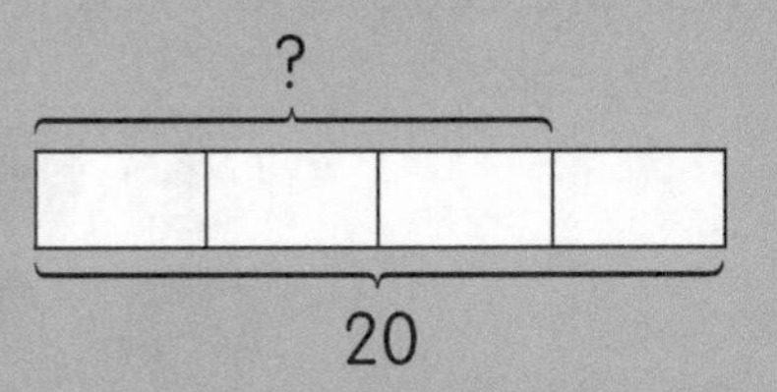

4 units ⟶ 20
1 unit ⟶ $20 \div 4 = 5$
3 units ⟶ $3 \times 5 = 15$

The number is **15**.

Check
$\frac{4}{\cancel{3}} \times \overset{5}{\cancel{15}} = 4 \times 5 = 20$

Practice Questions

Answer all questions. Show your work and write your statements clearly.

1. Henry ate $\frac{1}{4}$ of a cake. His cousin ate $\frac{3}{8}$ of the same cake. What fraction of the cake did they eat altogether?

2. One third of Michael's marbles are blue and $\frac{4}{9}$ of them are green. What fraction of his marbles are blue and green?

3. Simon ate $\frac{2}{9}$ of a melon and Agnes ate $\frac{1}{3}$ of it. What fraction of the melon was left?

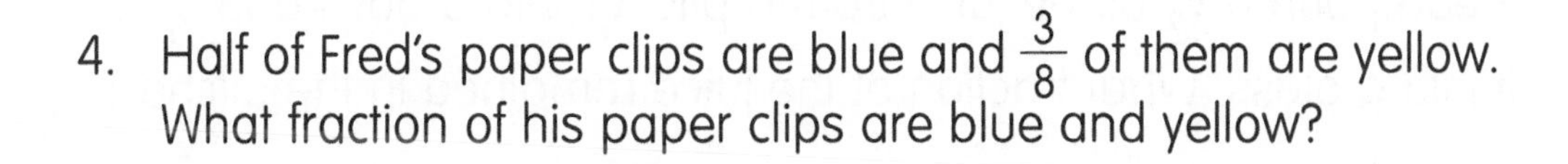

4. Half of Fred's paper clips are blue and $\frac{3}{8}$ of them are yellow. What fraction of his paper clips are blue and yellow?

5. Pamela had a ribbon that was $\frac{7}{12}$ yd long. She cut away $\frac{1}{3}$ yd. What was the length of the ribbon left? Express your answer in the simplest form.

6. Doug ate $\frac{3}{10}$ of a loaf of bread for breakfast and $\frac{3}{5}$ of it for lunch. What fraction of the loaf of bread was left?

7. Freda poured $\frac{7}{12}$ of the juice from a pitcher into a bowl and $\frac{1}{3}$ of it into a glass. What fraction of the juice remained in the pitcher?

8. Mr. Nicholson bought some fruits. $\frac{1}{2}$ of them were apples, $\frac{1}{4}$ were pears, and $\frac{1}{8}$ were oranges. The rest were strawberries. What fraction of the fruits were strawberries?

9. In each of the set of fractions, one fraction is not equivalent to the other three. Circle this fraction and then replace it with one that is equivalent to the others in the set by changing its numerator.

(a) $\frac{6}{12}$ $\frac{1}{2}$ $\frac{2}{4}$ $\frac{3}{8}$

(b) $\frac{4}{6}$ $\frac{2}{3}$ $\frac{7}{9}$ $\frac{8}{12}$

10. Carrie spent $5\frac{1}{4}$ hours doing her homework. Aaron spent $4\frac{5}{8}$ hours doing his homework. What was the difference in time taken by Carrie and Aaron? Give your answer in hours.

11. In a class of 40 students, 25 are boys. What fraction of the class are girls? Simplify your answer.

12. A rope is 3 ft long. $\frac{3}{5}$ of it was cut off. What is the length of the remaining piece? Give your answers in feet.

13. What is $1\frac{3}{4}$ of a minute? Give your answer in seconds. (1 minute = 60 seconds)

14. If $\frac{3}{7}$ of a number is 42, what is the number?

15. A furniture shop owner ordered 200 chairs. He sold $\frac{3}{5}$ of them at $42 each. How much money did he collect?

16. In a school hall, there are 26 rows of seats. There are 12 seats in each row. If $\frac{7}{8}$ of the seats are occupied, how many seats are not occupied?

17. Bag P has 36 ribbons. $\frac{2}{3}$ of them are red. Bag Q has 60 ribbons. $\frac{5}{12}$ of them are red. Which bag has more red ribbons?

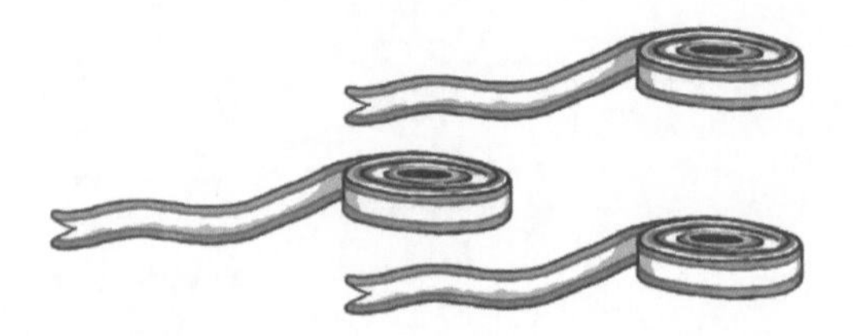

18. Andrew had some stamps. He gave $\frac{1}{4}$ of them to his brother. He gave his sister $\frac{1}{12}$ of the total stamps more than what he gave his brother. If Andrew had given away 42 stamps in total, how many stamps did he have left?

19. Joe took $\frac{1}{4}$ day to paint a fence. Steve took $\frac{2}{3}$ of the time taken by Joe to paint a similar fence. What was the difference in the time taken (in hours) by Steve and Joe? (1 day = 24 hours)

Worked Example 1

A bakery sold $\frac{2}{3}$ of its muffins in the morning and $\frac{1}{6}$ of the muffins in the afternoon. A total of 250 muffins were sold. How many muffins remained unsold?

$\frac{2}{3} + \frac{1}{6} = \frac{4}{6} + \frac{1}{6} = \frac{5}{6}$

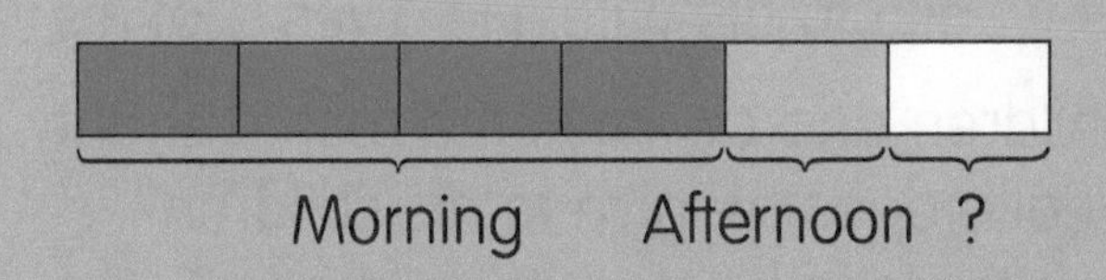

5 units ⟶ 250
1 unit ⟶ 250 ÷ 5 = 50

50 muffins remained unsold.

Worked Example 2

At a party, $\frac{5}{12}$ of the guests were women, $\frac{1}{4}$ were children, and the rest were men. There were 312 men. How many women were at the party?

$$1 - \frac{5}{12} - \frac{1}{4} = \frac{12}{12} - \frac{5}{12} - \frac{3}{12}$$
$$= \frac{4}{12}$$

$\frac{4}{12}$ of the guests were men.

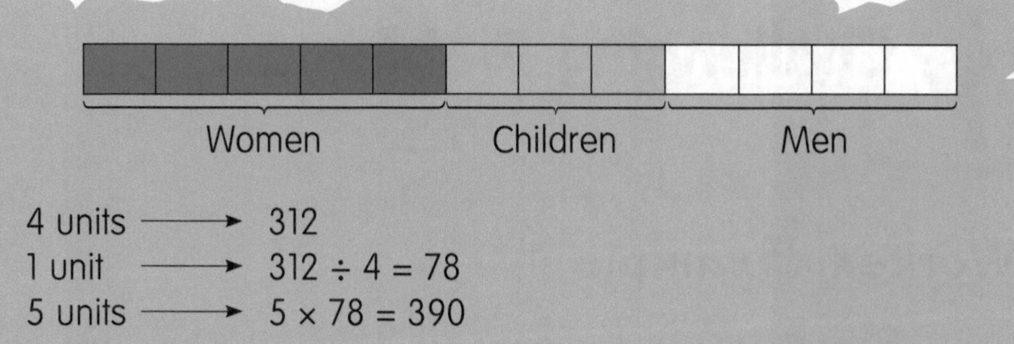

4 units ⟶ 312
1 unit ⟶ $312 \div 4 = 78$
5 units ⟶ $5 \times 78 = 390$

There were **390** women at the party.

Worked Example 3

A rich man gives $\frac{3}{10}$ of his wealth to his wife. He gives $\frac{3}{7}$ of his remaining wealth to his children and donates the rest to charity.
(a) What fraction of his wealth does he give to his children?
(b) What fraction of his wealth does he donate to charity?

(a)

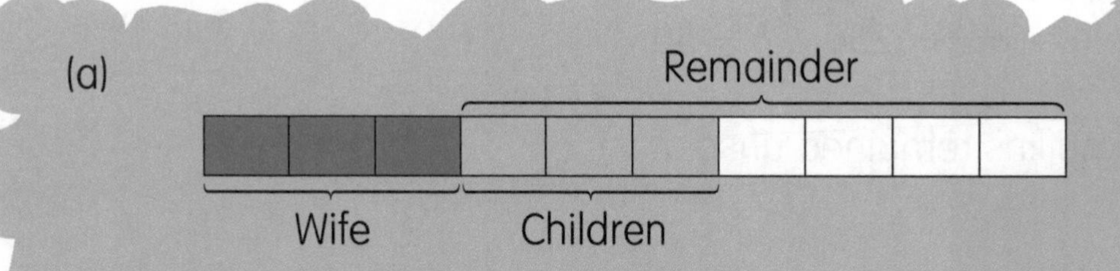

From the model, he gives $\mathbf{\frac{3}{10}}$ of his wealth to his children.

(b)

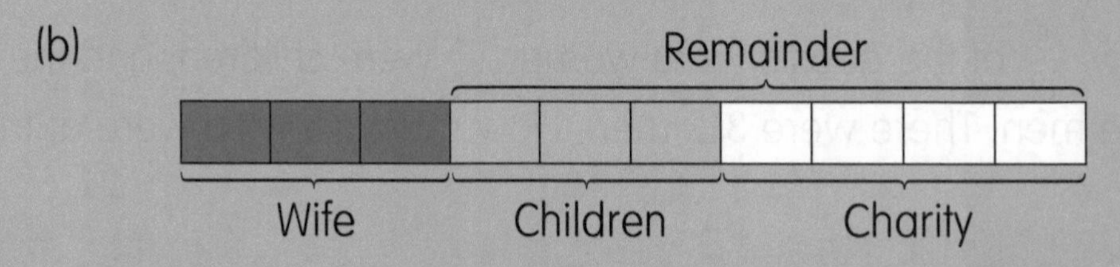

From the model, $\frac{4}{10} = \frac{2}{5}$.

He donates $\mathbf{\frac{2}{5}}$ of his wealth to charity.

Worked Example 4

The figure below shows 18 squares. 5 squares are shaded. If $\frac{2}{3}$ of the squares are to be left unshaded, how many more squares need to be shaded?

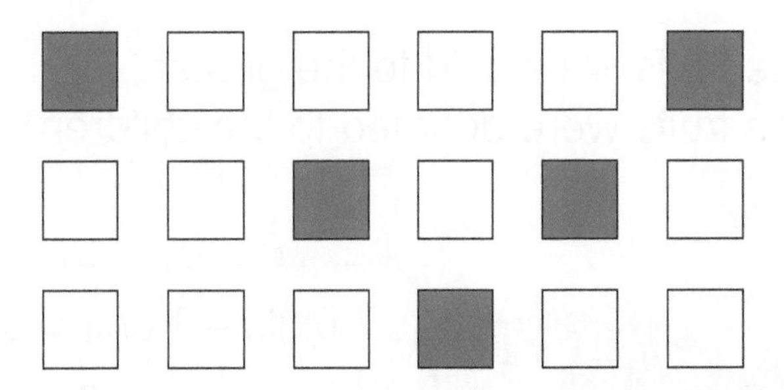

$\frac{2}{3} \times 18 = 12$ squares

12 squares are to be left unshaded.

$18 - 12 = 6$

6 squares need to be shaded.

5 squares are already shaded.

$6 - 5 = 1$

1 more square needs to be shaded.

Worked Example 5

A fruit seller sold $\frac{1}{7}$ of his fruits to a hotel owner. He sold $\frac{1}{3}$ of the remaining fruits to a grocer. He donated the rest of the fruits to a children's home.

(a) What fraction of the fruits were sold to the grocer?

(b) What fraction of the fruits were donated to the children's home?

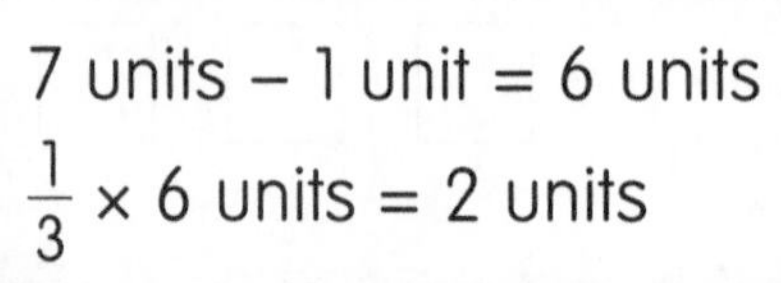

(a)

Remaining fruits

hotel grocer

From the model, 2 out of 7 equal parts were sold to the grocer.

$\frac{2}{7}$ of the fruits were sold to the grocer.

(b)

Remaining fruits

hotel owner grocer

$$1 - \frac{1}{7} - \frac{2}{7} = \frac{7}{7} - \frac{1}{7} - \frac{2}{7} = \frac{4}{7}$$

From the model, 4 out of 7 equal parts represent fruits donated to the children's home.

$\frac{4}{7}$ of the fruits were donated to the children's home.

Answer all questions. Show your work and write your statements clearly.

1. What is the value of $9 - \frac{1}{2} - \frac{5}{8}$?

2. How many $\frac{1}{7}$s are there in $4\frac{3}{7}$?

3. How many $\frac{1}{9}$s are there in $3\frac{1}{3}$?

4. The table below shows the time taken for an object to travel from one point to another point.

	Time taken (hours)
A to B	$\frac{1}{4}$
B to C	$\frac{7}{12}$
C to D	$\frac{5}{6}$

How long (in hours) does the object take to travel from point A to point D through points B and C?

5. Sharon had 7 m of cloth. She used $\frac{3}{5}$ m to make a handkerchief and $\frac{9}{10}$ m to make a shirt. How many meters of cloth were left?

6. Find a fraction which is halfway between $\frac{3}{5}$ and $\frac{4}{5}$.

Extension: Find a fraction that is one-third away, and another fraction that is two-thirds away, between $\frac{3}{5}$ and $\frac{4}{5}$.

7. Cecilia and Charles shared one pizza. If Cecilia ate $\frac{1}{5}$ of it and Charles ate half of the remaining pizza, what fraction of the pizza was left?

8. Fiona used $\frac{1}{6}$ of a ribbon to decorate a gift. She then gave $\frac{3}{5}$ of the remainder to her sister. What fraction of the ribbon was left? Express your answer in the simplest form.

9. In a class, $\frac{1}{4}$ of the students like board games. $\frac{7}{12}$ of the students like video games and the remaining 4 students like card games. How many students are there in the class?

10. A total of 960 people visited the Arts Museum. $\frac{1}{5}$ of them were boys, $\frac{7}{20}$ were girls, $\frac{3}{10}$ were men and the rest were women. How many more men than women were there?

11. The figure shows 15 triangles, 6 of which are shaded. If $\frac{2}{3}$ of the triangles are to be shaded, how many more triangles need to be shaded?

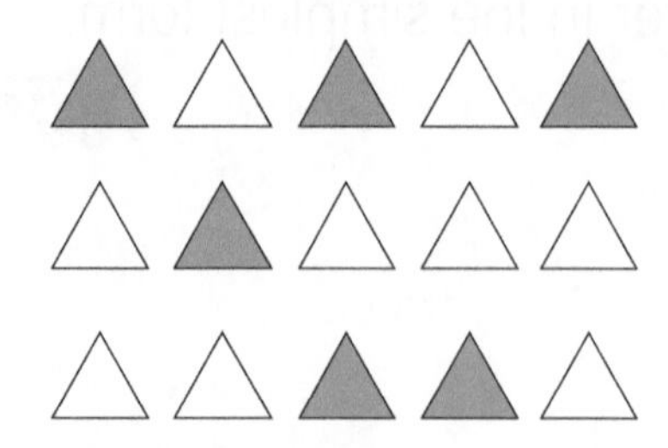

Hint: See Worked Example 4.

12. Shirley gave $\frac{2}{3}$ of her rare coins to her niece. After donating half of the remaining rare coins to a church, she still had 5 coins left. How many rare coins did Shirley have at first?

13. An equal number of men and women attended a party. After 2 hours, $\frac{4}{5}$ of the men and $\frac{3}{4}$ of the women left. If 36 men remained, how many women left the party?

14. Larry has $\frac{3}{4}$ as many badges as Mabel. Susan has $\frac{2}{3}$ as many badges as Larry. If all three children have 153 badges in total, how many badges does Larry have?

Hint: Use a model drawing.

15. William's candies are 12 more in number than $\frac{1}{5}$ of Glen's candies. If both of them have a total of 144 candies, how many candies does William have?

16. The number of books Mr. Jason has is 34 fewer than $\frac{3}{5}$ of the number of books Mrs. Roderick has. They have a total of 2,566 books altogether. How many books does Mr. Jason have?

17. Rod P is 6 cm longer than rod Q. $\frac{3}{5}$ of the length of rod Q is equal to half the length of rod P. What is the length of rod Q?

    Hint: Use a model drawing.

18. Two-thirds of Eddie's books is equal to $\frac{3}{7}$ of Linda's books. If Linda has 15 more books than Eddie, how many books do Eddie and Linda have in total?

    Hint: Use a model drawing.

Worked Example 1

The sum of two numbers is 42.3. Their difference is 8.9. What are the two numbers?

?

Greater number

8.9

42.3

Smaller number

?

Method 1

Let the greater number be 1 unit.

2 units ⟶ $42.3 + 8.9 = 51.2$
1 unit ⟶ $51.2 \div 2 = 25.6$

The greater number is 25.6.

$25.6 - 8.9 = 16.7$ or $42.3 - 25.6 = 16.7$

The smaller number is 16.7.

The two numbers are **16.7** and **25.6**.

Method 2

Let the smaller number be 1 unit.

2 units ⟶ $42.3 - 8.9 = 33.4$
1 unit ⟶ $33.4 \div 2 = 16.7$

The smaller number is 16.7.
$16.7 + 8.9 = 25.6$ or $42.3 - 16.7 = 25.6$

The greater number is 25.6.

The two numbers are **16.7** and **25.6**.

Worked Example 2

Cally has $17.35 and Simon has $32.65. How much money must Simon give Cally so that each of them has the same amount of money?

Method 1

Before

Cally: $17.35

Simon: $32.65

After

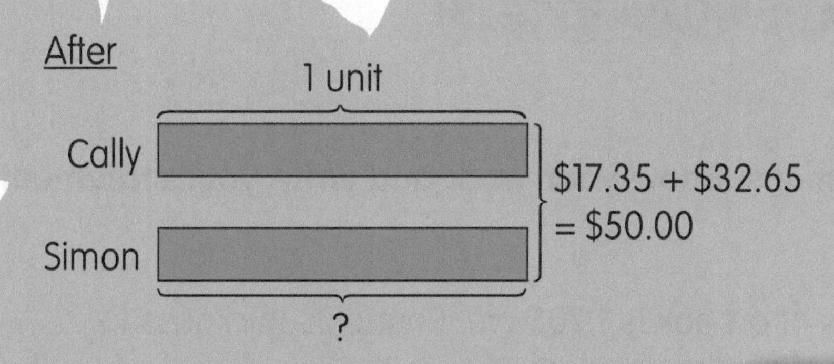

2 units ⟶ $50.00

1 unit ⟶ $50.00 ÷ 2 = $25.00

Check:
$17.35 + $7.65
= $25.00

$32.65 – $25.00 = $7.65

Simon must give Cally **$7.65** so that both of them will have the same amount of money.

Method 2

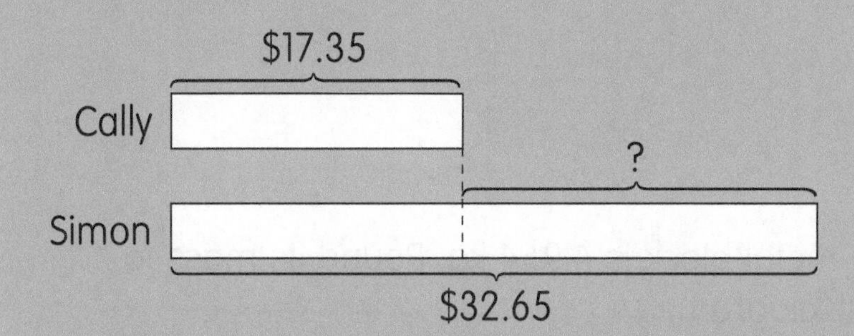

$32.65 – $17.35 = $15.30

Simon has $15.30 more than Cally.

$15.30 ÷ 2 = $7.65

Simon must give Cally **$7.65** so that both of them will have the same amount of money.

Answer all questions. Show your work and write your statements clearly.

1. The thickness of a book is 1.705 cm. Round its thickness to
   (a) the nearest centimeter,
   (b) one decimal place,
   (c) two decimal places.

2. The mass of a metal block is 4.954 kg. Round its mass to
   (a) the nearest kilogram,
   (b) one decimal place,
   (c) two decimal places.

3. The distance between two towns is 8.199 km. Round the distance to the nearest
   (a) kilometer,
   (b) tenth of a kilometer,
   (c) hundredth of a kilometer.

4. The runner-up in a 100-meter race completed it in 10.56 seconds, which was 1.09 seconds slower than the winner. How long did the winner take to complete the race?

5. Gerald spent $19.90 on a birthday cake and $16.50 on a roasted chicken. He paid the cashier with two $20 bills. How much change should he get?

6. What are the smallest and greatest numbers that, when rounded to the nearest hundredth, give the following numbers? Give your answers correct to 3 decimal places.
   (a) 5.34 (b) 385.25 (c) 187.50

7. The decimals below form a pattern. Fill in the blanks to complete the pattern.

   0.12, 0.27, ________, 0.57, ________, 0.87, 1.02

8. The sum of two decimals is 52.5. Their difference is 12.9. What are the two decimals?

9. Mrs. Bond plans to buy 3 dolls that cost $49.85 each. If she has only $10 bills, estimate the number of $10 bills she needs to buy the dolls.

Worked Example 1

Four calculators and three pens cost $65.20. Two calculators and five pens cost $41.00. What is the cost of one pen?

calculator	calculator	pen	pen	pen	
calculator	calculator				$65.20

calculator	calculator	pen	pen	pen	pen	pen	
calculator	calculator	pen	pen	pen	pen	pen	2 × $41 = $82

2 × (2 calculators and 5 pens) = 2 × $41
4 calculators and 10 pens = $82

4 calculators and 3 pens = $65.20 (given)

10 pens – 3 pens = $82 – $65.20
7 pens ⟶ $16.80
1 pen ⟶ $16.80 ÷ 7 = $2.40

The cost of one pen is **$2.40**.

Worked Example 2

Shaun bought a total of 13 poles. Each yellow pole was 1.2 m long. Each red pole was 1.5 m long. If the total length of the poles that he bought was 17.4 m, how many yellow poles and how many red poles did he buy?

Method 1

Use guess and check method.

Guess	1st	2nd	3rd
Number of yellow poles	5	6	7
Total length of yellow poles	5 × 1.2 m = 6 m	6 × 1.2 m = 7.2 m	7 × 1.2 m = 8.4 m
Number of red poles	8	7	6
Total length of red poles	8 × 1.5 m = 12 m	7 × 1.5 m = 10.5 m	6 × 1.5 m = 9 m
Total length of poles	6 m + 12 m = 18.0 m	7.2 m + 10.5 m = 17.7 m	8.4 m + 9 m = 17.4 m
Is the total length 17.4 m?	No	No	Yes

From the table, he bought **7** yellow poles and **6** red poles.

Method 2

Suppose all 13 poles were yellow.
Then, their total length would be $13 \times 1.2 = 15.6$ m.

Each red pole was $(1.5 - 1.2)$ m $= 0.3$ m longer than a yellow pole.

This means the extra $(17.4 - 15.6)$ m $= 1.8$ m would have come from the red poles.

1.8 m = 180 cm
0.3 m = 30 cm

180 cm ÷ 30 cm = 6
Shaun bought **6** red poles.

$13 - 6 = 7$
Shaun bought **7** yellow poles.

Check:
$6 \times 1.5 + 7 \times 1.2$
$= 9.0 + 8.4$
$= 17.4$

Answer all questions. Show your work and write your statements clearly.

1. Candice is paid $1.20 for every toy she sells. For every 15 toys that she sells, she is paid an extra $5.00. How much will she be paid if she sells 100 toys?

2. The table shows the parking charges at a shopping mall.

	Charges
From 7:00 A.M. to 6:00 P.M.	$3.50 per hour or part thereof
After 6:00 P.M.	$2.50 per hour or part thereof

Mr. Anderson parked his car from 3:00 P.M. to 7:45 P.M. at the shopping mall. How much did he have to pay?

3. Nelson is thinking of a number. When he divides it by 6 and adds 2.3 to the answer, he gets 4. What number is Nelson thinking of?

4. The cost of 4 pears is $1.40. The cost of 6 oranges is $2.40. Mrs. Wilson bought a total of 12 pears and oranges for $4.45. How many pears and oranges did she buy?

5. Three erasers and two pens cost $3.85. Three pens and two erasers cost $4.40. What is the cost of one eraser?

6. The total cost of 5 watches and 4 bags is $169.10. The total cost of 9 watches and 8 bags is $314.30. What is the difference between the cost of a watch and that of a bag?

7. Bob sold 17 ribbons altogether. Each blue ribbon was 1.7 m long. Each green ribbon was 2.3 m long. The total length of the ribbons that he sold was 31.9 m. How many blue ribbons and green ribbons did he sell?

8. Garry has a total of 15 nickels and dimes in his wallet. The coins have a total value of $1.05. How many nickels and dimes are there?

9. Each bag of red beans had a mass of 1.5 kg and each bag of green beans had a mass of 1.8 kg. Mr. Smith sold 10 bags of beans. The total mass of the bags that he sold was 16.2 kg. How many bags of red beans and green beans did he sell?

6 Angles

Worked Example 1

(a) How many right angles does a $\frac{1}{2}$-turn make?
(b) How many right angles does a rhombus have?

(a) A right angle is 90° and a $\frac{1}{2}$-turn is equivalent to 180°.

$180° \div 90° = 2$

A $\frac{1}{2}$-turn makes **2** right angles.

(b) **A square, which is a special type of rhombus, has 4 right angles. On the other hand, a rhombus has no right angles, although its diagonals meet at right angles.**

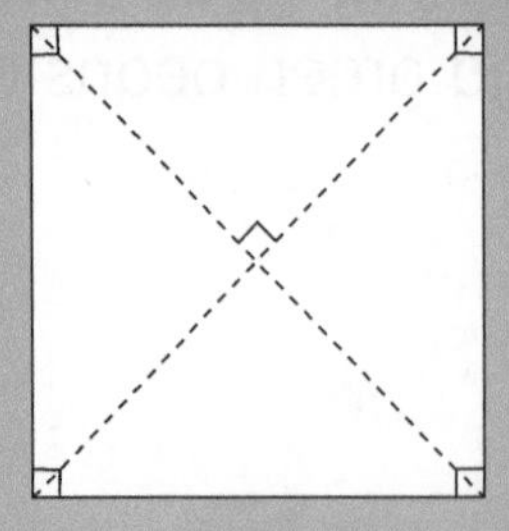

Square

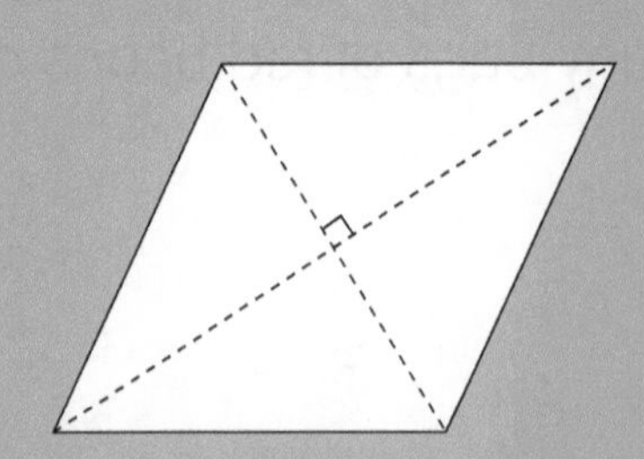

Rhombus

Worked Example 2

David turned 45° clockwise and then made a $\frac{3}{4}$-turn counterclockwise. He is now facing South. Where was he facing before he made the turns?

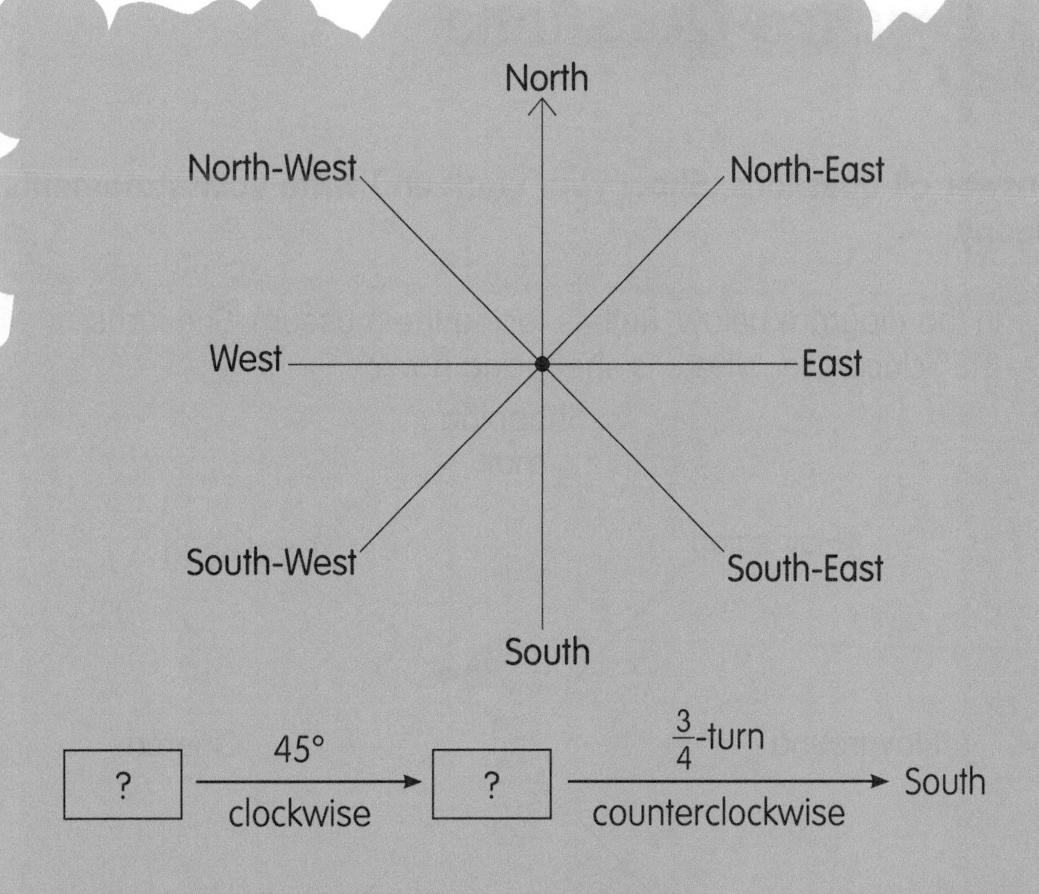

From the South, perform the two turns in the opposite direction:

(i) $\frac{3}{4}$-turn clockwise

(ii) 45° counterclockwise

North-East $\xleftarrow[\text{counterclockwise}]{45^\circ}$ East $\xleftarrow[\text{clockwise}]{\frac{3}{4}\text{-turn}}$ South

He was facing **North-East**.

Practice Questions

Answer all questions. Show your work and write your statements clearly.

1. In the diagram below, Ruth is facing the museum. She turns 315° clockwise. Where is she facing now?

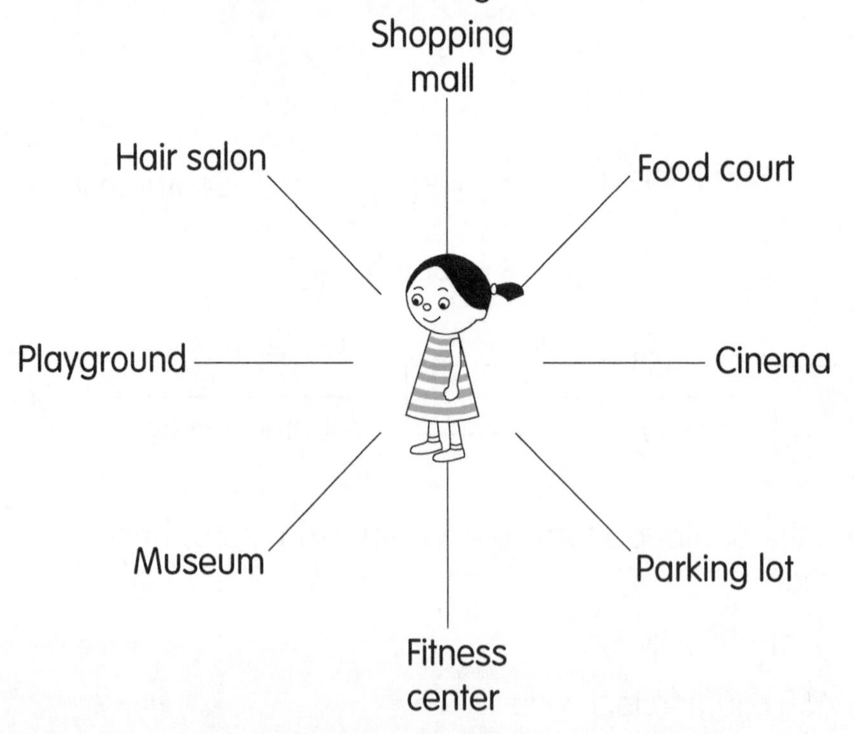

Hint: $315^\circ = 360^\circ - 45^\circ$ or $315^\circ = 180^\circ + 90^\circ + 45^\circ$

2. Susan left home at 2:40 P.M. When she reached the post office, she noticed that the minute hand of the clock had moved 90° clockwise. What time did she reach the post office?

Hint: The minute hand makes an angle of 360° in 1 hour.

3. In the figure below, how many marked angles are less than 90°?

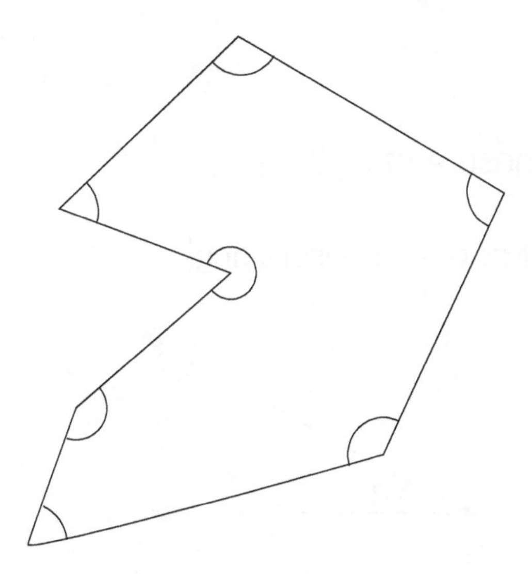

4. What is measure of angle p?

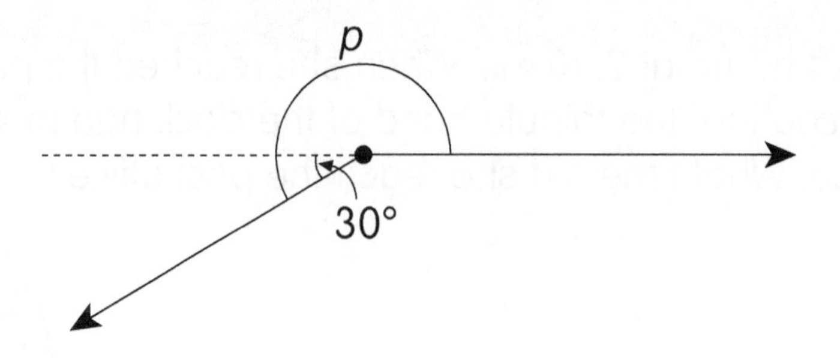

5. What is measure of angle r?

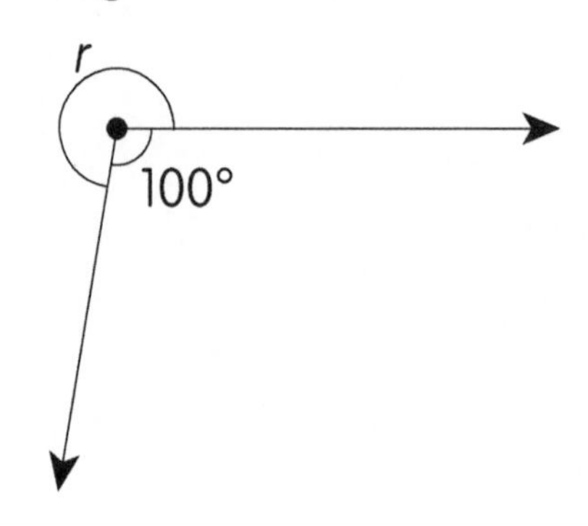

6. What is the measure of $\angle n$?

Hint: Use a protractor to measure angle n.

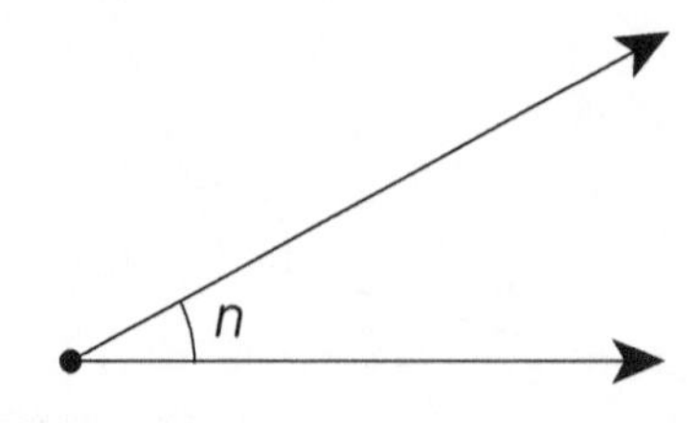

7. In the figure below, one of the angles is a right angle. Name the angle.

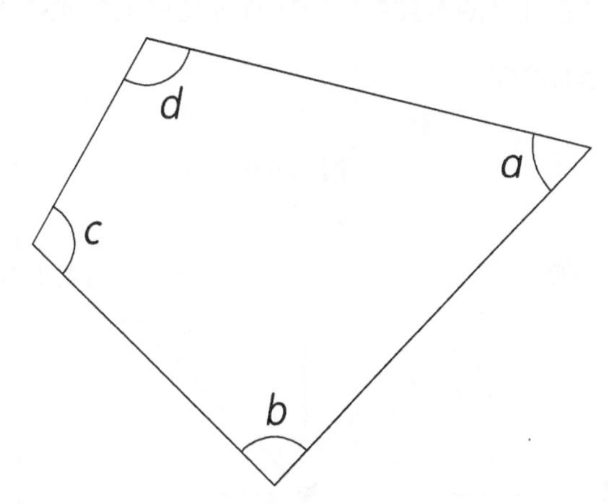

Hint: Use a protractor to confirm your answer.

8. The figure below shows a clock at 2:30 A.M. How many $\frac{1}{4}$-turns will the minute hand take to reach 4:00 A.M?

9. Joseph made a $\frac{1}{2}$-turn clockwise before turning 45° counterclockwise. If he faced North-West at first, where did he face after turning?

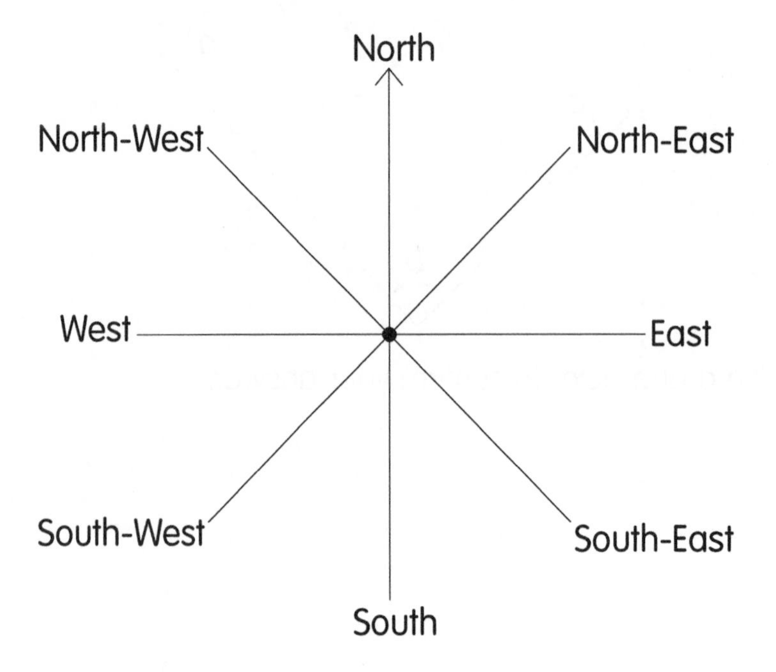

10. The minute hand of a clock moved from 1:05 P.M. to 1:20 P.M. What angle did the minute hand move?

11. In the diagram below, Joan is facing the pet shop. If Joan turns 225° counterclockwise, where will she be facing?

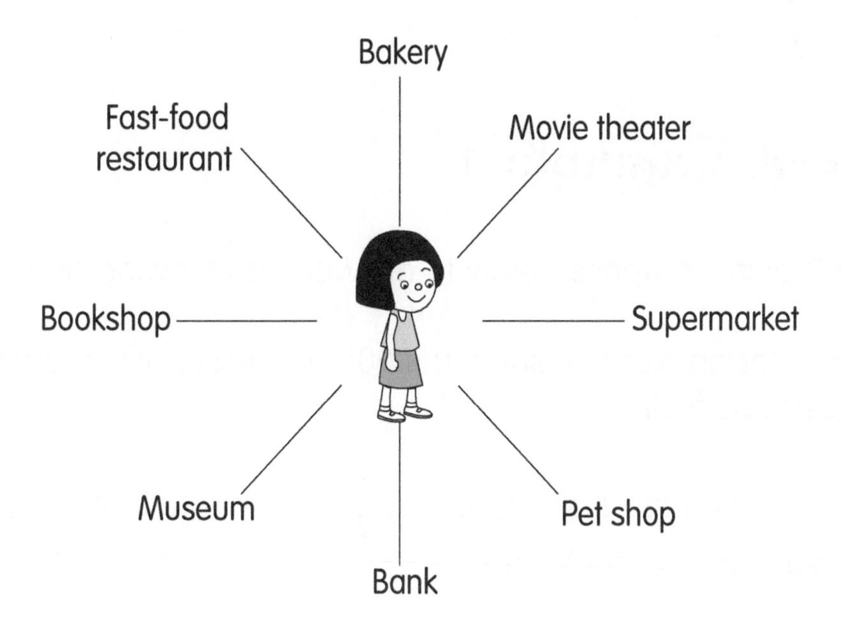

Hint: $225° = 180° + \frac{1}{4} \times 180°$

12. Study the figures below. Read the following statements about angles *p* and *q*. Which statement best describes the relationship between the two angles?
    A. The measure of angle *p* is greater than the measure of angle *q*.
    B. The measure of angle *q* is greater than the measure of angle *p*.
    C. Angle *p* and angle *q* have the same measure.

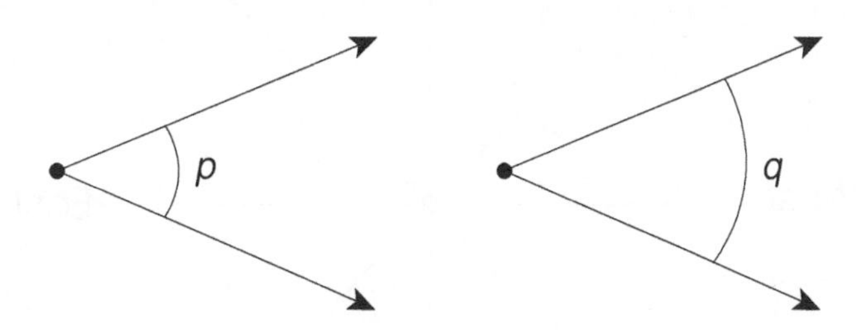

Hint: Use a protractor to confirm your answer.

Worked Example 1

Use the 8-point compass below to answer the following questions.

(a) Jean is facing North. If she turns 90° clockwise, which direction will Jean be facing?

(b) Zoe is facing East. If she makes a $\frac{1}{2}$-turn counterclockwise, which direction will Zoe be facing?

(c) Paul was facing West at first. He turned counterclockwise and ended up facing North-East. What angle did Paul turn?

(d) Louis made a $\frac{3}{4}$-turn clockwise and ended up facing South-West. Which direction was Louis facing at first?

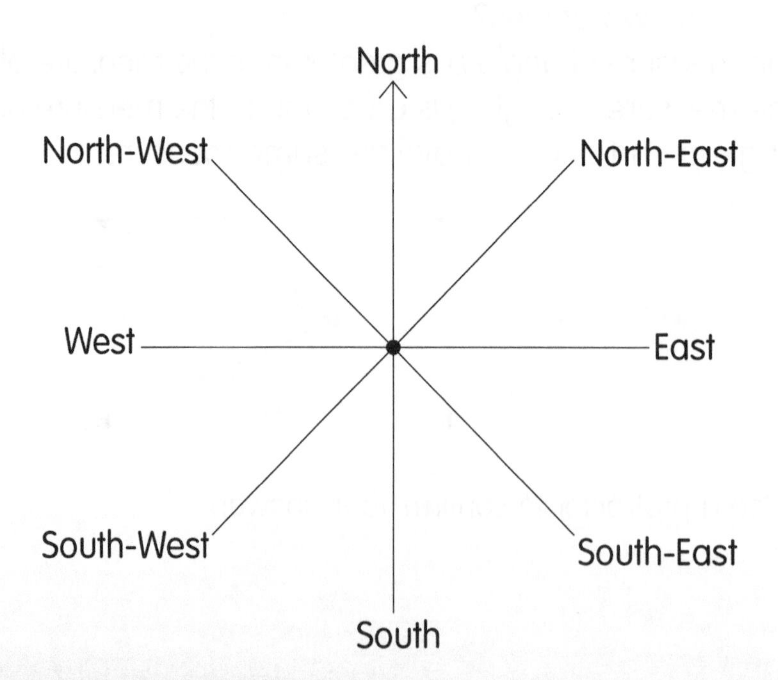

(a)

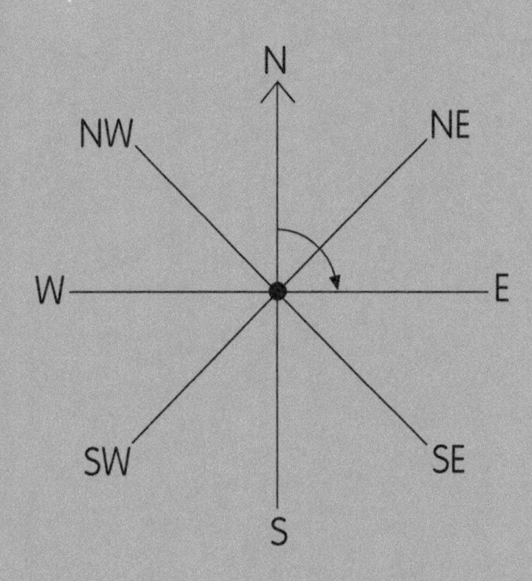

Jean will be facing **East**.

(b)

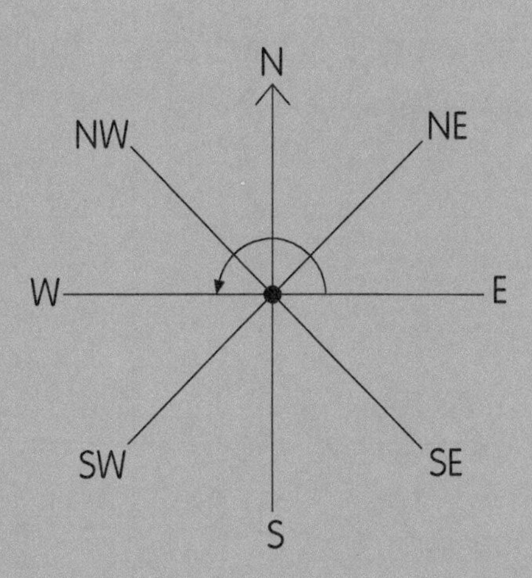

Zoe will be facing **West**.

(c)

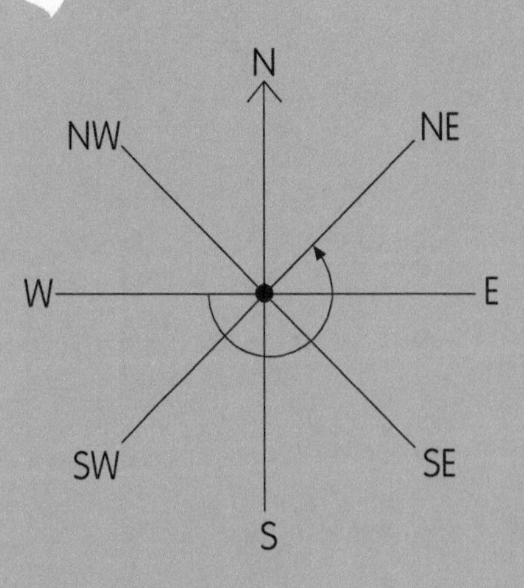

Paul turned **225°** counterclockwise.

(d) From South-West, work backwards by making a $\frac{3}{4}$-turn (or 270°) counterclockwise.

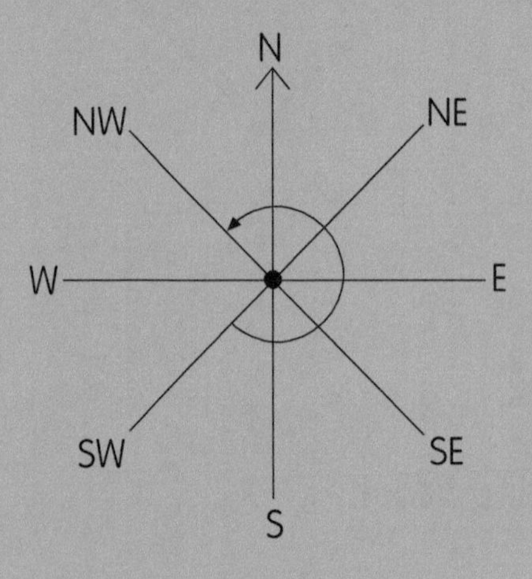

Louis was facing **North-West** at first.

Worked Example 2

Find the angle formed by the hands of a clock at 2:20.
There are 12 facing numerals on the clock.

Note that the angle between two neighboring numerals on the clock is $\frac{1}{12}$ of a circle.

$\frac{1}{12} \times 360° = 30°$

The angle between two neighboring numerals on the clock is 30°.

In 60 minutes, the hour hand moves 30°.

In 20 minutes, the hour hand moves $\frac{1}{3} \times 30° = 10°$.

The angle between the numerals 2 and 4 on the clock is $30° \times 2 = 60°$.

$60° - 10° = 50°$

The angle formed by the hands of a clock at 2:20 is **50°**.

Note: A common mistake is to give the incorrect answer of 60°, ignoring the fact that the hour hand has correspondingly moved as well. In fact, the hour hand has moved $\frac{30°}{60 \text{ mins}} \times 20 \text{ mins} = 10°$.

Answer all questions. Show your work and write your statements clearly.

1. From 3:00 P.M. to 3:30 P.M.,
   (a) what angle did the minute hand move,
   (b) what angle did the hour hand move?

2. A clock shows 12:30. What is the angle between the hour and minute hands?

3. Study the diagram and complete the table below.

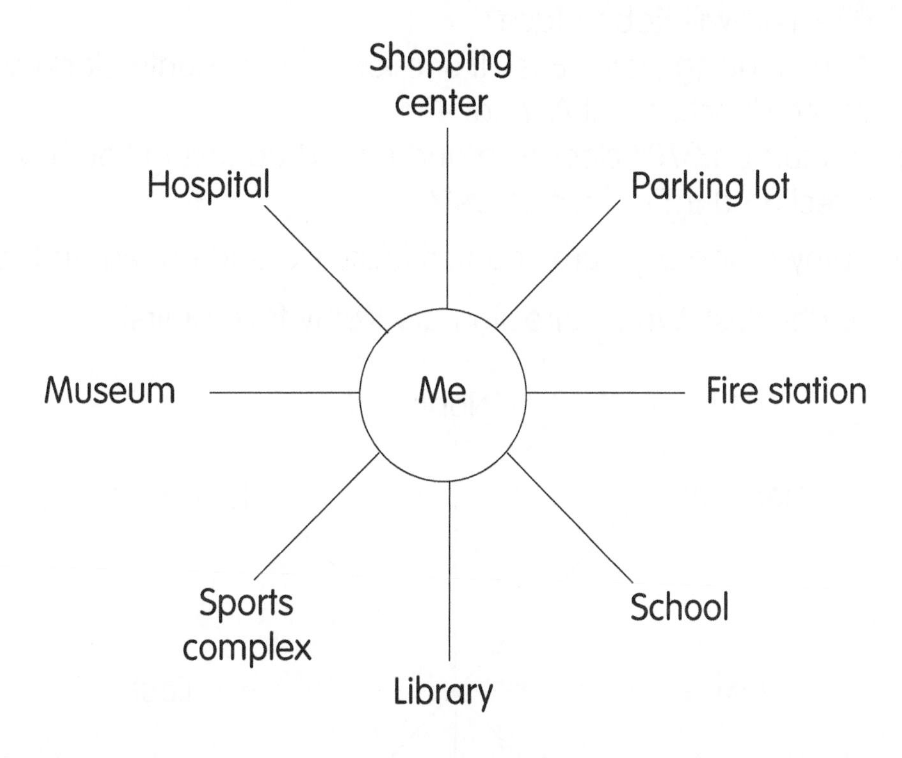

	I am facing	If I turn	I will face
(a)	Library	180° counterclockwise	
(b)	School	135° clockwise	
(c)	Museum	225° clockwise	
(d)		45° clockwise	Parking lot
(e)	Hospital	____ clockwise	Library
(f)	Sports complex	____ counterclockwise	Fire station
(g)	Shopping center	225° ____________	School
(h)	Parking lot	135° ____________	Museum

4. Use the 8-point compass to answer the following questions.
   (a) Robert is facing South-West. If he turns 180° clockwise , which direction will Robert face?
   (b) Ann is facing North-East. If she turns 135° counterclockwise, which direction will Ann face?
   (c) Tim turned 270° clockwise and ended up facing South. Which direction did Tim face at first?
   (d) Kathy made a $\frac{3}{4}$-turn counterclockwise and ended up facing North-West. Which direction did Kathy face at first?

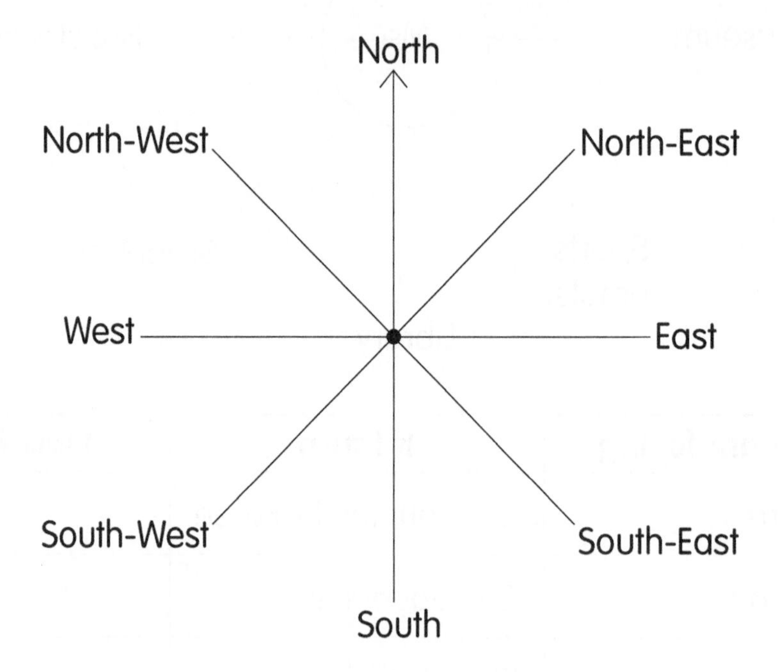

5. How many seconds does it take a second hand on a watch to sweep through 90°?

   Hint: The second hand moves 360° in 60 seconds.

6. How many angles smaller than a right angle are there in the figure below?

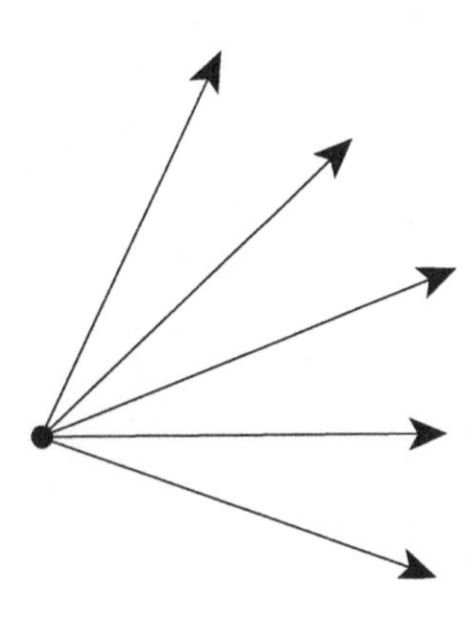

7. What is the smaller angle formed by the hands of a clock at 4:40?

8. Sketch a closed figure with 5 equal angles.

9. Sketch a closed figure with 8 equal angles.

10. On the grid below, Juliana starts her journey at point P. She walks 2 units towards the West and turns 90° counterclockwise and walks another 1 unit. Next, she moves 2 units to the East before turning 90° clockwise to move 1 more unit. Label the point on the grid where Juliana stops with the letter Q.

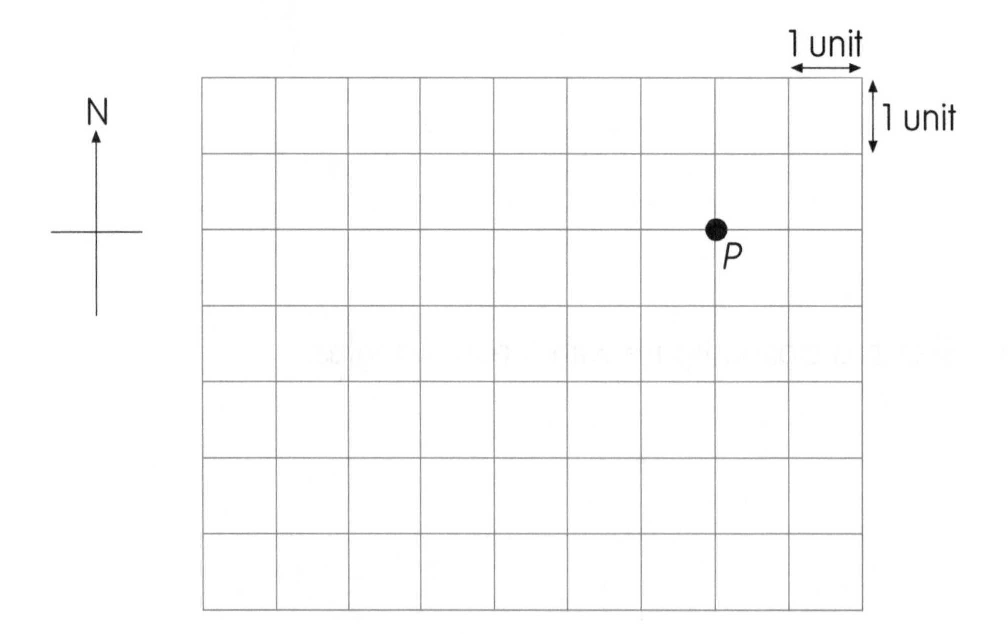

7 Perpendicular and Parallel Lines

Worked Example 1

Draw one line segment perpendicular to, and one line segment parallel to $\overline{AB}$.

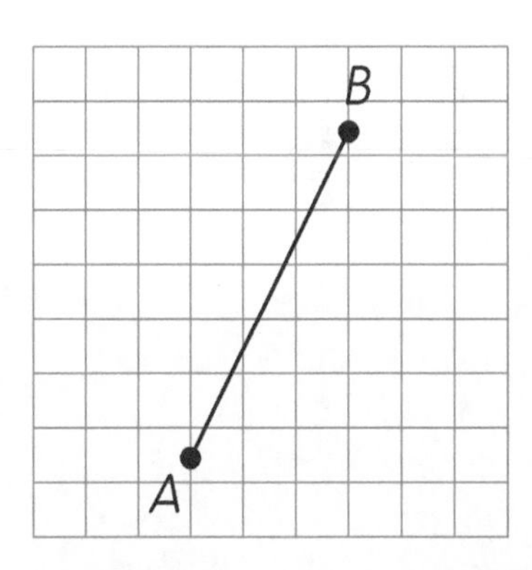

Many line segments can be drawn perpendicular and parallel to $\overline{AB}$.
Two such line segments are shown below.

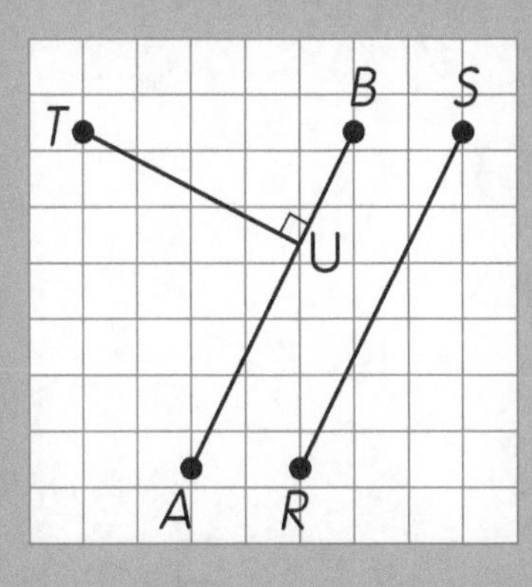

$\overline{RS}$ is parallel to $\overline{AB}$.
$\overline{TU}$ is perpendicular to $\overline{AB}$.

Worked Example 2

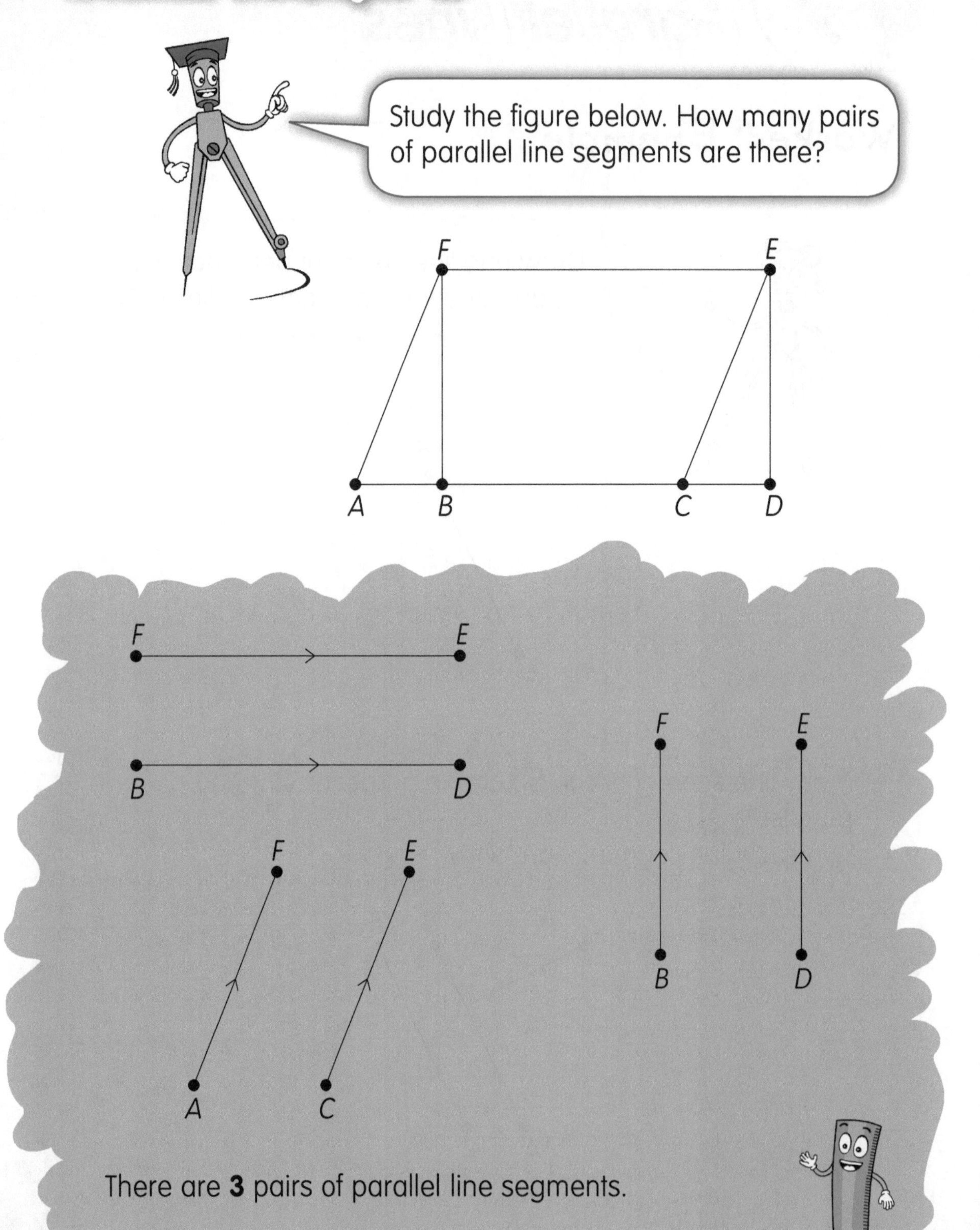

There are **3** pairs of parallel line segments.

Worked Example 3

Study the diagram and answer the questions that follow.

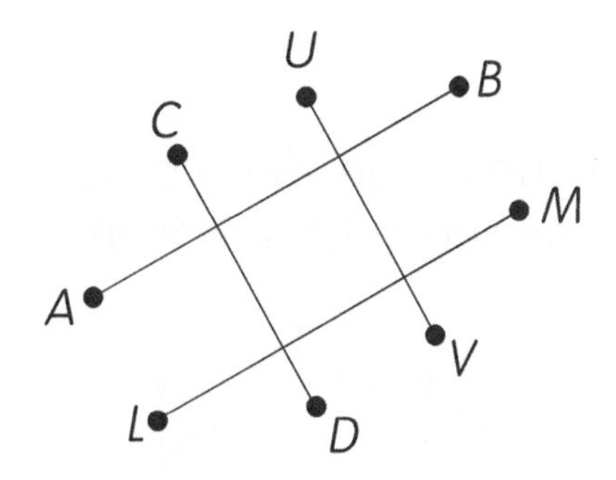

(a) Which line segment is perpendicular to line segment $\overline{AB}$?

(b) Name a pair of parallel line segments.

(c) How many right angles are there?

Solution:

(a) **Line segment $\overline{\textbf{CD}}$** or **$\overline{\textbf{UV}}$** is perpendicular to line segment $\overline{AB}$.

(b) A pair of parallel line segments are **$\overline{\textbf{AB}}$** and **$\overline{\textbf{LM}}$**, or **$\overline{\textbf{CD}}$** and **$\overline{\textbf{UV}}$**.

(c) **16** right angles.

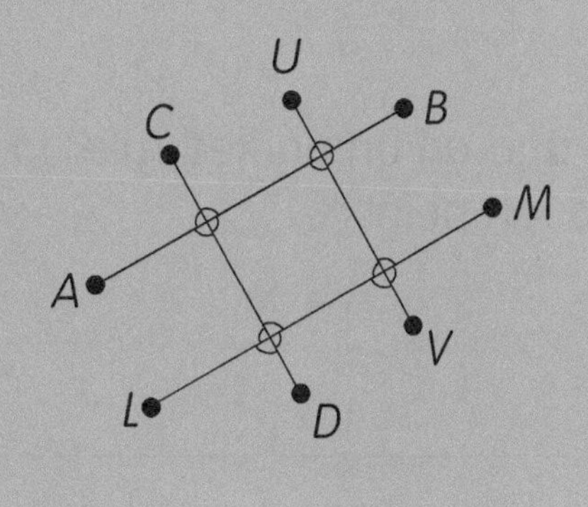

Answer all questions. Show your work and write your statements clearly.

1. The figure is made up of two identical squares. How many pairs of perpendicular line segments are there?

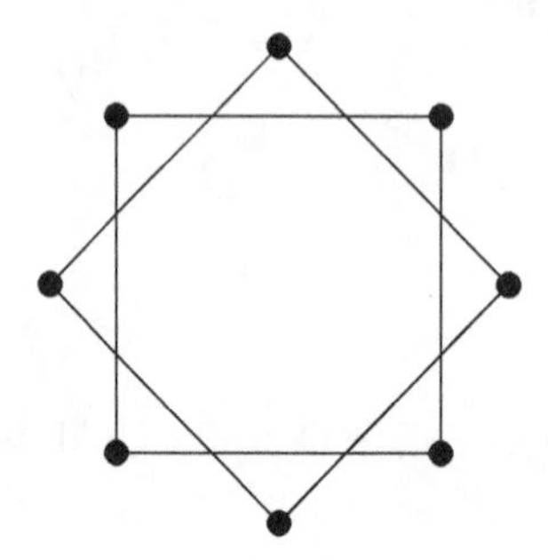

2. In the figure below, name a line segment that is perpendicular to $\overline{DE}$.

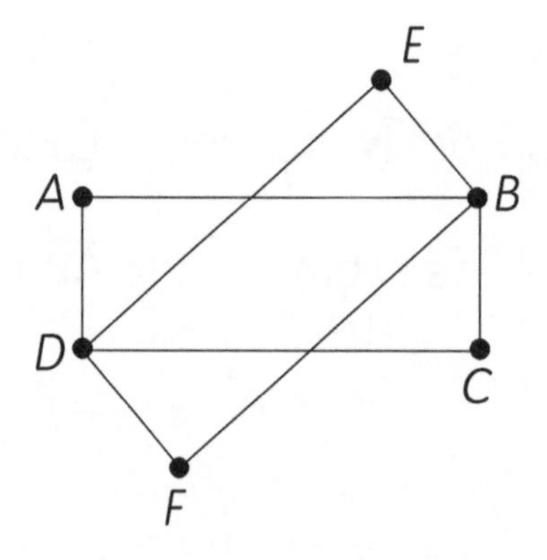

3. Use a set square and an unmarked ruler to draw a line segment parallel to $\overline{AB}$ through point X.

A ——————————————————————— B

4. Which of the following letters have a pair of parallel line segments?

5. How many pairs of parallel line segments are there in the figure below?

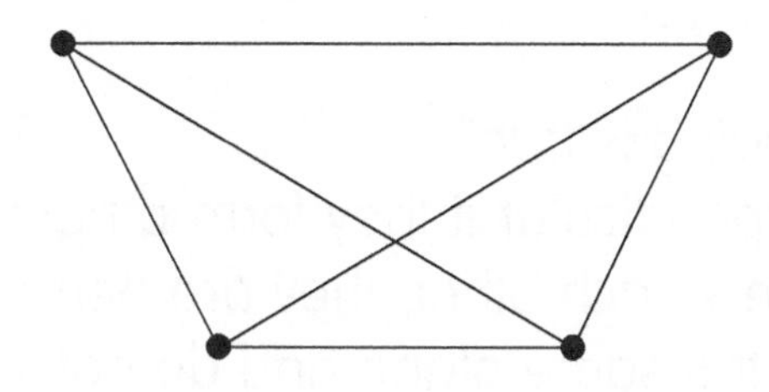

6. In the figure below, which line segment is perpendicular to $\overline{OE}$?

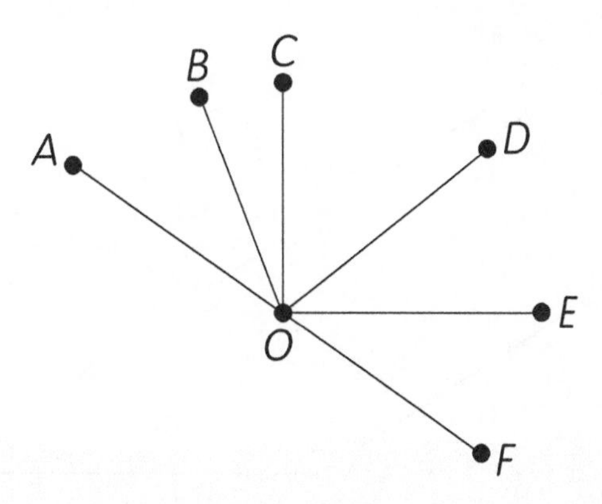

7. In the figure, X is a point not on line segment $\overline{CD}$.

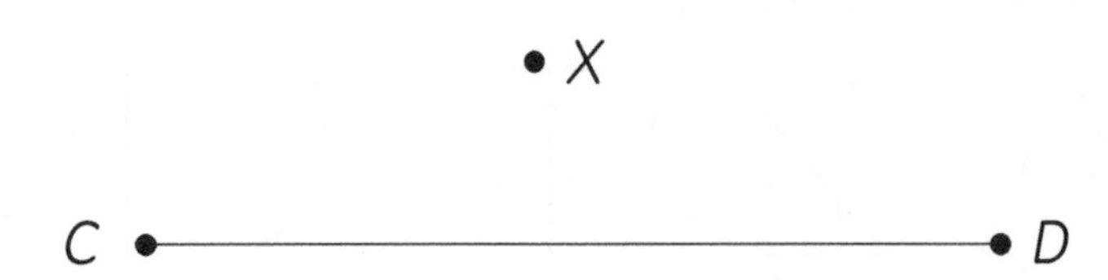

(a) Copy line segment $\overline{CD}$ and point X on a piece of paper.
(b) Draw a line segment perpendicular to $\overline{CD}$ starting from point X.
(c) Draw two more line segments to make a rectangle.

8. Which of the following is true?
(a) Two lines are perpendicular if they form a right angle.
(b) If two lines intersect each other, they are perpendicular.
(c) If two lines lie on the same plane and do not intersect, they are parallel.
(d) If two lines are perpendicular, they form four right angles.

9. How many pairs of perpendicular lines are there in the figure?

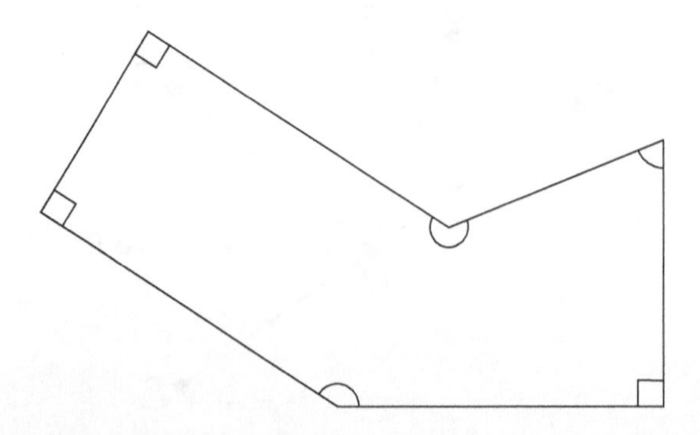

10. In the figure below, how many pairs of perpendicular line segments are there?

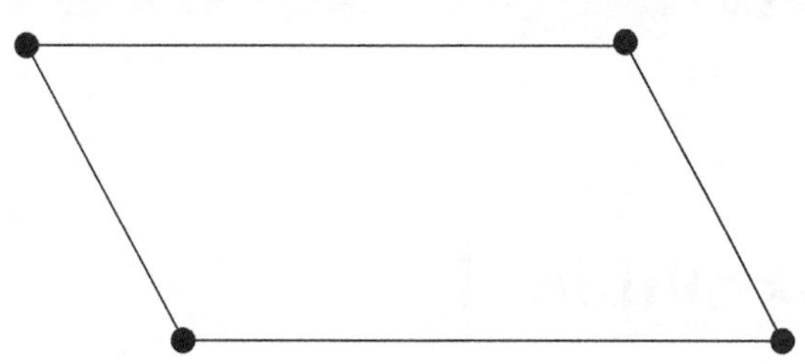

11. In the figure below, how many pairs of parallel line segments are there?

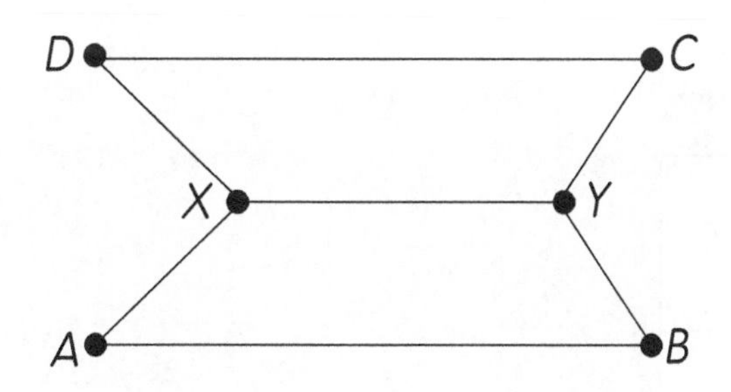

12. Study the figure below.
    (a) How many line segments are parallel to $\overline{AK}$?
    (b) How many line segments are parallel to $\overline{FG}$?

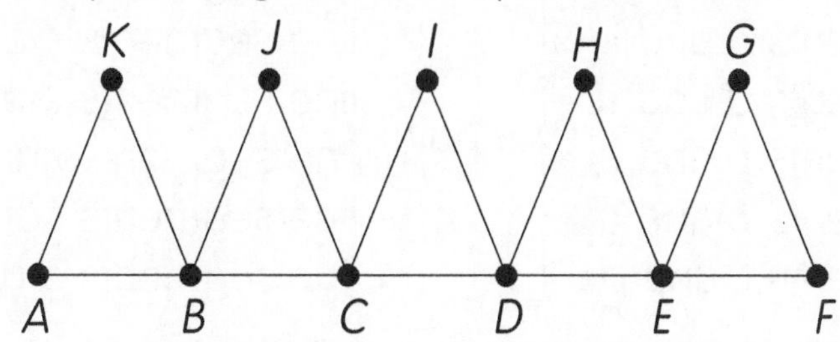

Worked Example 1

How many pairs of parallel lines are there in each of the figures shown below?

(a)

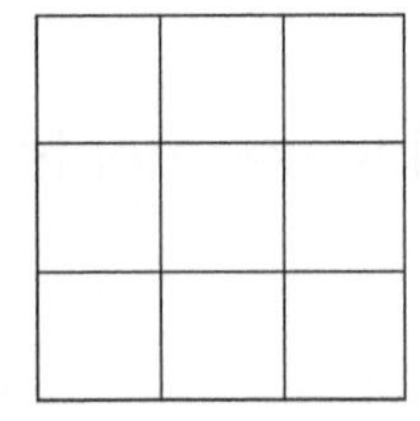

(b)

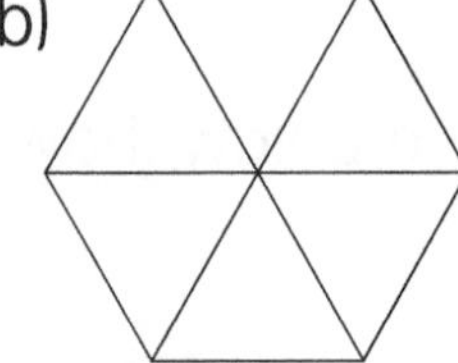

(a)

Observe that the figure is made up of 4 horizontal line segments (*a*, *b*, *c*, *d*) and 4 vertical line segments (*e*, *f*, *g*, *h*).

Pairs of horizontal parallel line segments are:
line segments *a* and *b*,
line segments *a* and *c*,
line segments *a* and *d*,
line segments *b* and *c*,
line segments *b* and *d*,
line segments *c* and *d*.
} 6 pairs

Pairs of vertical parallel line segments are:
line segments *e* and *f*,
line segments *e* and *g*,
line segments *e* and *h*,
line segments *f* and *g*,
line segments *f* and *h*,
line segments *g* and *h*.
} 6 pairs

There are a total of **12** pairs of parallel line segments .

(b)

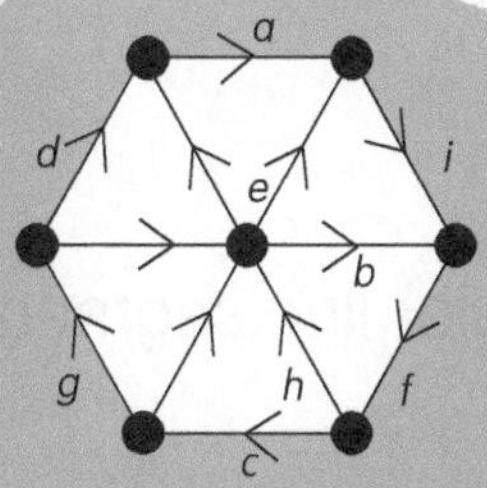

Pairs of parallel line segments are:

line segments *a* and *b*,
line segments *a* and *c*,
line segments *b* and *c*,
} 3 pairs

line segments *d* and *e*,
line segments *d* and *f*,
line segments *e* and *f*,
} 3 pairs

line segments *g* and *h*,
line segments *g* and *i*,
line segments *h* and *i*.
} 3pairs

There are a total of 3 + 3 + 3 = **9** pairs of parallel line segments.

Worked Example 2

In the figure below, name a pair of perpendicular line segments.

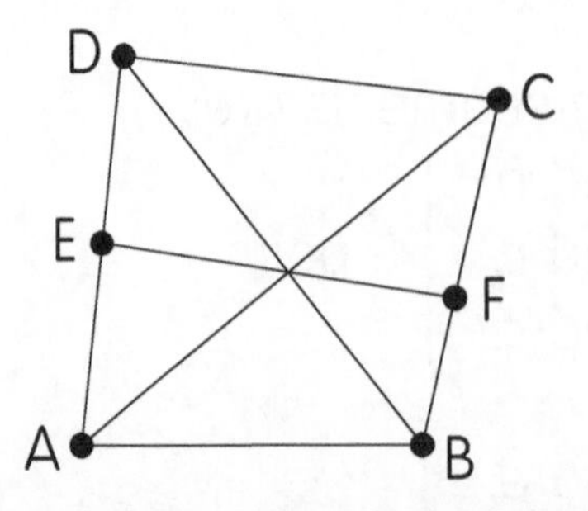

The pair of perpendicular line segments is:
$\overline{\mathbf{AC}}$ and $\overline{\mathbf{BD}}$, or $\overline{\mathbf{AD}}$ and $\overline{\mathbf{DC}}$.

Answer all questions. Show your work and write your statements clearly.

1. In the figure, $\overline{AB}$ is perpendicular to $\overline{BC}$ and $\overline{AD}$ is perpendicular to $\overline{DC}$. Is angle measure *B* equal in size to angle measure *D*?

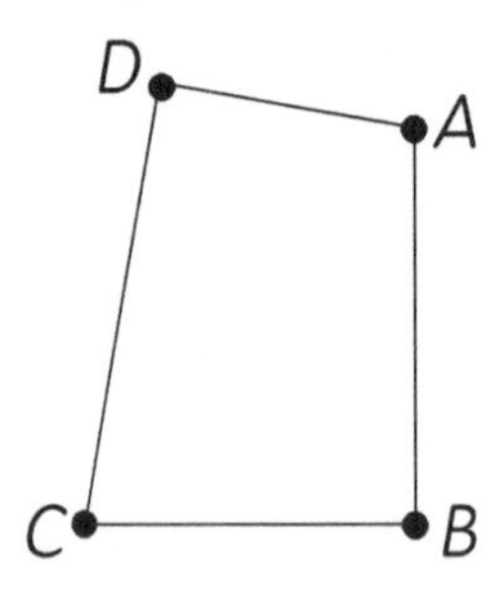

2. How many pairs of perpendicular line segments are there in the figure below?

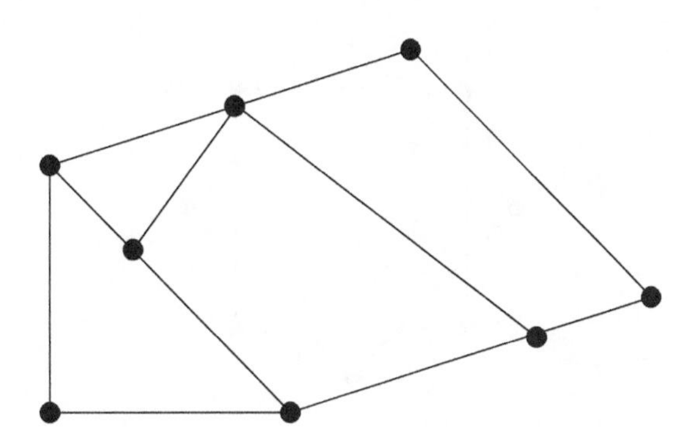

3. Study the figure below. *PQVW* and *RSTU* are rectangles. How many different line segments are parallel to $\overline{WV}$?

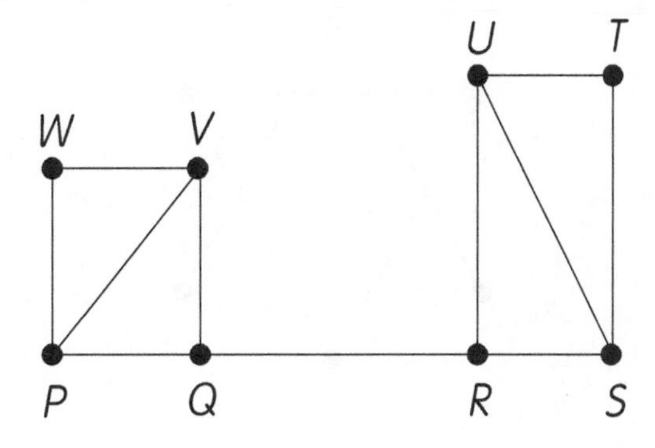

4. How many pairs of perpendicular line segments are there in the figure below?

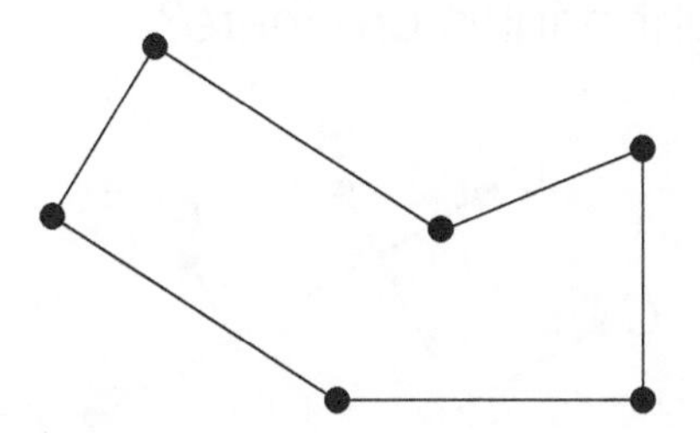

5. The figure below is made up of two identical squares. How many pairs of perpendicular line segments are there?

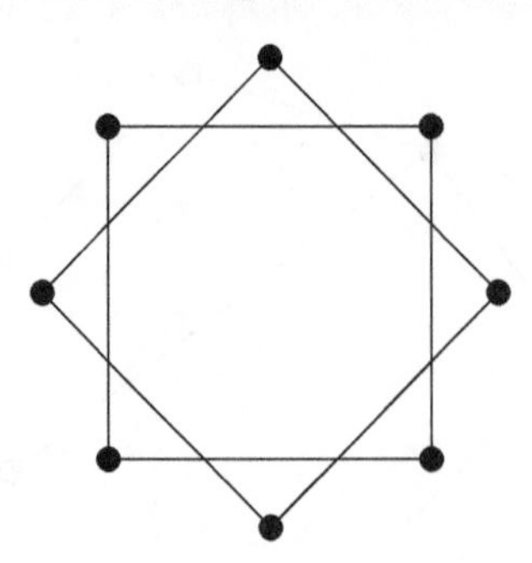

6. How many pairs of parallel line segments are there in the figure below?

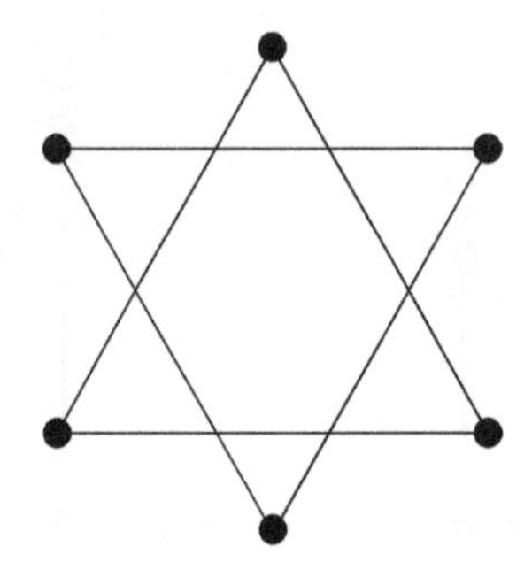

7. Look at the figure below.
   (a) Which line segment is perpendicular to AB?
   (b) Name a pair of parallel lines.
   (c) How many right angles are there?

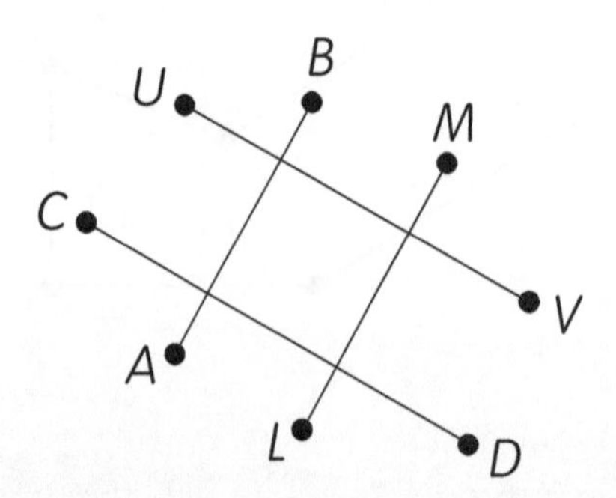

8. Look at the figure below.
   (a) Name the line segments that are parallel to $\overline{FE}$.
   (b) Name the line segments that are perpendicular to $\overline{FE}$.
   (c) Name the line segments that are parallel to $\overline{DE}$.
   (d) Name the line segments that are parallel to $\overline{CD}$.
   (e) Name the line segments that are perpendicular to $\overline{FB}$.

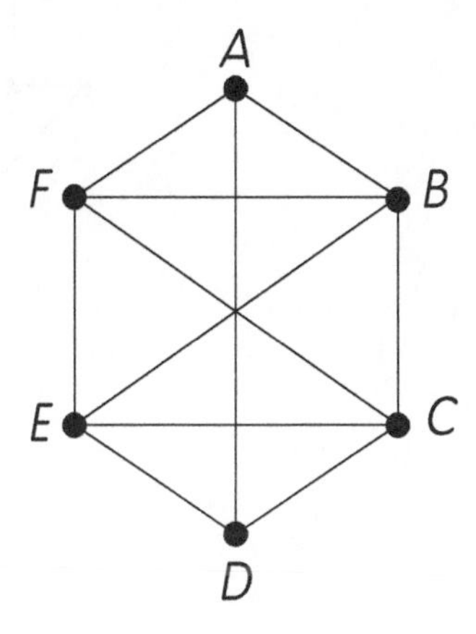

9. Study the figure below. *ABWX* and *CDUV* are rectangles. How many different line segments are parallel to $\overline{VU}$?

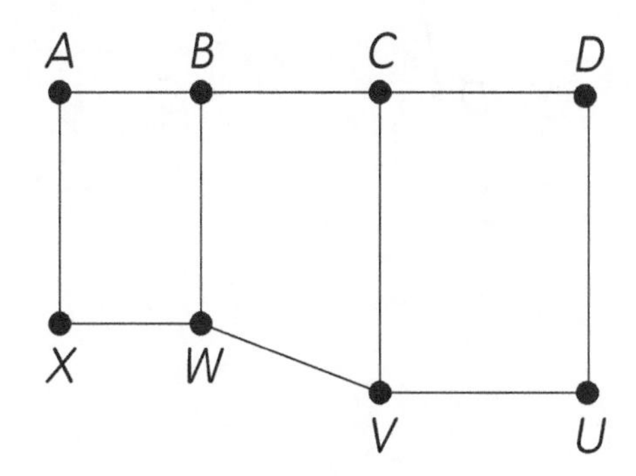

10. How many pairs of perpendicular line segments are there in each of the figures below?

(a)

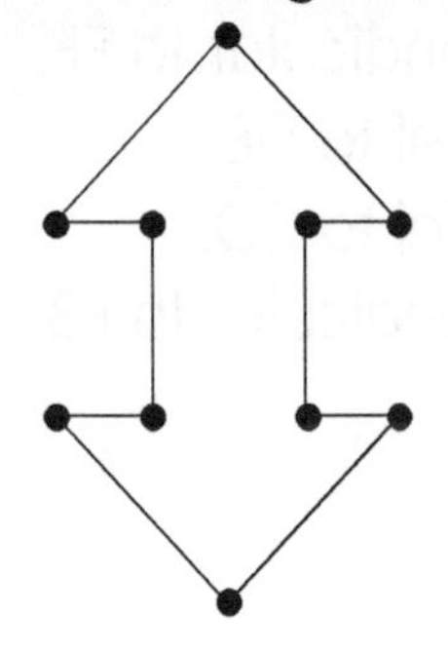

(b)

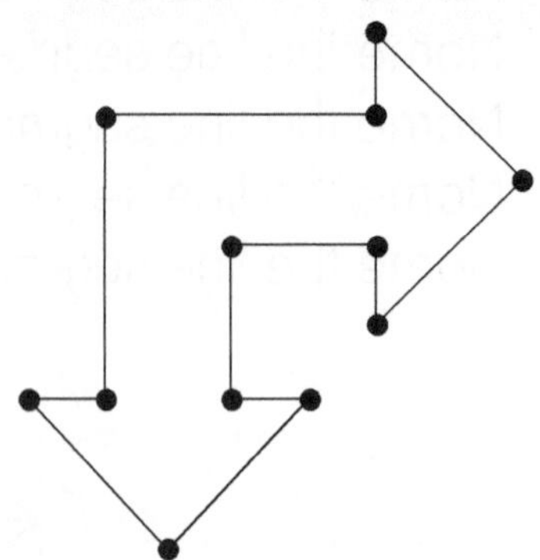

11. In the figure below, $\overline{AB}$ is perpendicular to $\overline{AD}$, and $\overline{BC}$ is perpendicular to $\overline{CD}$. Is the measure of angle A the same as the measure of angle C?

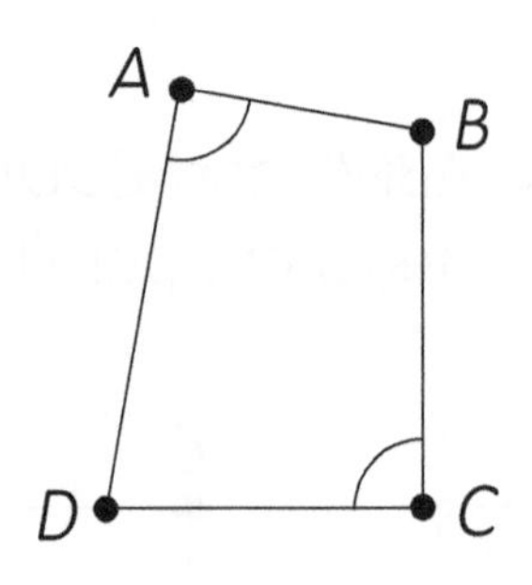

8 Tiling Patterns and Symmetry

Worked Example 1

In each of the figures below, determine whether the dotted line is a line of symmetry.

(a)

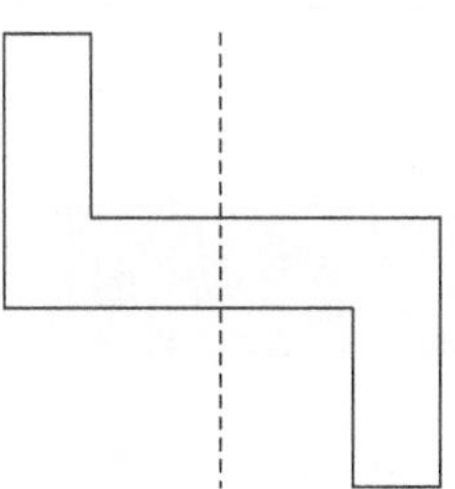

(b)

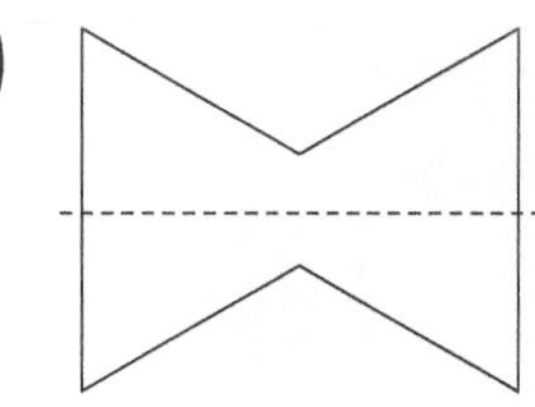

(c)

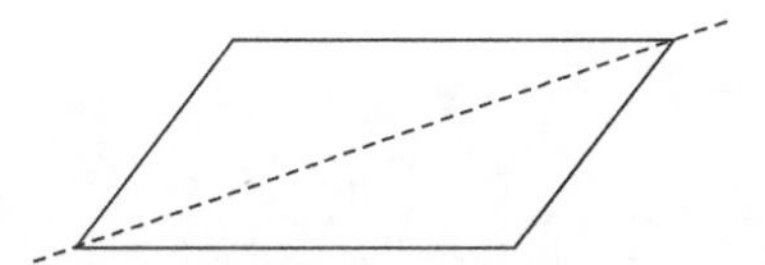

(d)

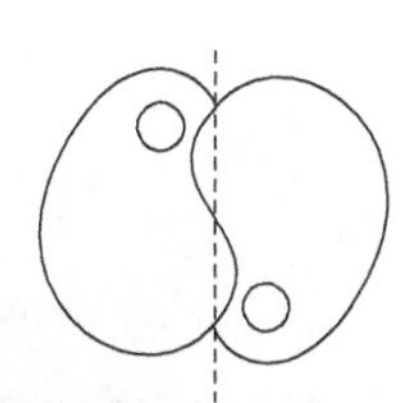

A figure has a line of symmetry when one half of it is the mirror image of the other half.

Another line of symmetry for (b) is

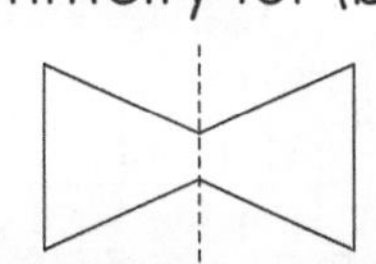

(a) **No**
(b) **Yes**
(c) **No**
(d) **No**

Extension: How can you modify figures (a) and (c), so that each has at least one line of symmetry?

Worked Example 2

Draw a line of symmetry to show a symmetric pattern in each of the following.

(a)

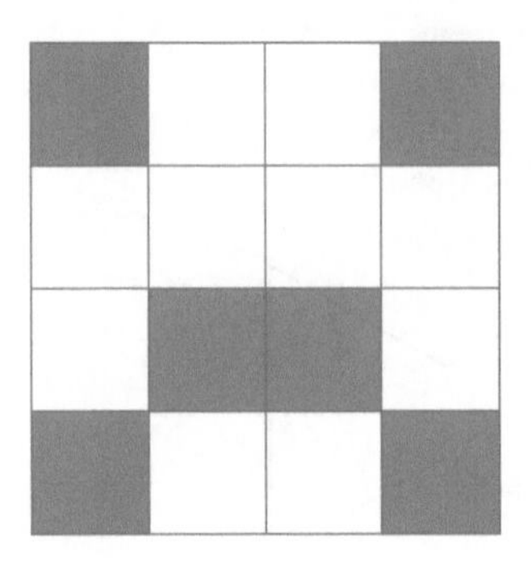

(b)

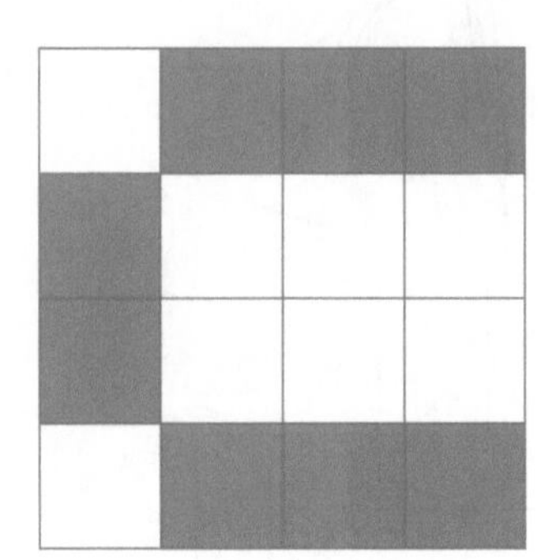

(a)

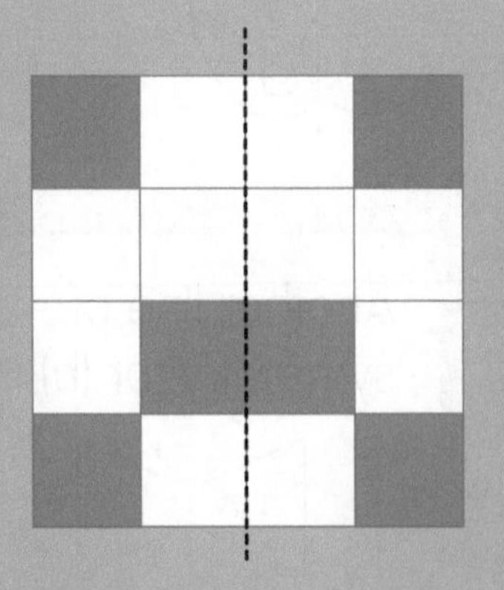

(b)

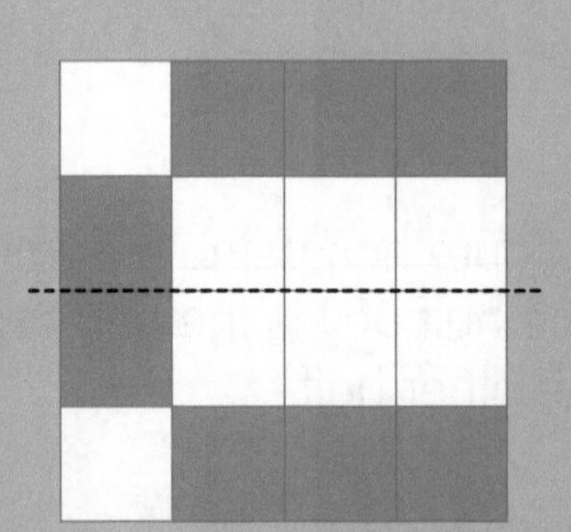

Think!
Would you say that a line of symmetry serves like a mirror line?

Practice Questions

Answer all questions. Show your work and write your statements clearly.

1. How many bricks have been removed from the wall below?

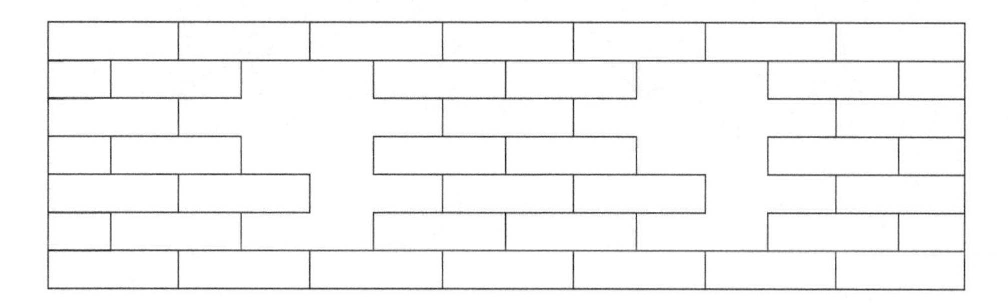

2. Name the line of symmetry in the figure below.

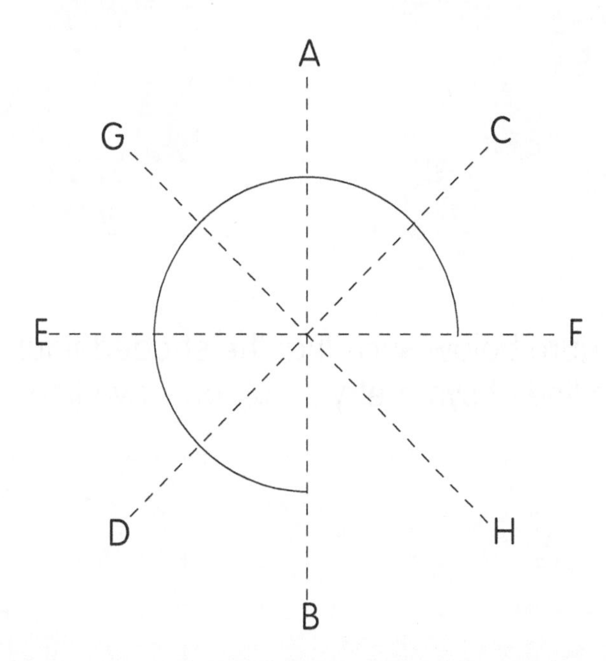

3. Which one of following figures is symmetric?

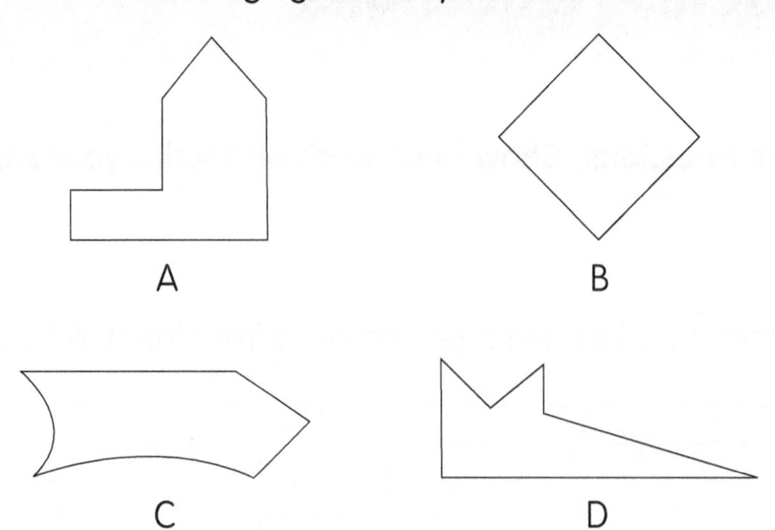

4. Draw a line of symmetry to show a symmetric pattern in each of the following.

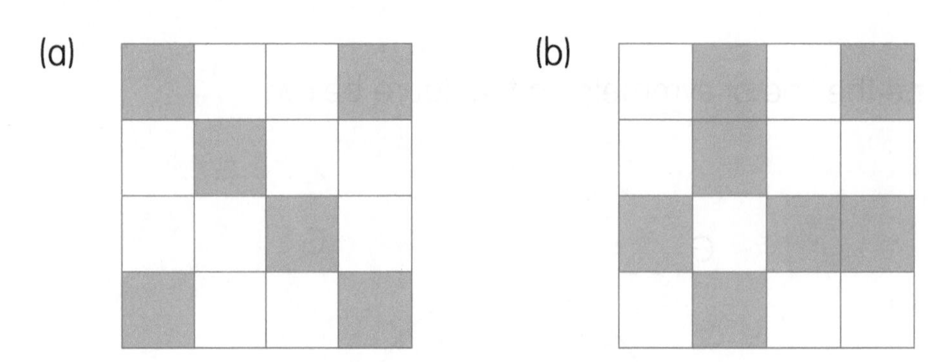

5. Shade the figure below such that the shaded figure has
(a) only one line of symmetry, (b) only two lines of symmetry.

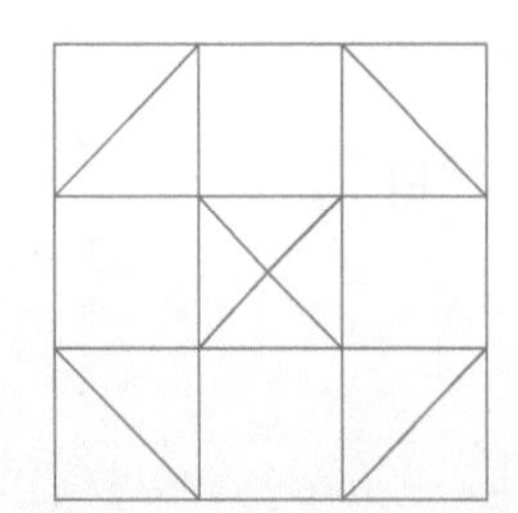

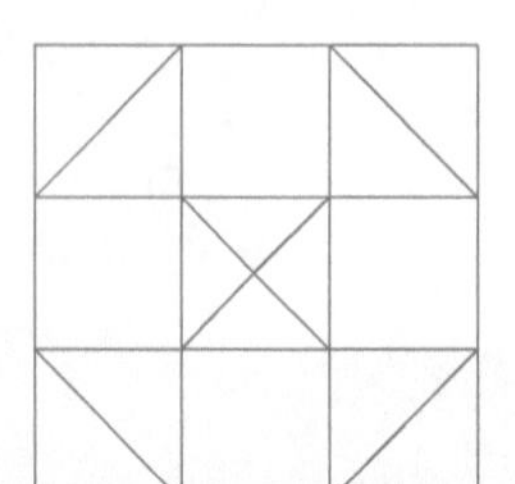

6. Edmund folded a piece of paper into halves and drew a line to divide one half of the paper into 2 parts, A and B, as shown below. He then cut along the line that he drew to obtain part A. Sketch the figure formed by part A when he unfolded the paper.

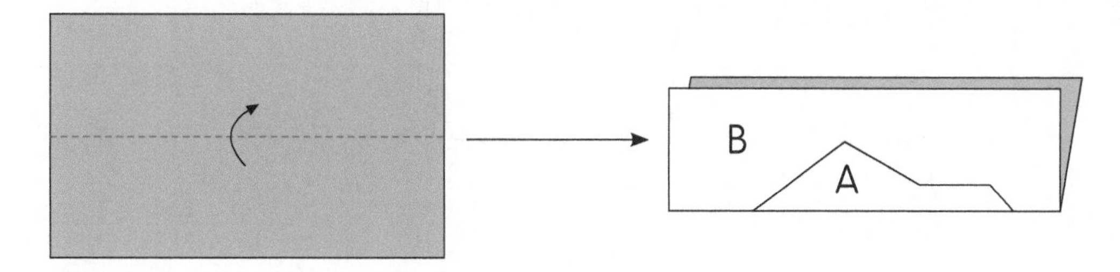

Hint: Act it out to verify your answer.

7. Mary wants to obtain the figure below.

She folds a piece of paper in half, as shown below. Draw the line that Mary should cut along in order to obtain the figure above.

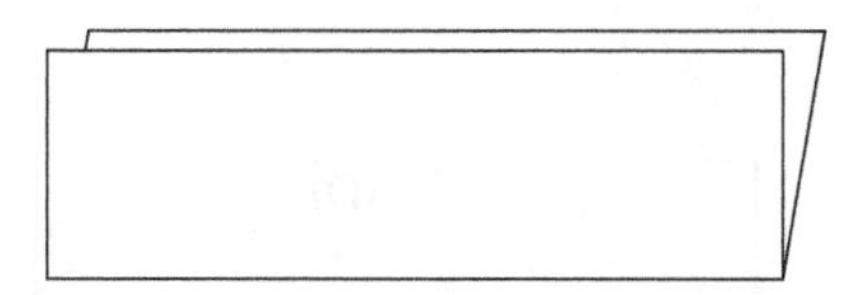

8. Alice folded a square paper in half two times as shown below.

She then made one straight cut. The figure obtained after cutting is shown below. On the figure above, draw the line that Alice had cut along in order to obtain the figure.

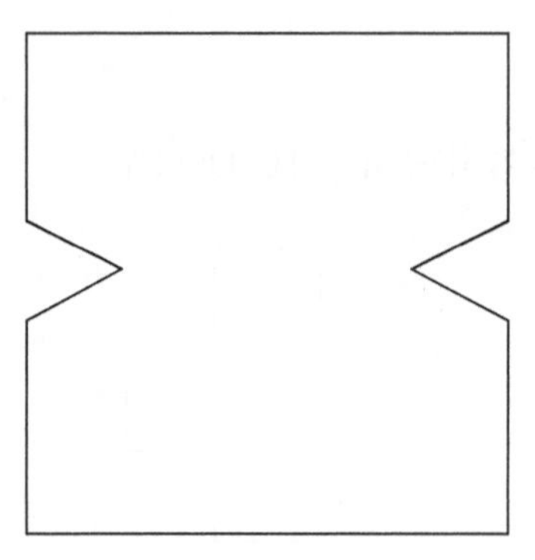

9. In each of the figures below, draw one more square to form a symmetric figure.

(a)

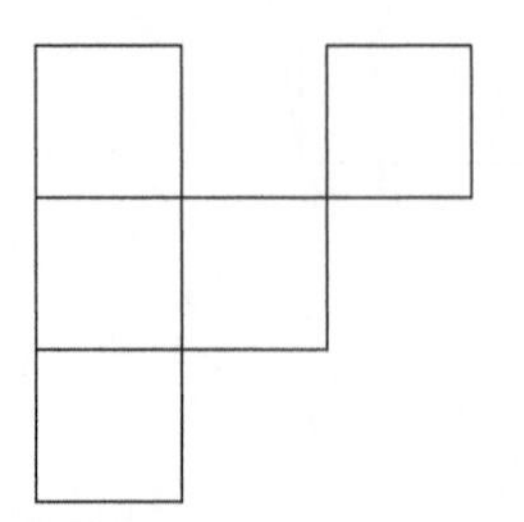

(b)

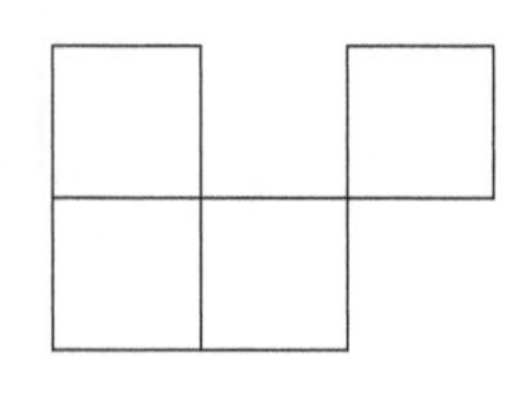

Challenging Problems

Worked Example 1

Look at the pattern formed by the shaded parts. Using the dotted pattern as the line of symmetry, complete the symmetric pattern.

(a)

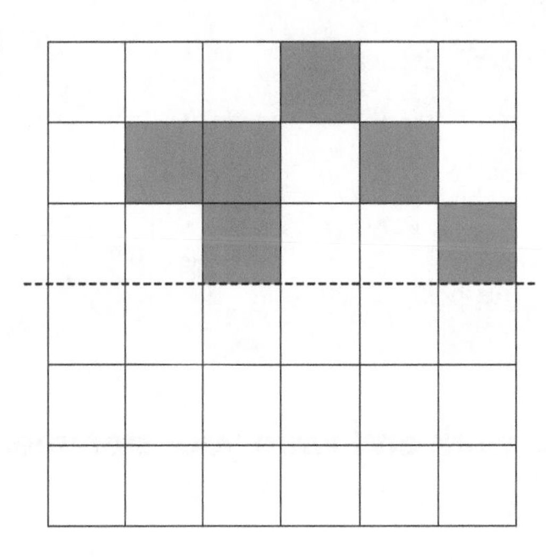

(b)

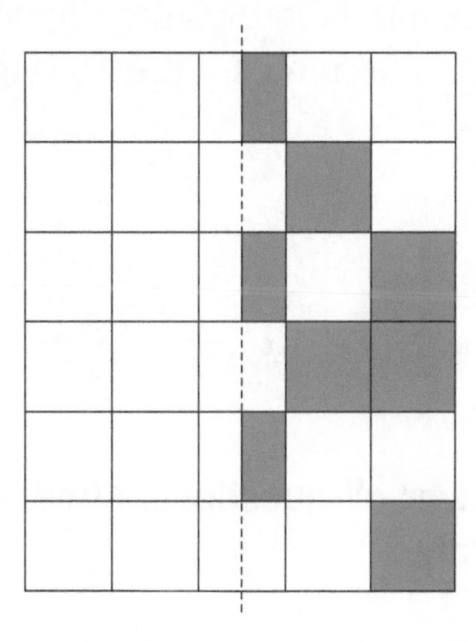

(a)

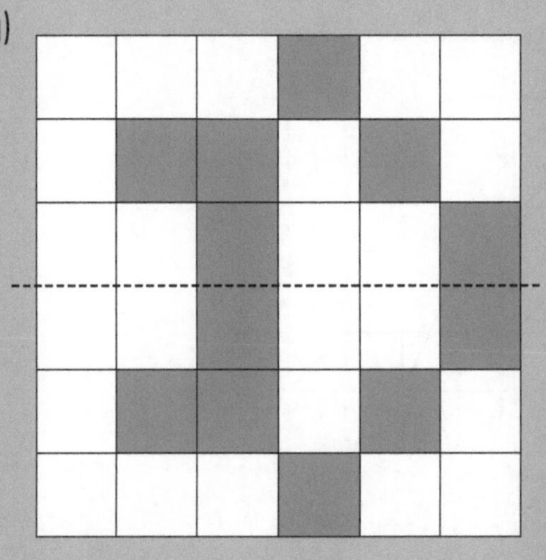

(b)

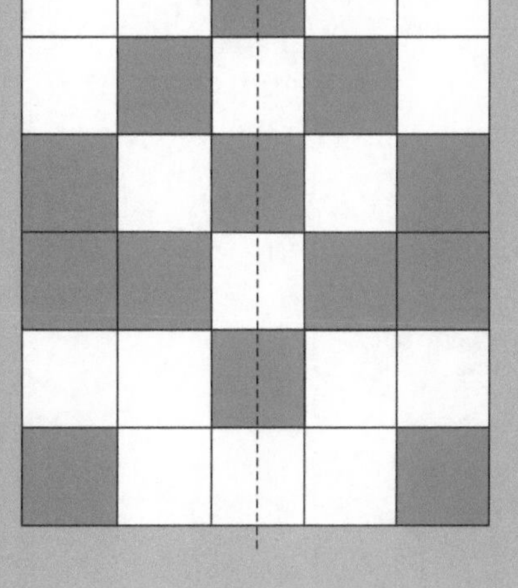

Worked Example 2

In the figure, draw two more squares to form a symmetric figure.

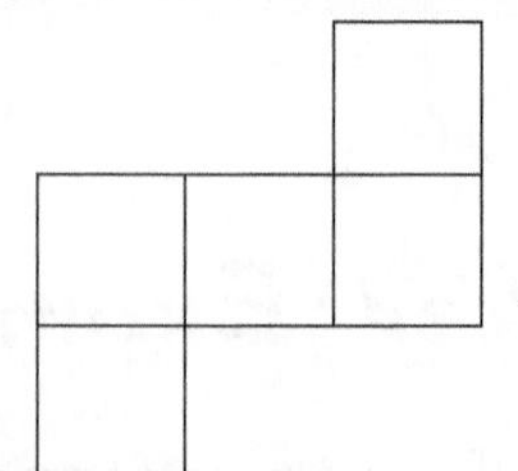

Answers vary.
Some examples are shown below.
The shaded squares are the drawn squares.

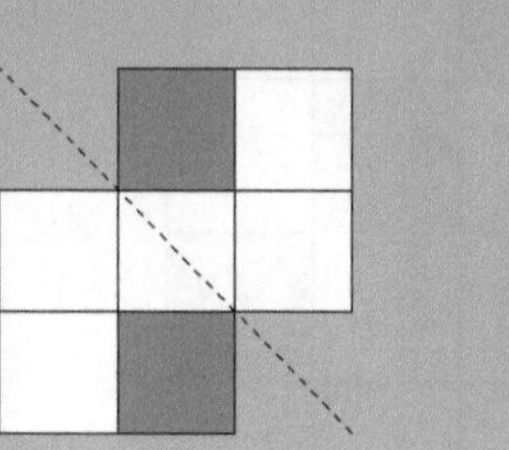

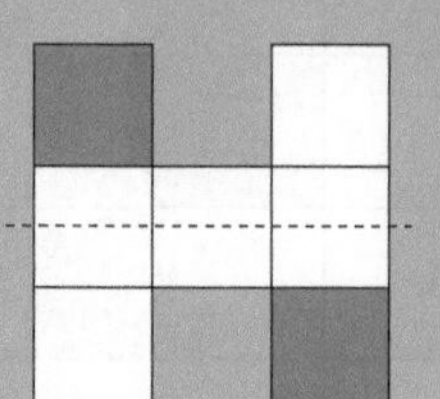

Answer all questions. Show your work and write your statements clearly.

1 Complete the symmetric figure using the dotted line as a line of symmetry.

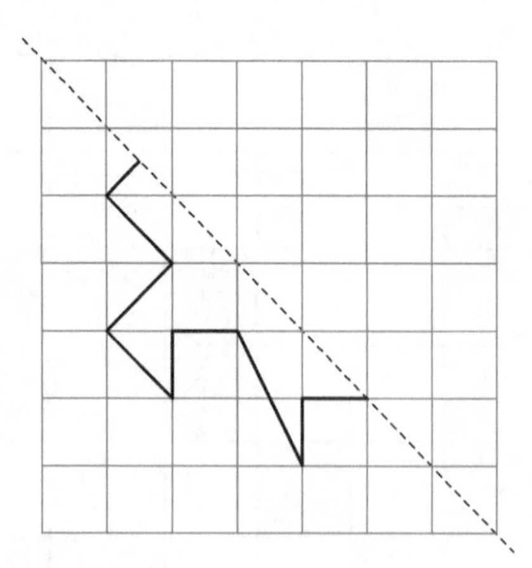

2. Look at the pattern formed by the shaded parts. Using the dotted line as the line of symmetry, complete the symmetric pattern.

(a)

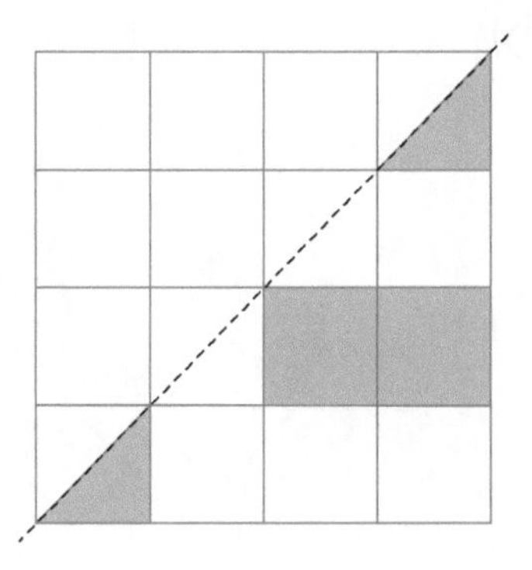

(b)

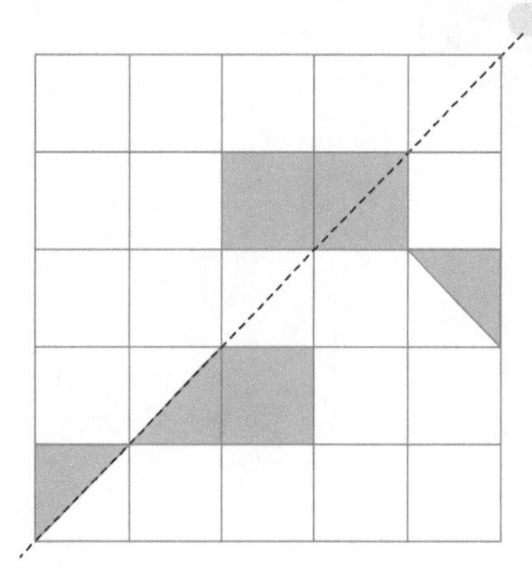

3. Look at the pattern formed by the shaded squares. Using the dotted line as the line of symmetry, complete the symmetric pattern.

(a)

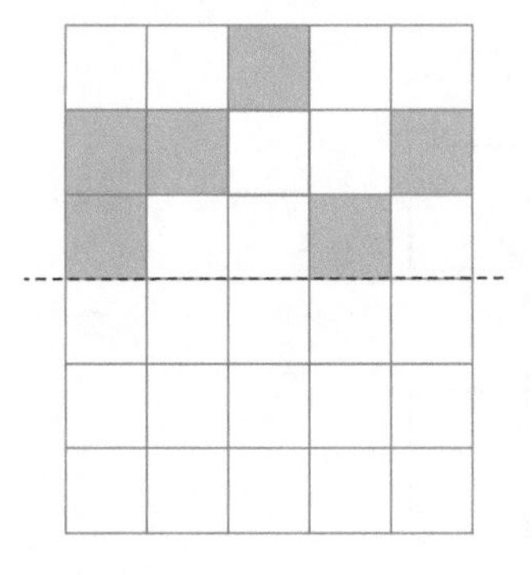

(b)

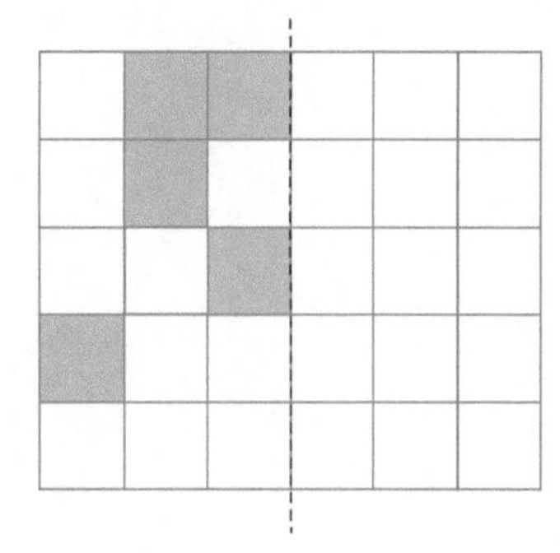

4. Look at the pattern formed by the shaded parts. Using the dotted line as the line of symmetry, complete the symmetric pattern.

(a)

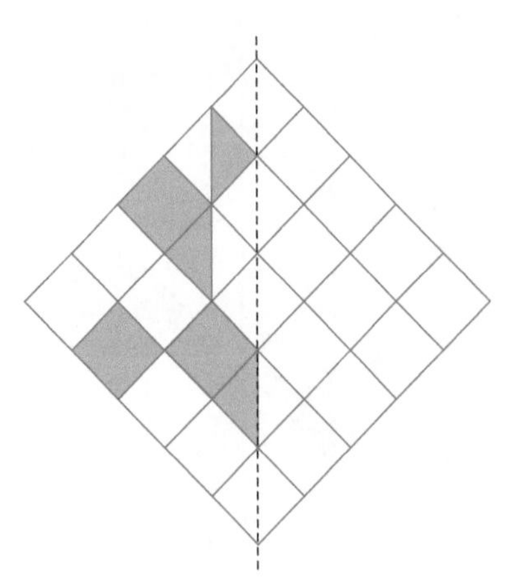

(b)

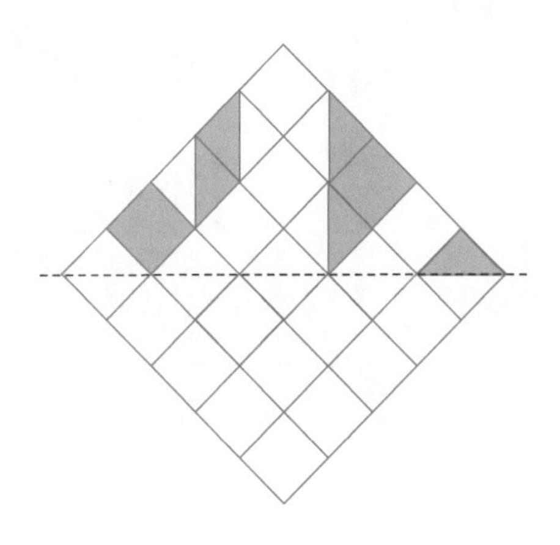

5. In the figure below, draw one more square to form a symmetric figure.

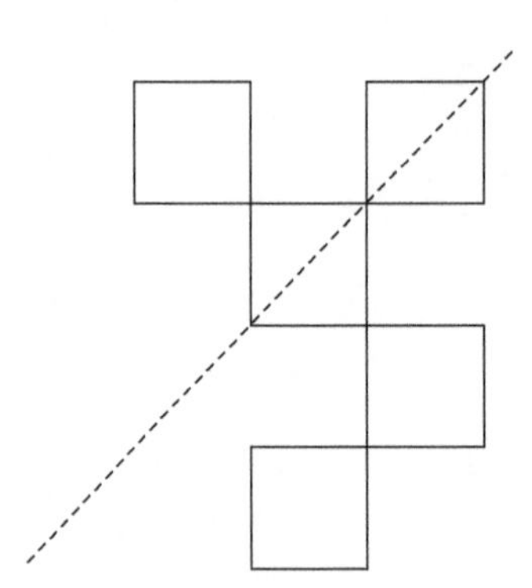

6. In each of the figures below, draw three more squares to form a symmetric figure. Draw the line of symmetry for each figure.

(a)

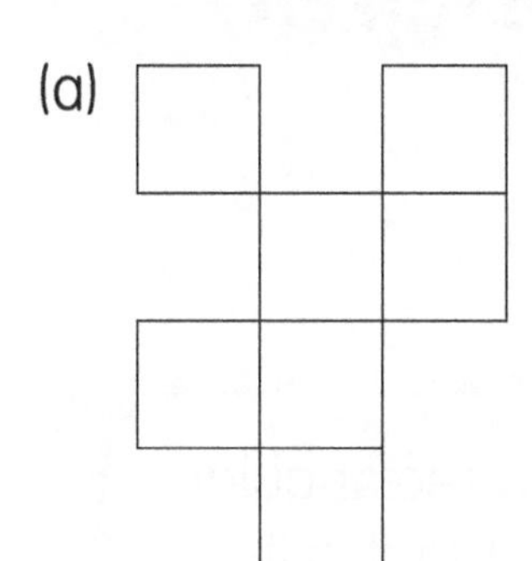

(b)

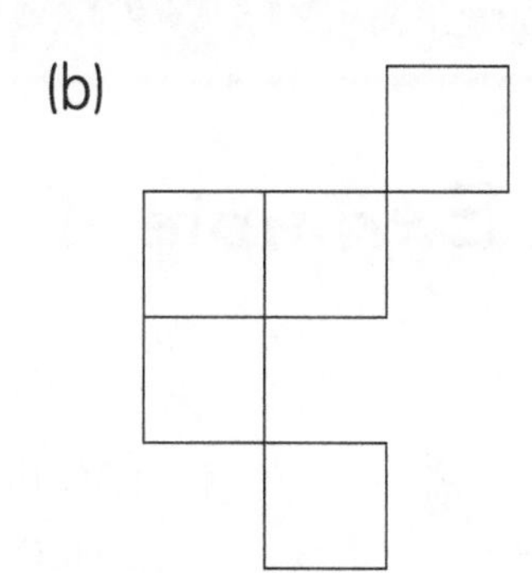

7. Jeremy has to use nine tiles (four black and five white) to form symmetric figures. One example is given below.

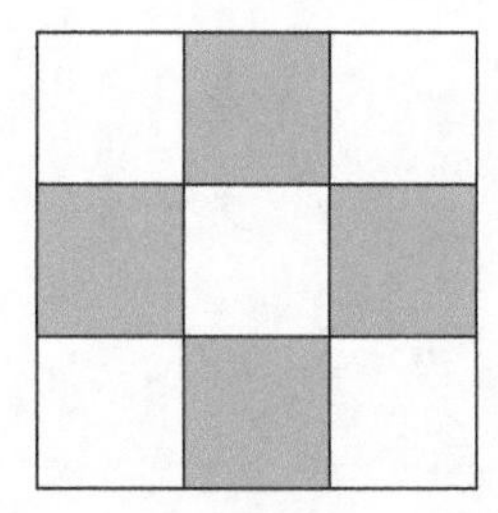

Help him form another two different symmetric figures using the nine tiles. Draw the line(s) of symmetry in each case.

9 Area and Perimeter

Worked Example 1

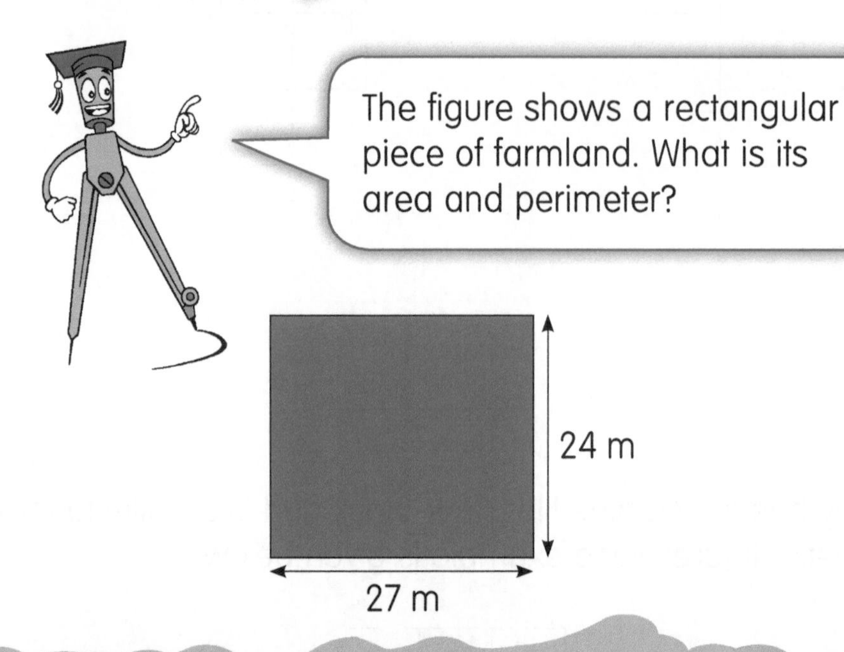

Area = length × width
$= 27 \text{ m} \times 24 \text{ m}$
$= 648 \text{ m}^2$

Its area is **648 m²**.

Perimeter = length + width + length + width
$= 27 \text{ m} + 24 \text{ m} + 27 \text{ m} + 24 \text{ m}$
$= 102 \text{ m}$

Its perimeter is **102 m**.

Another way to find the perimeter is:
27 + 24 = 51
51 × 2 = 102

Worked Example 2

The figure is made up of two squares, A and B. The perimeter of square B is 48 cm. What is the area of the entire figure?

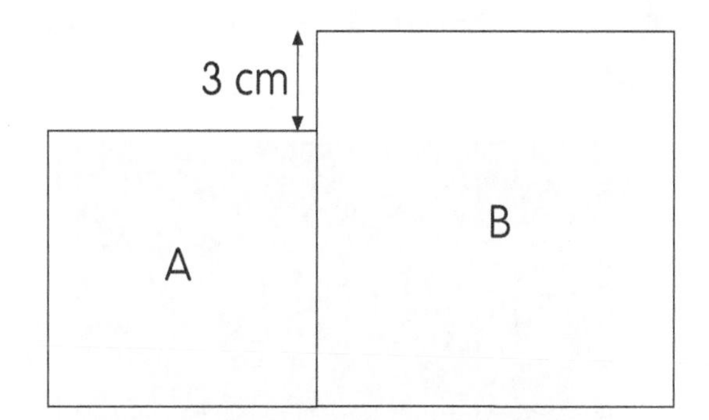

Perimeter of square B = 48 cm
Length of square B = 48 cm ÷ 4
= 12 cm

Length of square A = 12 cm − 3 cm
= 9 cm

Area of square A = 9 cm × 9 cm
= 81 cm^2

Area of square B = 12 cm × 12 cm
= 144 cm^2

Area of entire figure = area of square A + area of square B
= 81 cm^2 + 144 cm^2
= 225 cm^2

The area of the entire figure is **225 cm^2**.

Worked Example 3

The figure represents the floor of a rectangular hall. How much will it cost to carpet the hall if one square meter of carpeting costs $10?

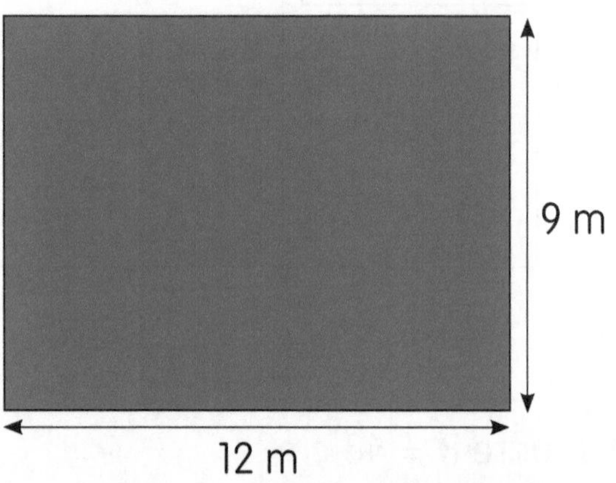

Area = 12 m × 9 m
= 108 m^2

The floor area is 108 m^2.

108 × $10 = $1,080

It will cost **$1,080** to carpet the hall.

1 m^2 ⟶ $10
108 m^2 ⟶ ?

Practice Questions

Answer all questions. Show your work and write your statements clearly.

1. If the area of the square is 1 square unit, estimate the area of the irregular shape.

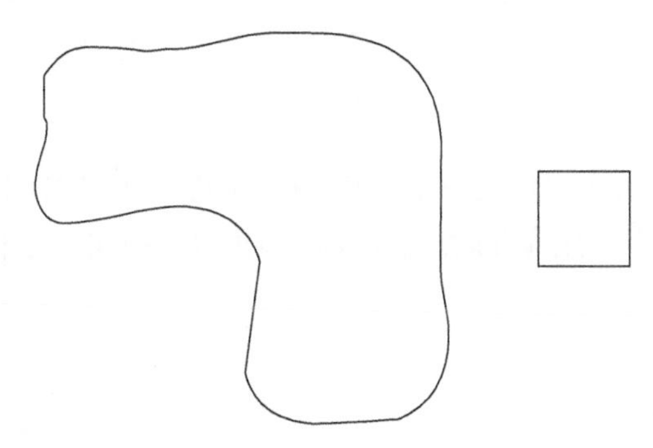

2. A piece of wire is 36 cm long. It is bent to form a square. What is the area of the square?

3. The figure below is made up of 6 identical squares. The perimeter of the figure is 28 cm. What is the area of each square?

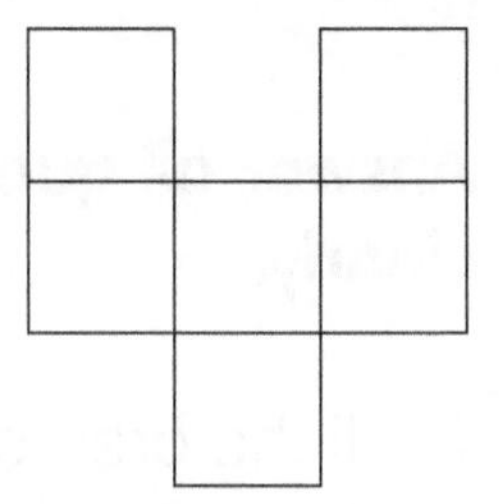

4. The figure below is made up of 9 identical squares and has a perimeter of 32 cm. What is the area of each square?

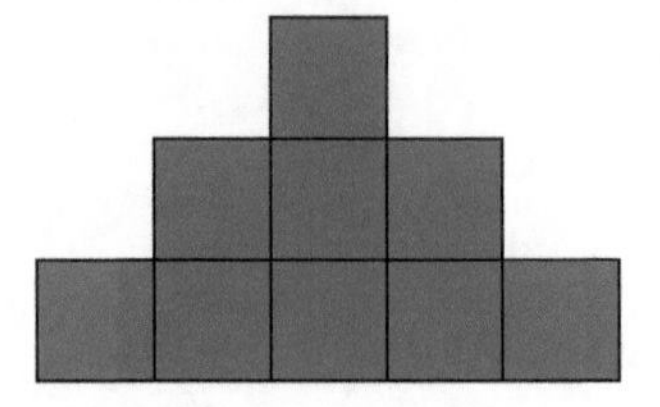

Hint: Count the number of sides of the squares that make up the perimeter.

5. The perimeter of a rectangular coffee table is 440 cm. If its width is 70 cm, what is its area?

6. A rectangular piece of land has a width of 9 m and an area of 162 m^2. How much will it cost to fence the land if the fence costs $18 per meter?

7. A small rectangle is drawn. A second rectangle is drawn around the small rectangle. A third rectangle is drawn around the two and so on. The distance between the sides is always 1 cm. By how much do the length, width, and perimeter increase from one rectangle to another?

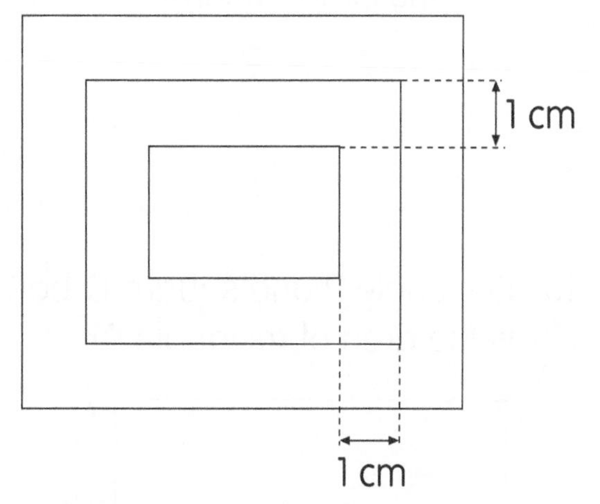

8. The figure below is made up of three squares of different sizes. The length of BC is 6 cm. CD is one-third of BC. The length of EF is 2 cm. What is the area of the largest square?

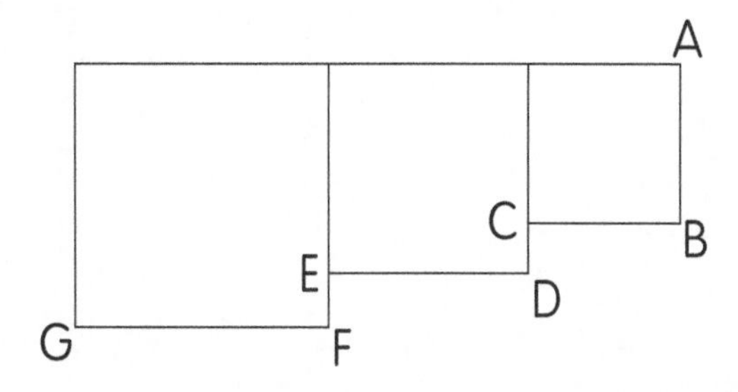

Hint: What is the side of the second largest square, and of the largest square?

9. The figure consists of two squares. What is the area of the shaded region?

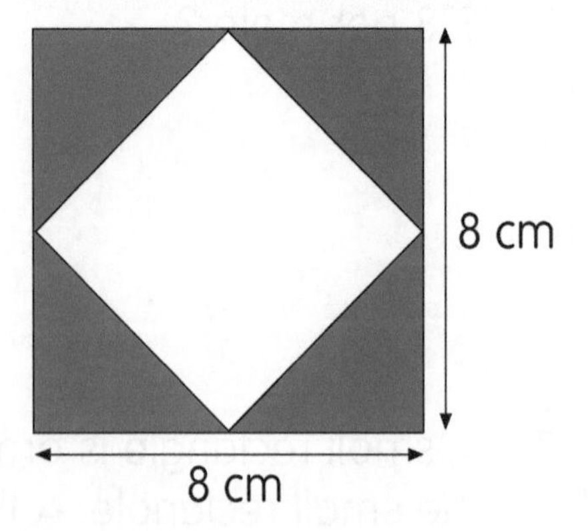

Hint: What is the difference in area between the smaller square and the larger square?

10. Rectangle P and square Q both have the same perimeter. What is the area of rectangle P?

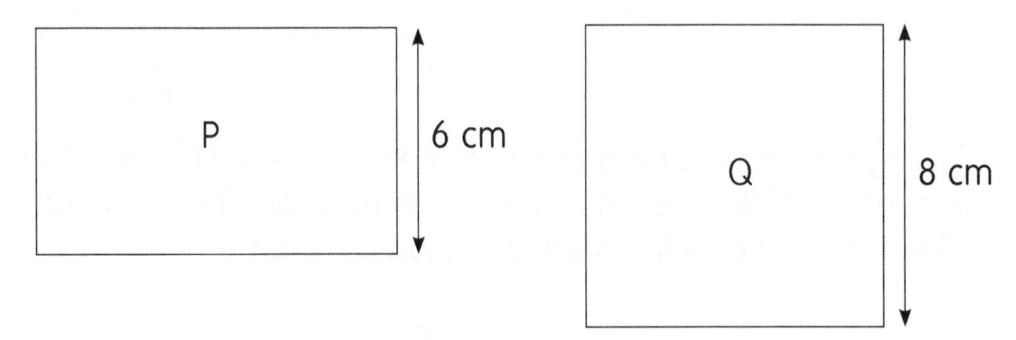

11. Mr. Paul uses a piece of wire to make a big square and a small square, as shown on the right. The area of the big square is 9 times the area of the small square. What is the length of the wire?

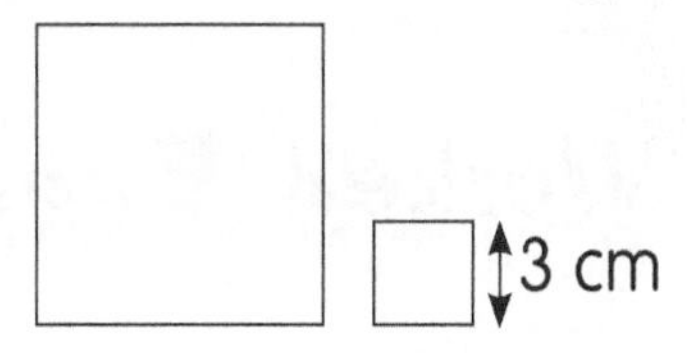

12. A rectangle has a perimeter of 52 cm and an area of 144 cm^2. Find its length and width if the dimensions are expressed in whole numbers.

Hint: Use guess and check.

Worked Example 1

What is the perimeter and area of the figure below?

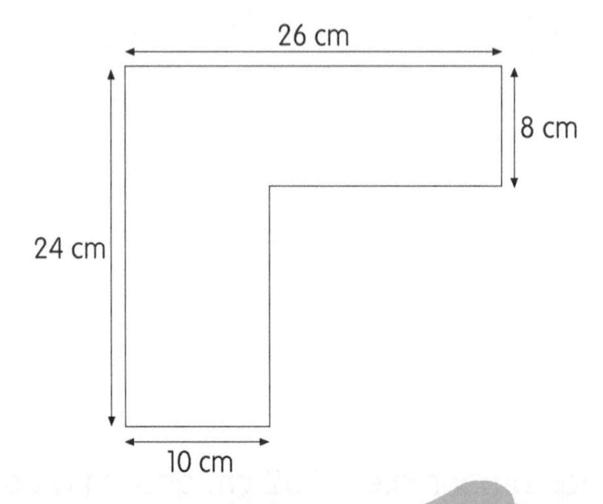

Shift the lines, as shown by the arrows.
They form a rectangle of length 26 cm and width 24 cm.

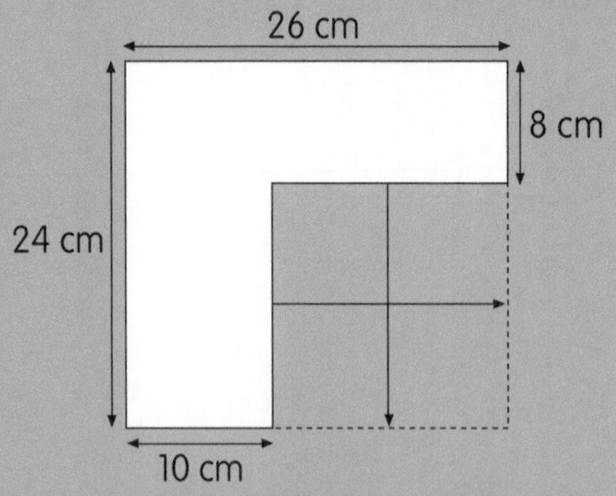

Perimeter = length + width + length + width
= 26 cm + 24 cm + 26 cm + 24 cm
= 100 cm

The perimeter of the figure is **100 cm**.

Method 1

Divide the figure into 2 rectangles, A and B, as shown.

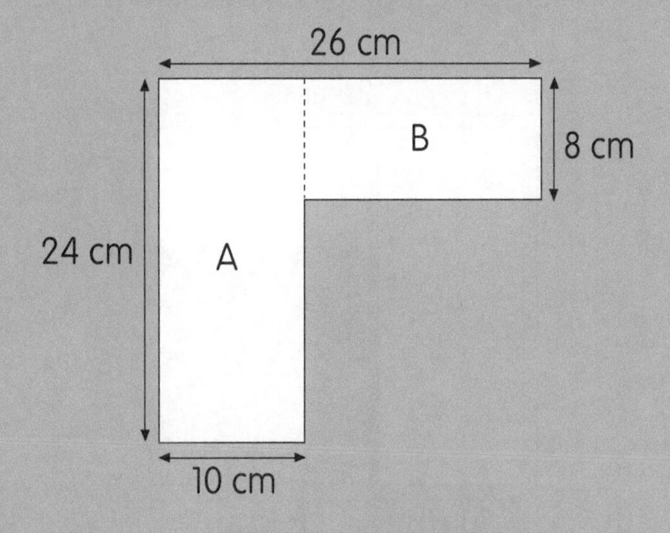

Area of rectangle A = length × width
$= 24 \text{ cm} \times 10 \text{ cm}$
$= 240 \text{ cm}^2$

Length of rectangle B = 26 cm – 10 cm = 16 cm

Area of rectangle B = 16 cm × 8 cm = 128 cm^2

Area of the figure = $240 \text{ cm}^2 + 128 \text{ cm}^2 = 368 \text{ cm}^2$

The area of the figure is **368 cm^2**.

Method 2

The area of the figure may also be calculated as follows:

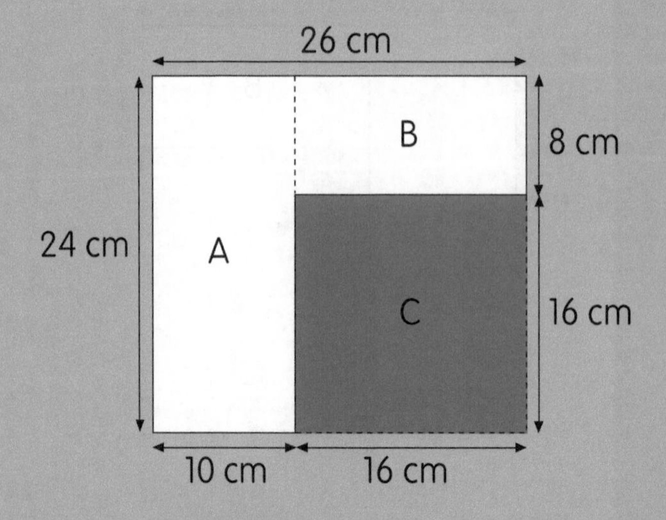

Area of figure = Area of rectangle (of sizes 26 cm by 24 cm) – Area of square C

$= 26 \times 24 \text{ cm}^2 - 16 \times 16 \text{ cm}^2$

$= \mathbf{368\ cm^2}$.

Worked Example 2

Find the area of the unshaded region of the two rectangles, A and B below.

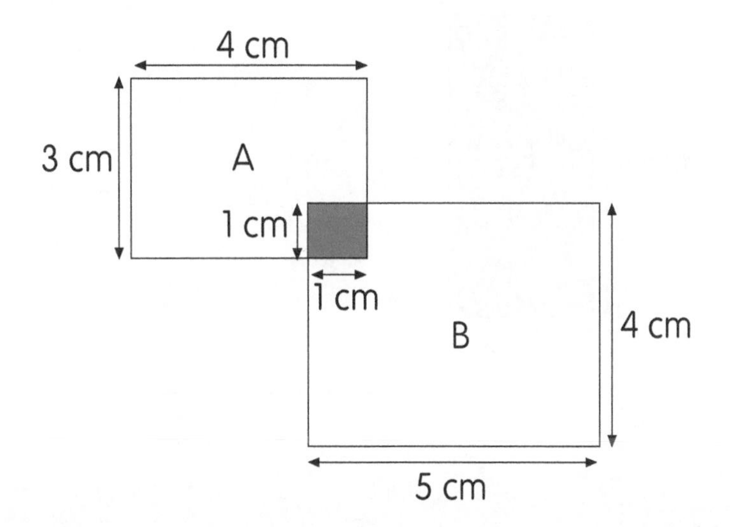

Note that the shaded region is part of both rectangles.

Area of rectangle A = 4 cm × 3 cm
= 12 cm^2

Area of rectangle B = 5 cm × 4 cm
= 20 cm^2

Area of shaded square = 1 cm × 1 cm
= 1 cm^2

Area of unshaded region = 12 cm^2 + 20 cm^2 – 1 cm^2 – 1 cm^2
= 30 cm^2

The area of the unshaded region of the two rectangles, A and B, is **30 cm^2**.

Worked Example 3

A rectangular piece of paper is folded, as shown below. What was the area of the piece of paper before it was folded?

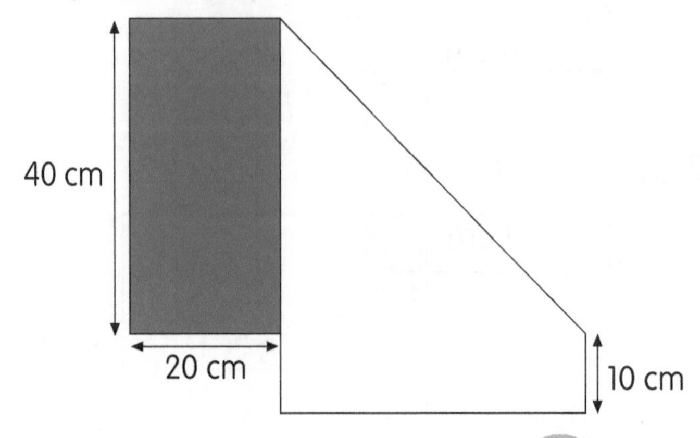

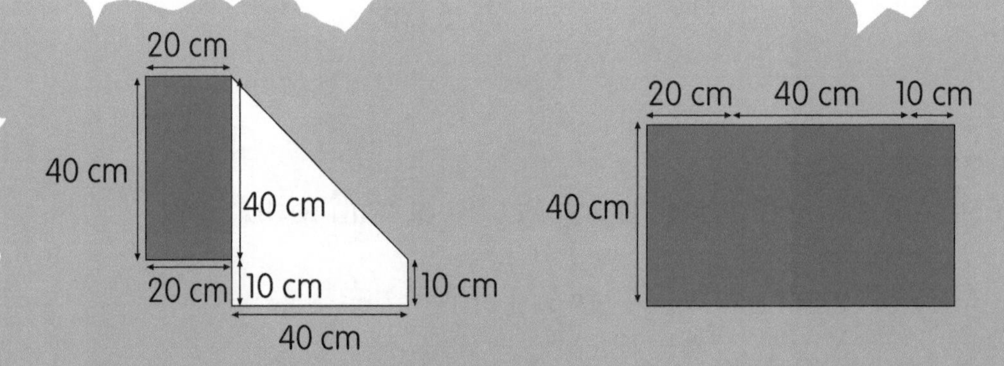

Length of rectangle = 20 cm + 40 cm + 10 cm
= 70 cm

Area of rectangle = 70 cm × 40 cm
= 2,800 cm^2

The area of the piece of paper before it was folded was **2,800 cm^2**.

Extension: Use a different method to figure out the area of the piece of paper.

Answer: 40 × 20 + 40 × 10 + 40 × 40 = **2,800 cm^2**.

Answer all questions. Show your work and write your statements clearly.

1. What is the perimeter of the figure below?

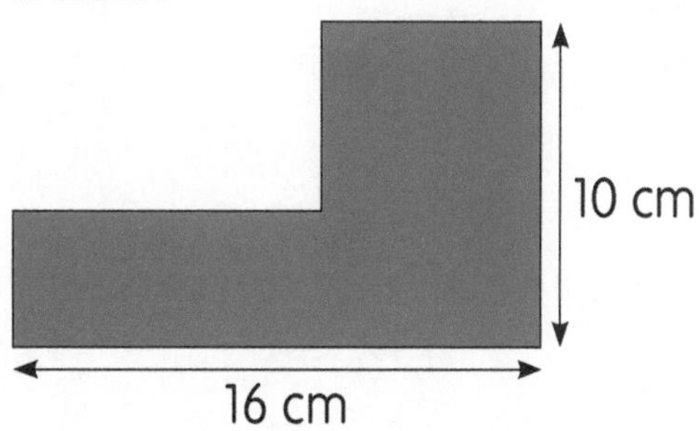

2. What is the perimeter of the figure below? All angles are right angles.

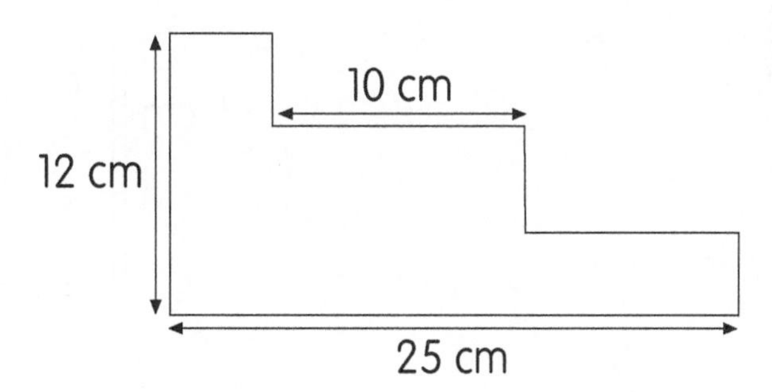

3. What is the total length of the bold lines? All angles are right angles.

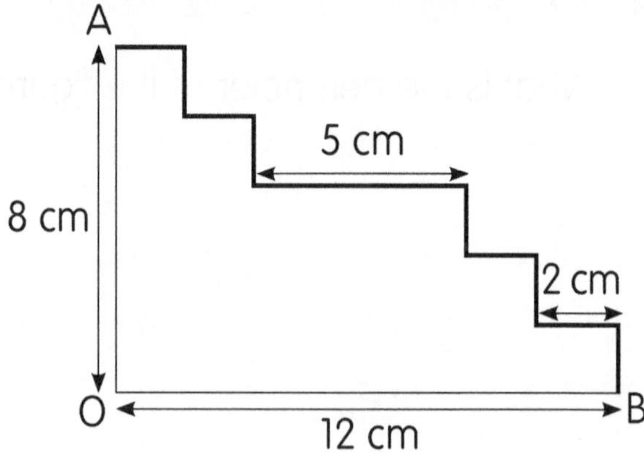

4. What is the area of the unshaded region of square A and rectangle B?

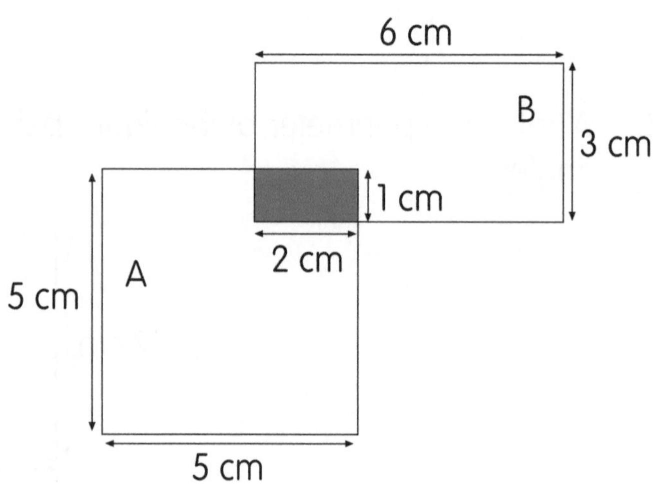

Hint: See Worked Example 2

5. A floor tiler charges $400 to tile a rectangular room. Another room is twice as long and twice as wide. How much will he charge to tile the other room?

Hint: Find out how much bigger the new area is.

6. The figure shows a cubic box of sides 1 cm. Cutting along sides *AD, BC, FG, EH,* and *BF* will form a flat shape. What is the perimeter of the resulting shape?

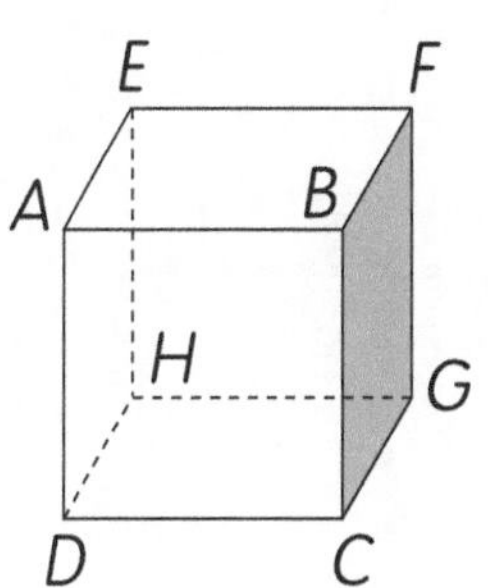

Hint: Sketch the two-dimensional shape.

7. In the figure below, *ABCD* is a square of sides 2 cm.
E, F, G, and *H* are the midpoints of the sides of the square *ABCD.*
I, J, K, and *L* are the midpoints of the square *EFGH.*
What is the area of square *IJKL*?

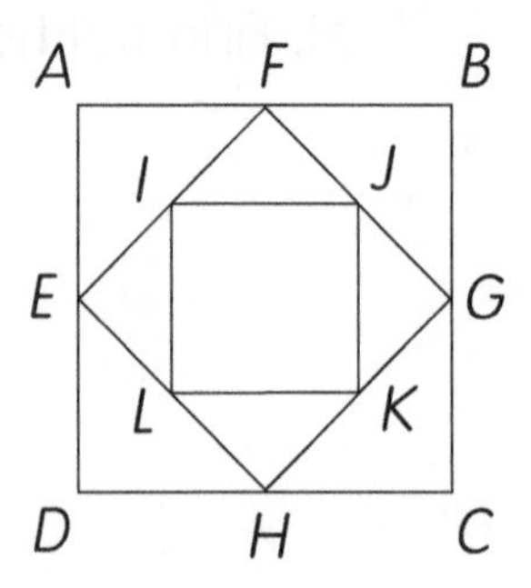

Hint: Area of square EFGH = $\frac{1}{2}$ × area of square ABCD

8. Square A and rectangle B have the same perimeter. Each side of square A is 12 cm. The length of rectangle B is 4 cm longer than its width. What is the width of rectangle B?

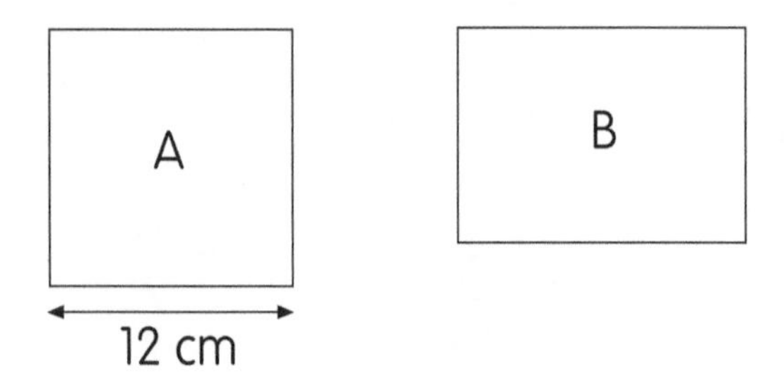

9. Daryl has some squares of side 1 cm and rectangles of length 3 cm and of width 1 cm.

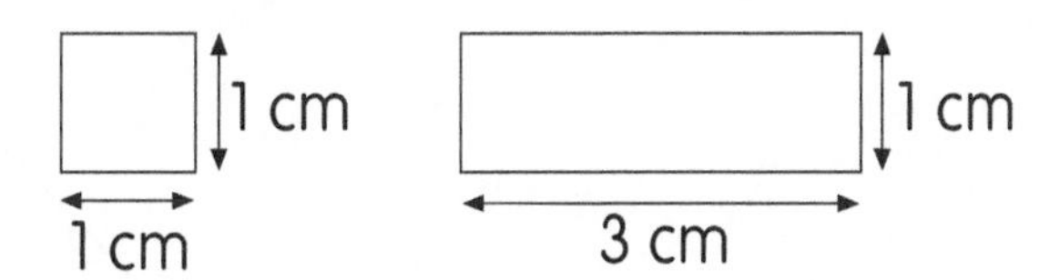

(a) He wants to make a big square of side 3 cm using the above squares and rectangles. How many such squares and rectangles does he need?
(b) Daryl also plans to make a rectangle of length 4 cm and width 3 cm using the above squares and rectangles. How many such squares and rectangles does he need?

Extension: How many possible ways can Daryl make the 3-cm square and the 4 × 3 rectangle?

10. Richard cuts a wire into two pieces to form a rectangle and a square, as shown below. The perimeter of square P is equal to the perimeter of rectangle Q. What is the area of rectangle Q?

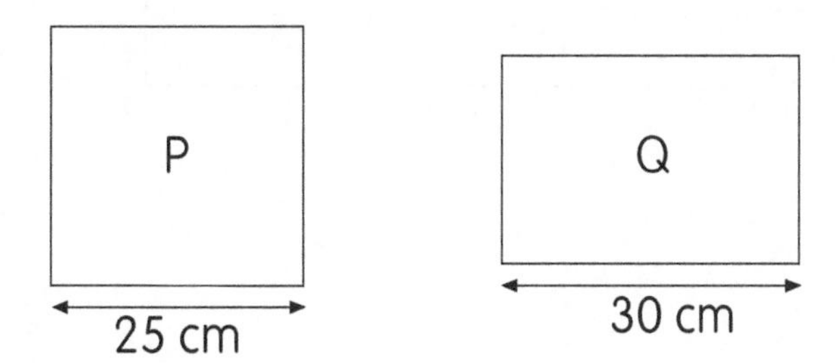

11. A rectangular piece of paper is folded, as shown below. What is the area of the piece of paper before it was folded?

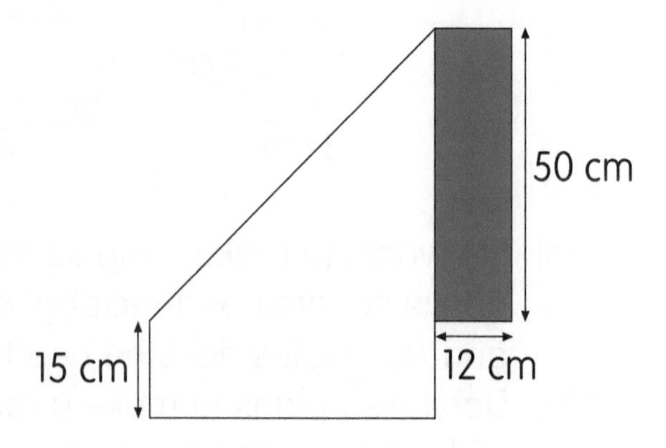

12. In the figure, the length of *PS* is one-third of *PQ*. The perimeter of the rectangle is 32 cm. What is the area of rectangle *PQRS*?

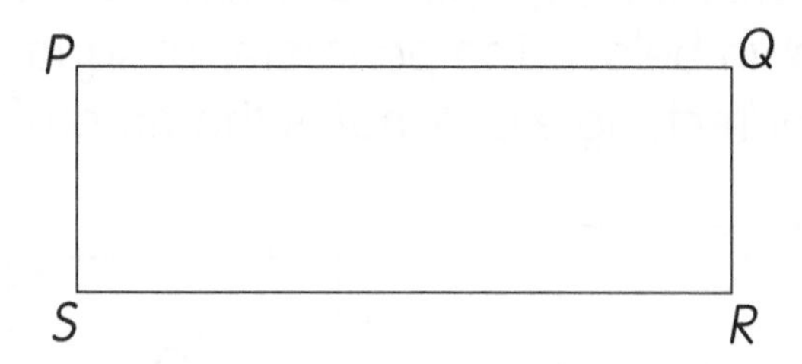

10 Tables and Graphs

Worked Example 1

The table shows some animals spotted by a group of students in a zoo.

Type of animal	John	Arnold	Sayed	Tyra	Lisa
Boar	2	4	3	1	3
Lion	3	5	4	3	4
Tiger	1	0	4	2	3
Snake	0	3	5	4	2
Elephant	5	2	4	0	3

(a) Who spotted the most number of tigers?
(b) Who spotted the least number of boars?
(c) How many elephants did the group spot in total?
(d) How many more lions than tigers did the group spot in all?
(e) Which type of animal was spotted the least number of times?

(a) Across the "tiger-row," the largest number is 4. It is under Sayed. So, **Sayed** spotted the most number of tigers.

(b) Under the "boar-row," the least number is 1. It is under Tyra. So, **Tyra** spotted the least number of boars.

(c) Under the "elephant-row," the numbers are 5, 2, 4, 0, and 3.

$$5 + 2 + 4 + 3 = 14$$

The group spotted **14** elephants in all.

(d) $3 + 5 + 4 + 3 + 4 = 19$
The group spotted 19 lions in all.

$1 + 0 + 4 + 2 + 3 = 10$
The group spotted 10 tigers in all.

$19 - 10 = 9$
The group spotted **9** more lions than tigers in all.

(e)

						Total
Boar	2	4	3	1	3	13
Lion	3	5	4	3	4	19
Tiger	1	0	4	2	3	10
Snake	0	3	5	4	2	14
Elephant	5	2	4	0	3	14

From the table, the smallest total is 10, which is the total number of tigers spotted by the five students.

The **tiger** was spotted the least number of times.

Worked Example 2

The bar graph below shows the number of different types of fruits that Sally bought from a supermarket.

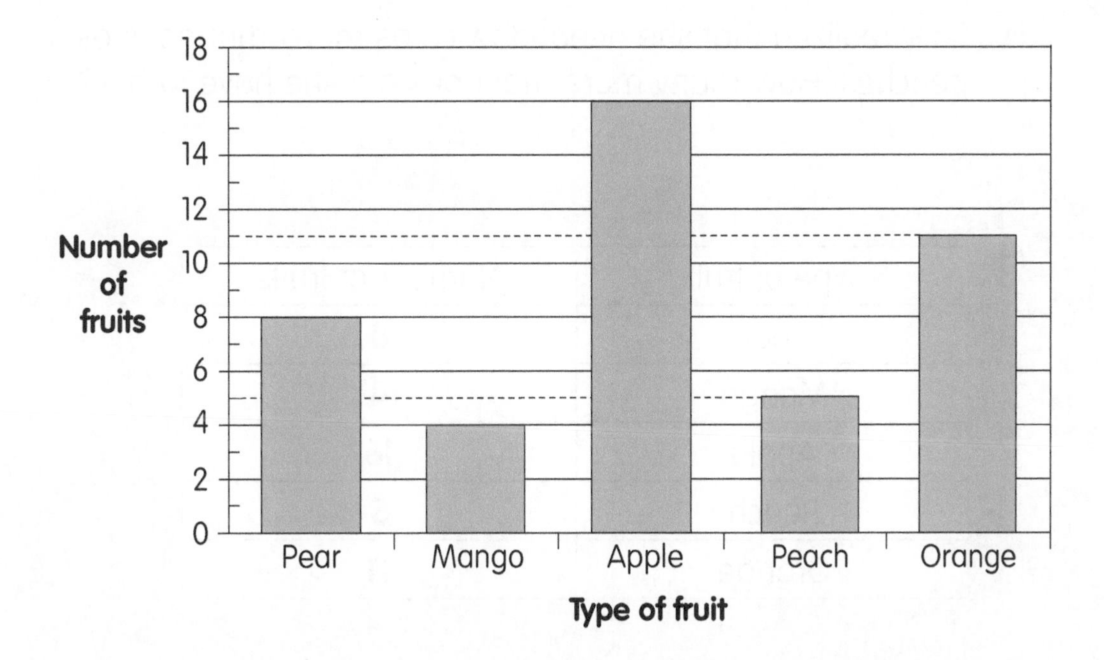

(a) Study the bar graph and complete the following table.

Type of fruit	Number of fruits
Pear	
Mango	
Apple	
Peach	
Orange	

(b) Use the data in the table to answer the following questions.

(i) How many fruits did Sally buy altogether?

(ii) How many fewer oranges than apples did Sally buy?

(iii) How many more oranges than mangoes did she buy?

(iv) Sally realized that she needed twice as many mangoes as peaches. How many more mangoes did she have to buy?

(a)

Type of fruit	Number of fruits
Pear	**8**
Mango	**4**
Apple	**16**
Peach	**5**
Orange	**11**

(b) (i) $8 + 4 + 16 + 5 + 11 = 44$
Sally bought **44** fruits altogether.

(ii) There are 16 apples and 11 oranges.
$16 - 11 = 5$
Sally bought **5** fewer oranges than apples.

(iii) There are 11 oranges and 4 mangoes.
$11 - 4 = 7$
She bought **7** more oranges than mangoes.

(iv) There are 5 peaches.
$2 \times 5 = 10$
She needed to buy 10 mangoes.

There are 4 mangoes
$10 - 4 = 6$
She had to buy **6** more mangoes.

Answer all questions. Show your work and write your statements clearly.

1. Mr. Lim is returning to his home in Singapore after a visit to relatives in the United States. Use the table below to help him find a flight leaving for Singapore in the afternoon. Circle the flight that he can take.

Destination	Departs 8:00 A.M.	Departs 3:00 P.M.	Departs 10:00 P.M.
Dubai	Flight 46	Flight 11	Flight 72
Singapore	Flight 55	Flight 80	Flight 54
Sydney	Flight 94	Flight 33	Flight 84
Liverpool	Flight 21	Flight 56	Flight 91

2. The number of medals won by contestants from top schools at a math competition is tabulated below.

School	A	B	C	D	E
Gold	13	12	9	7	2
Silver	15	8	7	8	12
Bronze	5	7	10	6	5

Fill in the blanks.

(a) School C won __________ bronze medals.

(b) School D won a total of __________ medals.

(c) School E won __________ more silver medals than school C.

(d) School __________ and school __________ won the same number of silver medals.

3. The graph below shows the number of math books sold by a particular bookshop in a particular year.

Title	Number of copies sold
Math is Cool!	★★★
Aha! Math	★★★★★★★★
Math for You ONLY!	★★★★
Beautiful Math	★★
My Numbers and I	★★★★★

Each ★ represents 9 copies.

(a) How many copies of *Aha! Math* were sold?
(b) The number of copies of *Math is Cool!* sold was 18 fewer than the number of copies of another book. Which book was it?
(c) Which book had the least number of copies sold?

4. A survey was conducted to find out the different modes of transport used by students in a particular school on Friday. The students were asked to indicate their main mode of transport. The results are tabulated in the bar graph below.

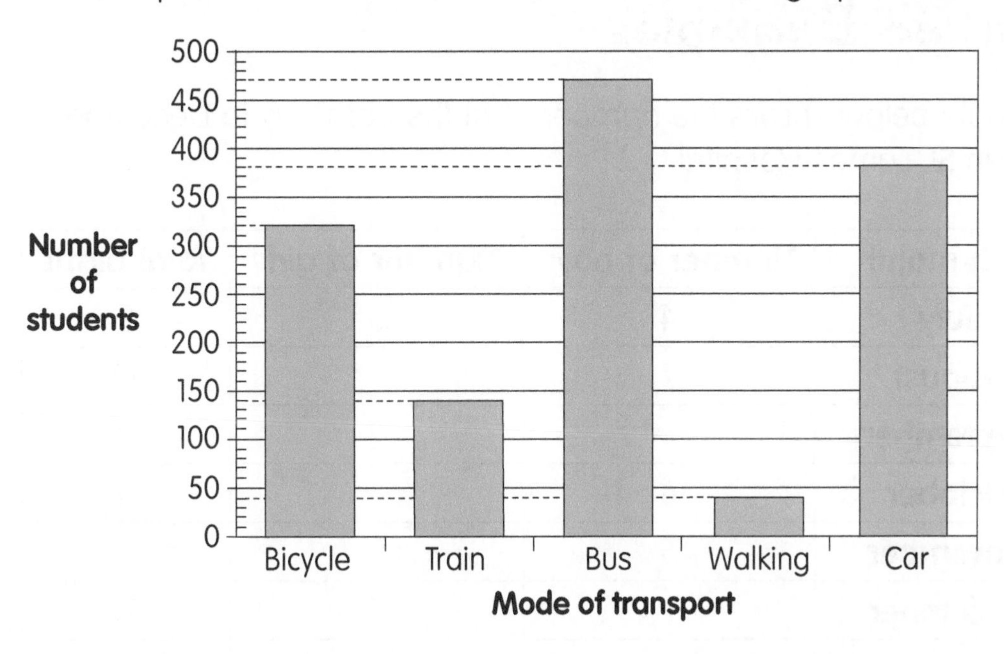

(a) Study the bar graph and complete the following table.

Mode of transport	Bicycle	Train	Bus	Walking	Car
Number of students					

(b) Use the data in the table to answer the following questions.
 (i) Which was the most common mode of transport?
 (ii) Which was the least common mode of transport?
 (iii) What was the total number of students who went to school on Friday?
 (iv) How many more students traveled by bus than by car?
 (v) How many fewer students walked than cycled to school?
 (vi) How many students would need to travel to school by car instead of by bus, so that the number of students who traveled by bus and by car are the same?

Worked Example

The table below shows the number of births from July to December 2009 in St. James Hospital.

Birth month	Number of boys	Number of girls	Total births
July	4	5	9
August	7		13
September		2	11
October	6		6
November	5	2	
December		7	11
Total			

(a) Complete the table.
(b) Use the data in the table to answer the following questions.
   (i) How many children in all were born in September and October 2009?
   (ii) How many children were born from July to December 2009?
   (iii) In which month was the least number of babies born?
   (iv) Joanne is the youngest among those born in September 2009.
   How many children born from July to December 2009 are
   (a) younger than her,
   (b) older than her?

(a)

Birth month	Number of boys	Number of girls	Total births
July	4	5	9
August	7	**6**	13
September	**9**	2	11
October	6	**0**	6
November	5	2	**7**
December	**4**	7	11
Total	**35**	**22**	**57**

(b) (i) 11 babies were born in September, and 6 in October.
$11 + 6 = 17$

17 children were born in September and October 2009.

(ii) From the table above, **57** children were born from July to December 2009.

(iii) From the table, 6 is the least number of births in a given month, which is October.

The least number of babies were born in **October**.

(iv) (a) Children who are younger than Joanne must be born after September, that is, those born from October to December.

$6 + 7 + 11 = 24$

24 children are younger than her.

(b) Children who are older than Joanne are those born in and before September.

Since Joanne is the youngest born in September, there are $11 - 1 = 10$ older children born in September.

$9 + 13 + 10 = 32$

32 children are older than her.

Answer all questions. Show your work and write your statements clearly.

1. The table below shows the number of students attending lessons for different subjects.

	Grade 3	Grade 4	Grade 5	Grade 6
English	?	65	87	84
Science	82	52	64	60
Math	123	131	97	136

(a) 321 students attend English lessons. How many Grade 3 students attend English lessons?
(b) How many more Grade 4 students attend English lessons than science lessons?
(c) How many more students attend math lessons than science lessons?

2. The bar graph below shows the number of students from Grade 1 to Grade 4 in a particular school.

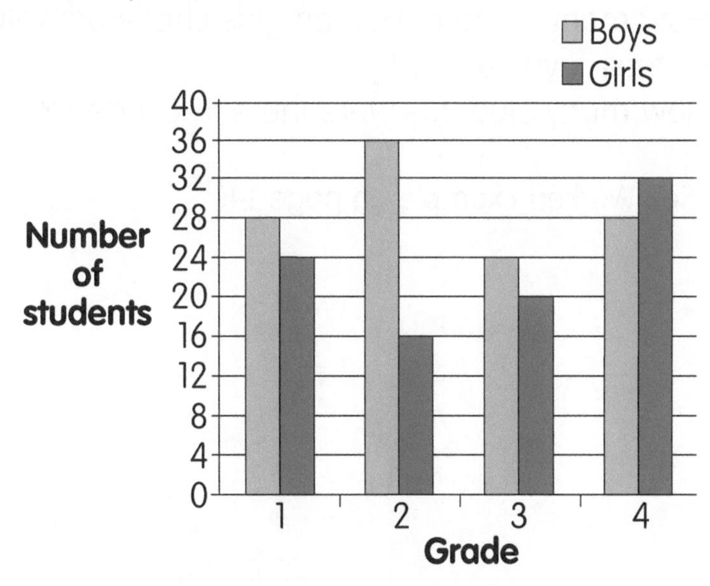

(a) How many girls are in Grade 1?
(b) How many boys are in Grade 3?
(c) How many students are in Grade 4?
(d) How many more boys than girls are there in Grade 2?

3. Students in Grade 4 classes were asked to choose their favorite activity among those listed in the table below.

Activity	Number of boys	Number of girls	Total
Badminton	13	8	21
Tennis		6	12
Soccer	11		16
Basketball	9	4	
Swimming		10	17
Total			

(a) Complete the table.

(b) Use the data in the table to answer the following questions.

(i) Which activity is the least popular among the students?

(ii) Which activity is the most popular among the boys?

(iii) How many more girls than boys chose swimming as their favorite activity?

(iv) How many more boys than girls chose basketball as their favorite activity?

(v) How many students were there in Grade 4?

Hint: See Worked Example on page 140.

4. The bar graph below shows the points scored by a group of students in a math examination.

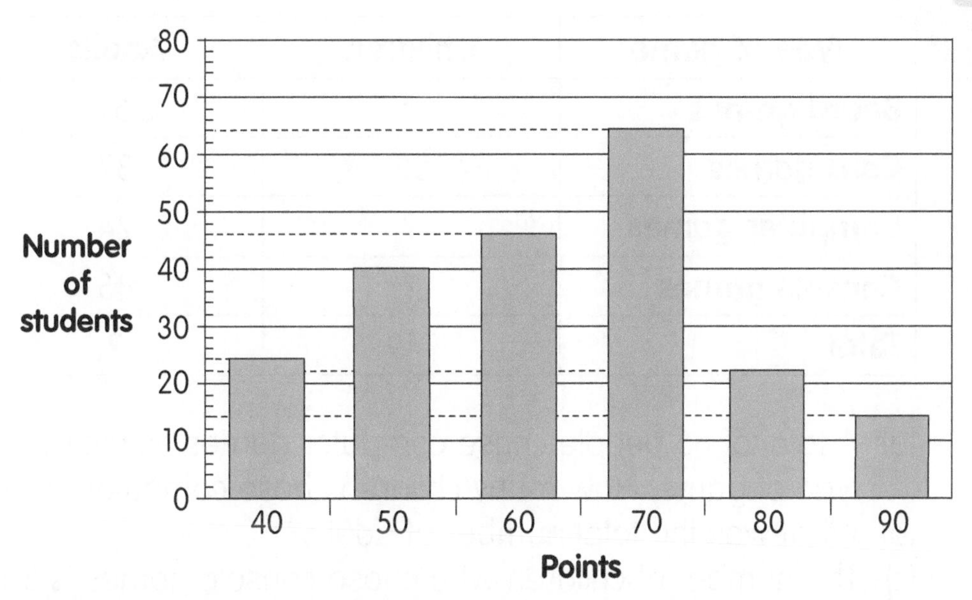

(a) Denise and 45 other students got the same points. How many points did Denise score?

(b) If grade A was 80 points and above, how many students obtained grade A?

(c) If the passing grade was 50 points and above, how many students passed the examination?

5. A group of people were asked to choose their favorite type of game among those listed in the table below.

Type of game	Children	Adults
Board games	?	51
Card games	32	37
Computer games	?	24
Console games	?	45
Total	149	?

(a) A total of 65 people chose computer games as their favorite type of game. How many children chose computer games?
(b) What was the total number of adults?
(c) The number of children who chose console games is 3 times the number of children who chose board games. How many children chose console games?

11 Volume

Worked Example 1

A rectangular container, measuring 25 cm by 21 cm by 18 cm, is $\frac{3}{5}$ filled with water. How much more water can it hold? Give your answer in liters and milliliters. (1 liter = 1,000 cm^3)

Capacity of rectangular container = length × width × height
= 25 cm × 21 cm × 18 cm
= 9,450 cm^3

Fraction of rectangular container not filled with water $= 1 - \frac{3}{5}$
$= \frac{2}{5}$

$\frac{2}{5} \times 25 \text{ cm} \times 21 \text{ cm} \times 18 \text{ cm} = 3{,}780 \text{ cm}^3$

3,780 cm^3 = 3 liters 780 milliliters

It can hold **3 liters 780 milliliters** more water.

Worked Example 2

Three metal cubes of sides 3 cm, 4 cm, and 5 cm respectively, are melted and recast into a bigger cube. What is the length of the new cube?

Volume of 3-cm cube = 3 cm × 3 cm × 3 cm = 27 cm^3

Volume of 4-cm cube = 4 cm × 4 cm × 4 cm = 64 cm^3

Volume of 5-cm cube = 5 cm × 5 cm × 5 cm = 125 cm^3

Volume of the bigger cube = 27 cm^3 + 64 cm^3 + 125 cm^3
= 216 cm^3

216 = 6 × 6 × 6

The length of the new cube is **6 cm**.

Worked Example 3

What is the maximum number of cubes of sides 3 cm that can be cut from a wooden block that measures 36 cm by 21 cm by 12 cm?

The dimensions of the block are multiples of 3.

$$\frac{36 \times 21 \times 12}{3 \times 3 \times 3} = 12 \times 7 \times 4 = 336$$

The maximum number of cubes of sides 3 cm that can be cut from the wooden block is **336**.

Extension: Given a wooden block measuring 21 cm by 18 cm by 13 cm, what would the most number of cubes of sides 3 cm that can be cut from it?

Hint: The answer is not 182.

Answer: 168

Answer all questions. Show your work and write your statements clearly.

1. The solid figure below is made up of 2-cm cubes. What is its volume?

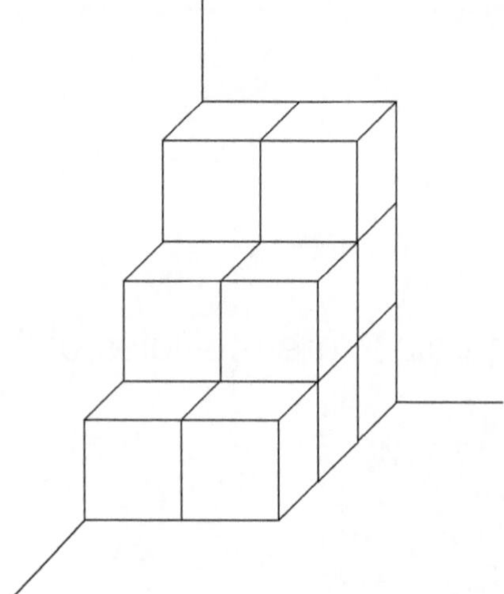

2. In the figure below, what is the volume of water needed to fill the container to its brim? Express your answer in liters and milliliters.

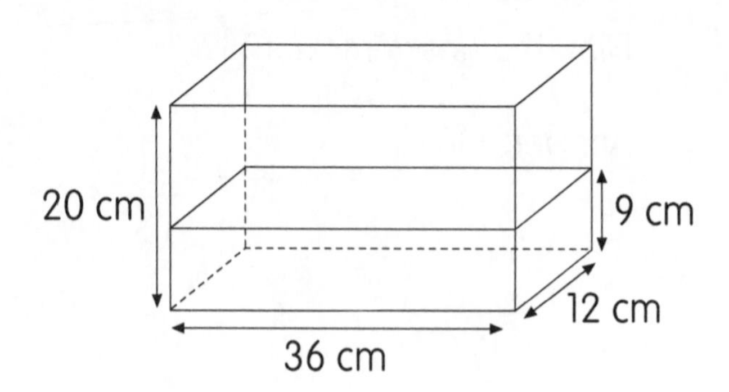

3. A rectangular tank, measuring 40 cm long and 25 cm wide, was filled with water up to a height of 15 cm. After some water was poured out from the tank, the height of the water dropped to 12 cm. How much water was poured out? Express your answer in liters.

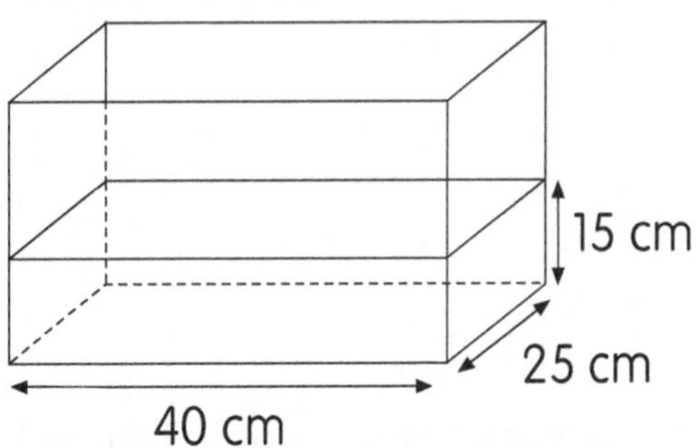

4. A rectangular container of length 45 cm, width 30 cm, and height 12 cm, was filled with water to a height of 7 cm. If 1,340 cm^3 of water is further added into the container, what is the volume of water in the container now?

5. A rectangular container of length 26 cm, width 21 cm, and height 15 cm, was completely filled with liquid. Mr. Perez poured all the liquid into another rectangular container that measured 30 cm by 25 cm by 18 cm. How much more of the liquid could the second container hold?

6. Three cubes of sides 1 cm, 6 cm, and 8 cm respectively are melted and recast into a bigger cube. What is the length of the new cube?

   Hint: See Worked Example 2.

7. A rectangular container of length 32 cm and width 18 cm, was filled with water to a height of 12 cm. When 9 L 35 mL of water was poured into the container, 4,247 cm^3 of water overflowed. What was the capacity of the container? (1 L = 1,000 cm^3)

8. A tank was $\frac{2}{3}$ filled with water. The tank became $\frac{3}{4}$ filled with water when another 5 L of water was added.
   (a) What was the capacity (in liters) of the tank?
   (b) How much more water was needed to fill the tank completely?

9. How many rectangular containers of oil are needed to fill up the empty tank?

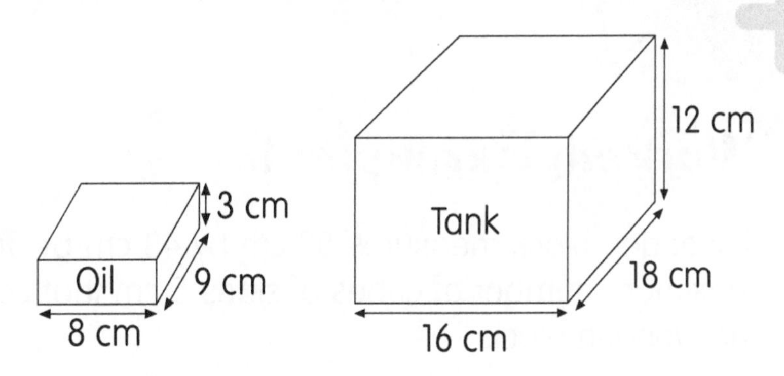

10. What is the maximum number of cubes of sides 2 cm that can fit into the box below?

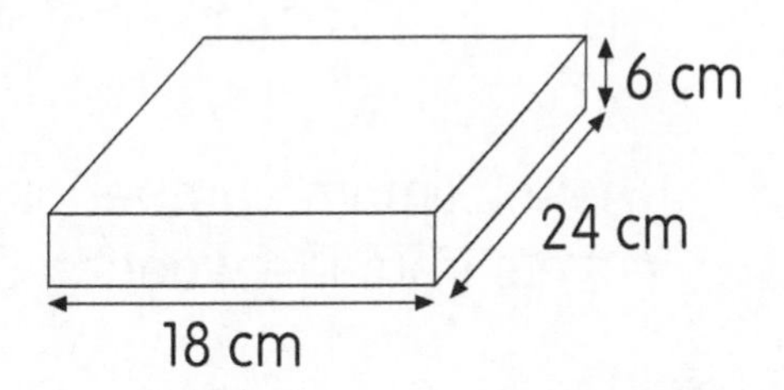

Challenging Problems

Worked Example 1

A wooden block measures 52 cm by 43 cm by 36 cm. Find the maximum number of cubes of sides 5 cm that can be cut out from the wooden block.

All the dimensions of the wooden block are not multiples of 5. Round down each dimension to its nearest multiple of 5.

$52 \approx 50$
$43 \approx 40$
$36 \approx 35$

$$\frac{50 \times 40 \times 35}{5 \times 5 \times 5} = 10 \times 8 \times 7$$
$$= 560$$

The maximum number of cubes of sides 5 cm that can be cut out from the wooden block is **560**.

Think!
What volume of the wooden block would be wasted?

Worked Example 2

Thirty 4-cm cubes are melted to form a solid. If thirty 2-cm cubes were used instead, how many more 2-cm cubes would be needed to form the same solid?

Volume of solid = volume of thirty 4-cm cubes
$= 30 \times 4 \times 4 \times 4\ \text{cm}^3$

Number of 2-cm cubes needed $= \dfrac{30 \times 4 \times 4 \times 4}{2 \times 2 \times 2}$
$= 240$

$240 - 30 = 210$

210 more 2-cm cubes would be needed.

Answer all questions. Show your work and write your statements clearly.

1. A rectangular aquarium is 36 cm long. It is half as wide as it is long and half as tall as it is wide. What is its capacity?

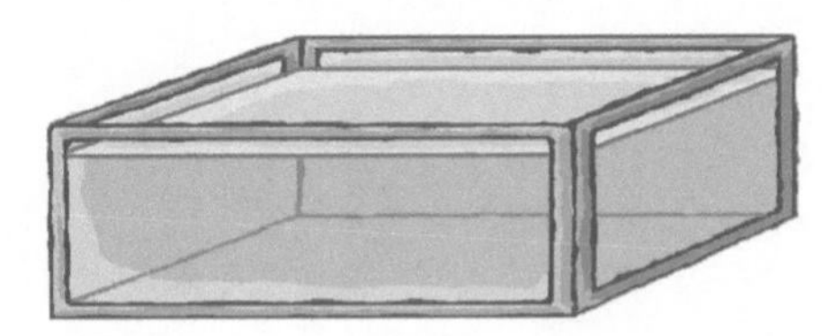

2. The base of a rectangular container measures 4 m by 8 m. Eight cubes are placed inside the container, covering the base completely. What is the length of each cube?

3. A rectangular container measures 19 cm by 22 cm by 30 cm. What is the maximum number of 3-cm cubes that can be put into the container?

   Hint: See Worked Example 1.

4. A rectangular prism measures 23 cm by 18 cm by 13 cm. What is the maximum number of cubes of sides 3 cm that can be cut from the rectangular prism?

5. A barrel is filled with 34 L of water. Mr. Ray drains water from the barrel to fill 8 identical buckets, leaving 1.6 L of water in the barrel. What is the capacity (in liters and milliliters) of each bucket?

6. The solid on the right is formed from wooden cubes of sides 2 cm. How many more cubes of sides 2 cm are needed to build a cube of sides 8 cm?

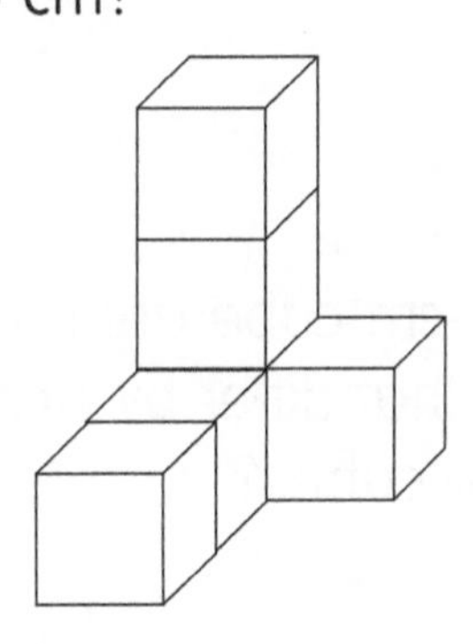

7. Tank P has a capacity twice that of tank Q and half that of tank R. Tank R can hold 12 L 624 mL more water than tank Q. What is the capacity of tank P?

8. A particular brand of liquid detergent is sold in 240-mL packs and 600-mL bottles. Adrian bought some packs of detergent and Sam bought some bottles of detergent. If they bought an equal volume of detergent, what was the least possible number of packs and bottles of detergent that each bought?

9. A 1-cm cube and a 12-cm cube are melted and recast into two new cubes with sides that differ by 1 cm only. What are the lengths of the two new cubes?

10. A container, measuring 100 cm by 80 cm by 50 cm, was completely filled with water. The water was used to fill 16 bottles, each of capacity 2 L. What was the height of water left in the container after all the bottles were filled?

11. A rectangular container, measuring 45 cm by 38 cm by 8 cm, is half-filled with water. After $\frac{1}{3}$ of the water is poured out, how much water will then have to be added to fill the container to its brim?

12 Solid Figures

Worked Example 1

Some unit cubes are stacked together to form the solid figure below. How many unit cubes are used to form the solid figure?

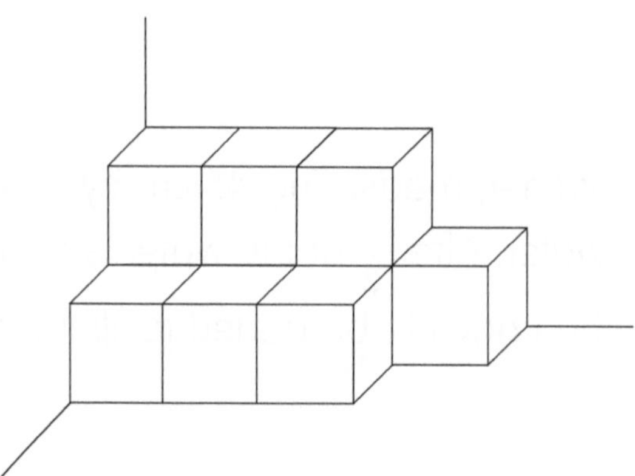

Top layer: 3
Bottom layer: 7
7 + 3 = 10

10 unit cubes are used to form the solid figure.

Each of the cubes on the top layer is supported by another cube below it.

Worked Example 2

The solid figure below is formed by stacking some unit cubes together. How many unit cubes are used to form the solid figure?

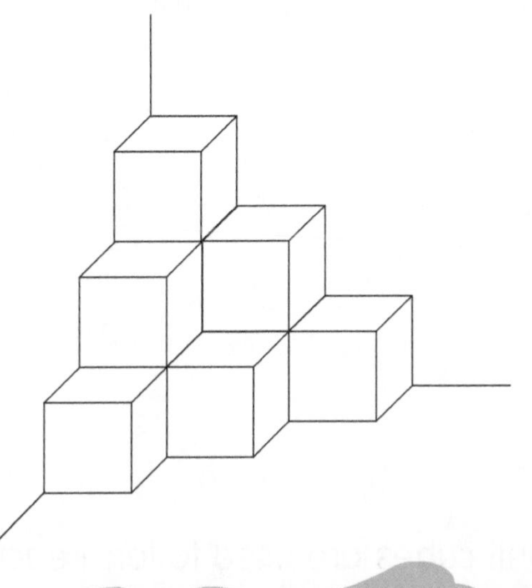

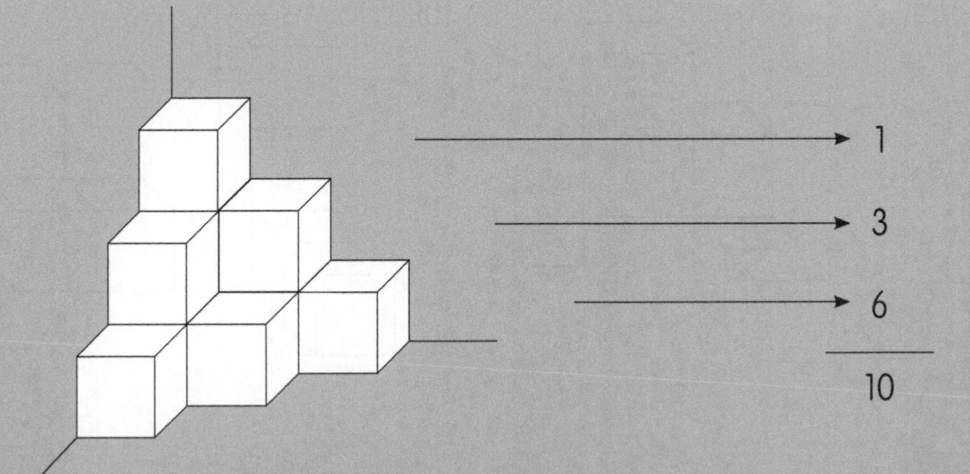

10 unit cubes are used to form the solid figure.

Practice Questions

Answer all questions. Show your work and write your statements clearly.

1. How many unit cubes are used to form each of the following solid figures?

(a)

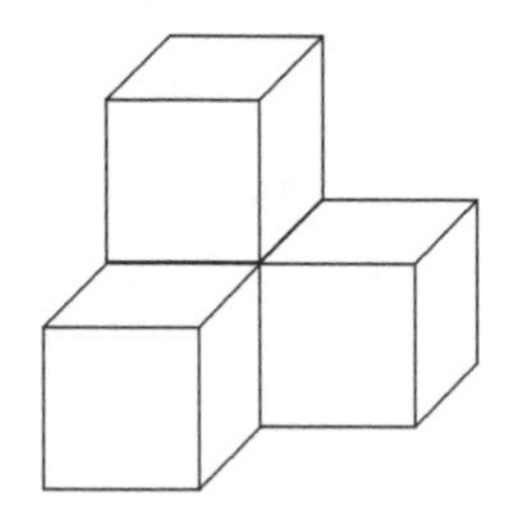

(b)

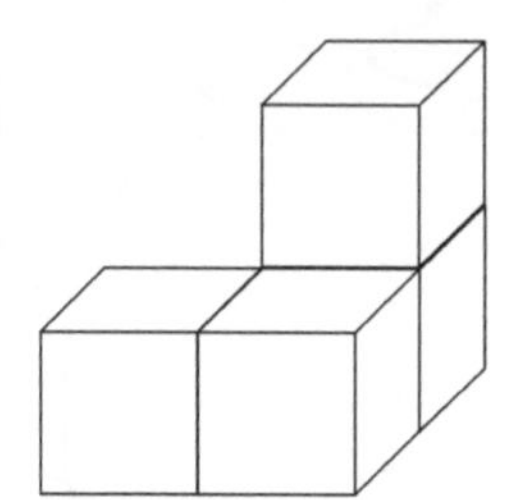

2. How many unit cubes are used to form each of the following solid figures?

(a)

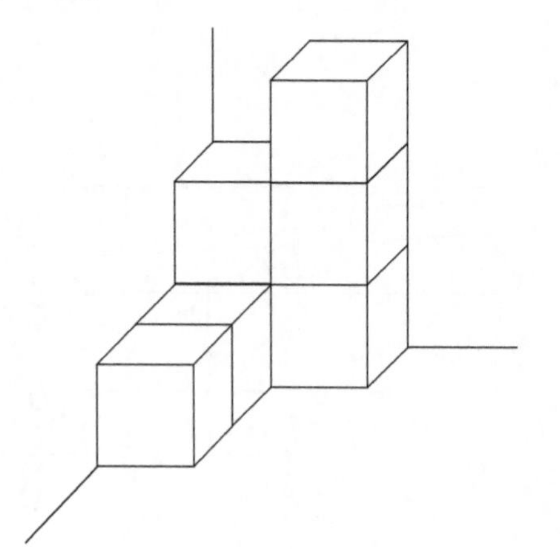

(b)

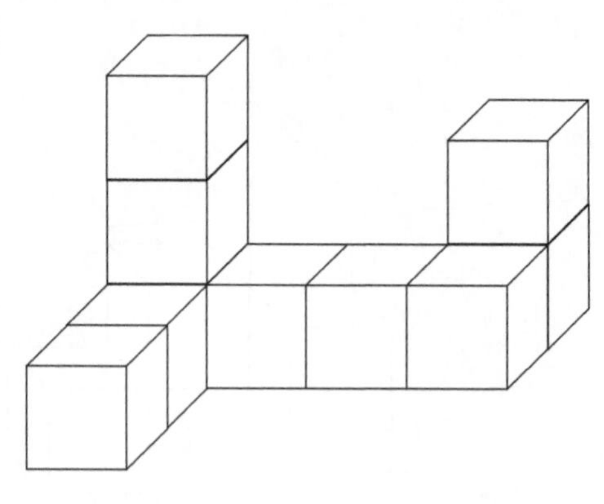

3. Some unit cubes are stacked together to form the solid figure below. How many unit cubes are used to form the solid figure?

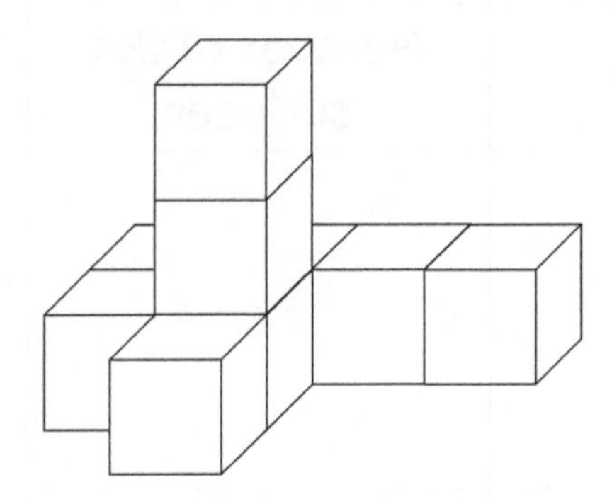

4. How many cubes are left in each solid figure if the shaded cube is removed?

(a)

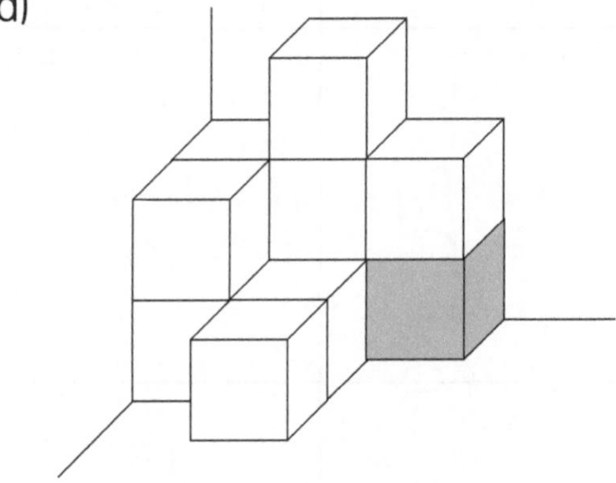

(b)

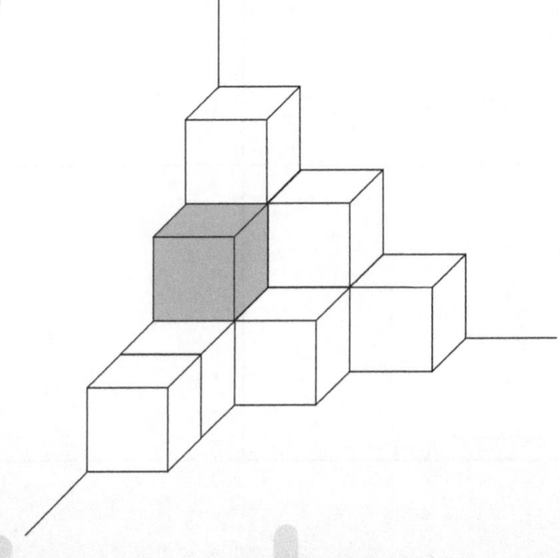

5. Solid figures have flat surfaces or curved surfaces. Look at each solid figure in the table below and complete the table.

Solid figure	Number of flat surfaces	Number of curved surfaces
Cube	6	0
Rectangular prism		
Triangular pyramid		
Square pyramid		
Cone		

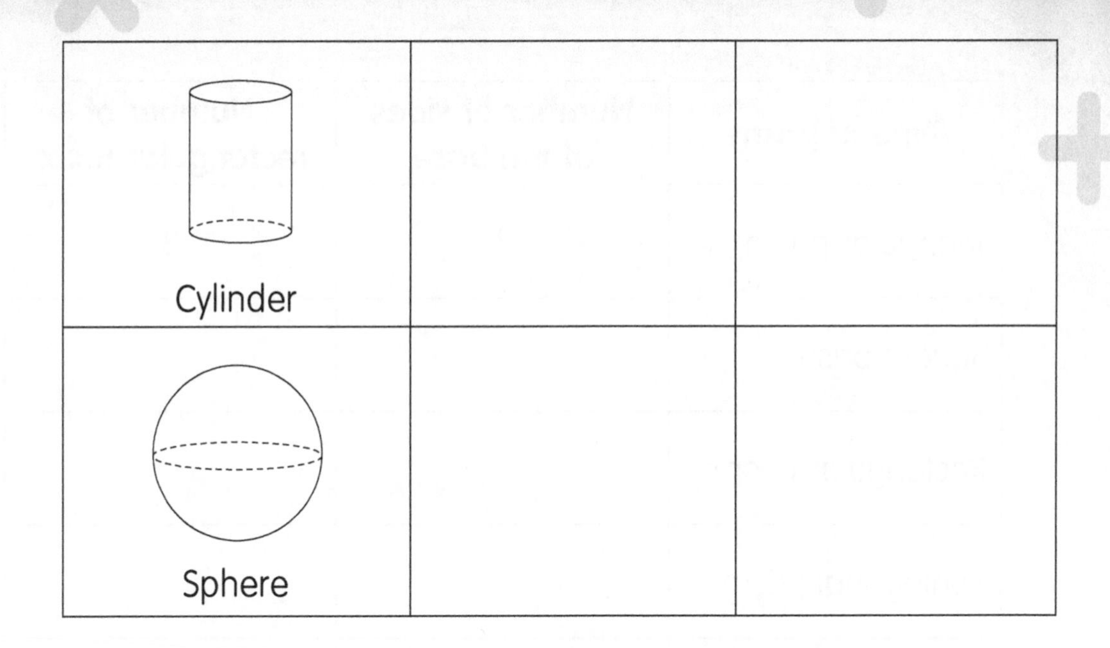

Cylinder		
Sphere		

6. Look at each of the following prisms and complete the table on the next page.

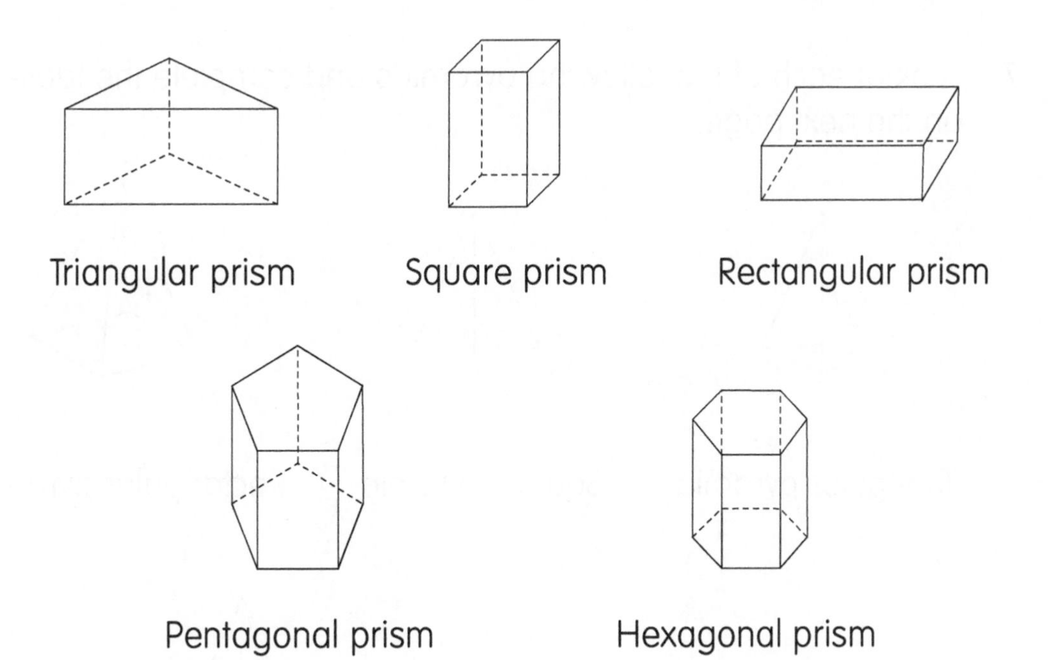

Type of prism	Number of sides of the base	Number of rectangular faces
Triangular prism	3	3
Square prism		
Rectangular prism		
Pentagonal prism		
Hexagonal prism		

7. Look at each of the following pyramids and complete the table on the next page.

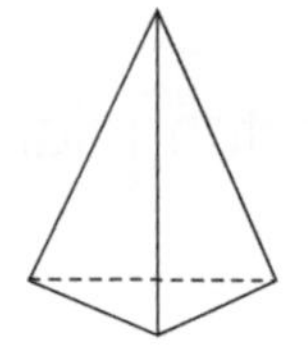

Triangular pyramid

Square pyramid

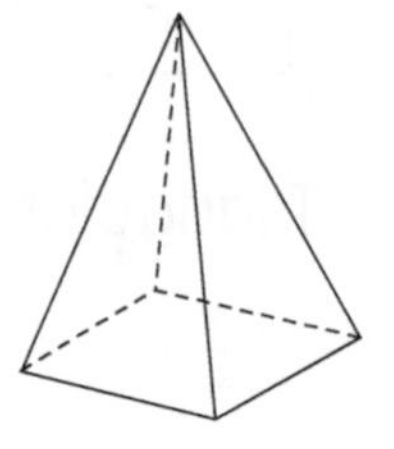

Rectangular pyramid

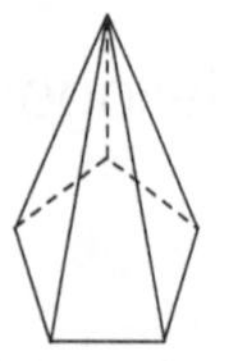

Pentagonal pyramid

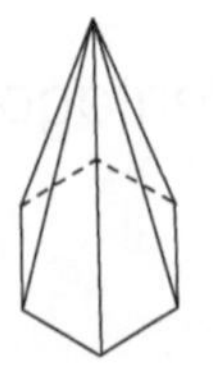

Hexagonal pyramid

Type of pyramid	Number of sides of the base	Number of triangular faces
Triangular pyramid	3	3
Square pyramid		
Rectangular pyramid		
Pentagonal pyramid		
Hexagonal pyramid		

Think!
How are pyramids different from prisms?

8. Which of the following solid figures are pyramids?

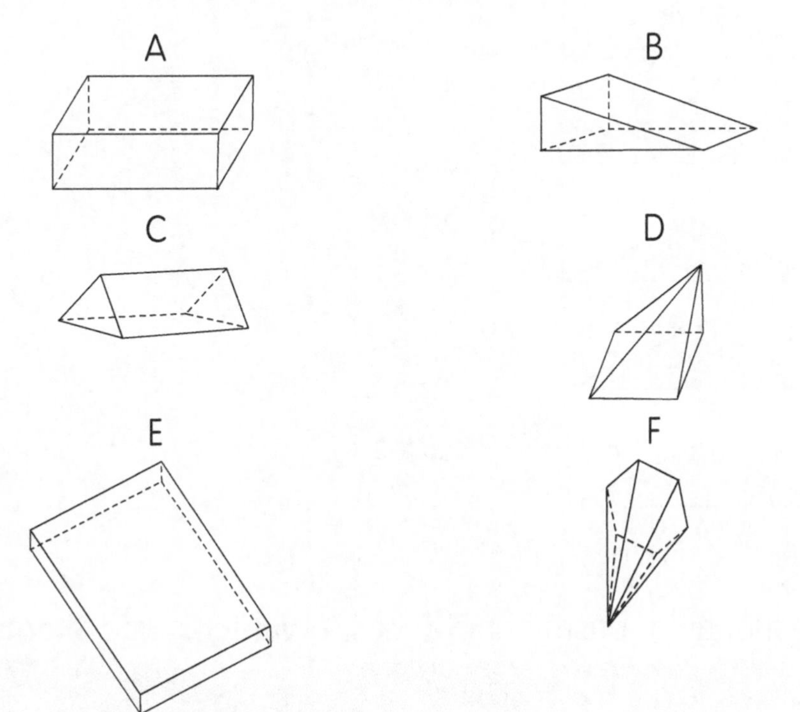

Hint: What is the definition of a pyramid?

Worked Example 1

How many faces, vertices, and edges does the triangular prism below have?

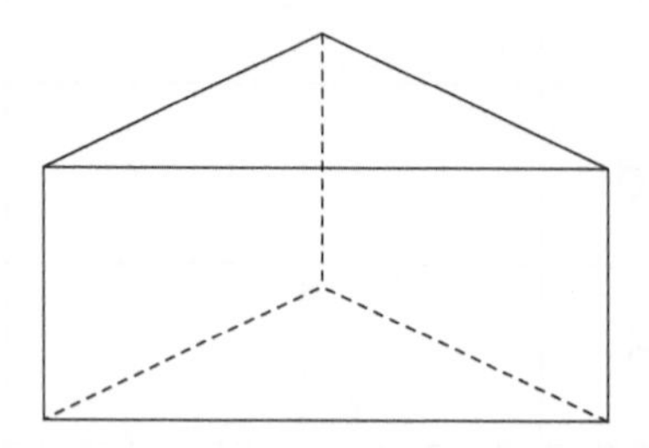

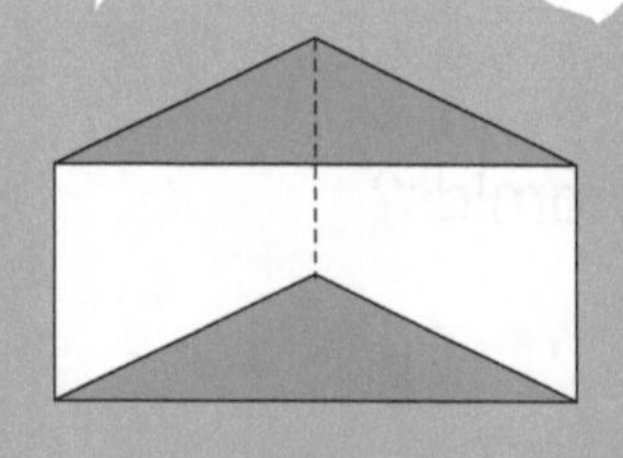

2 triangular faces + 3 rectangular faces = 5 faces

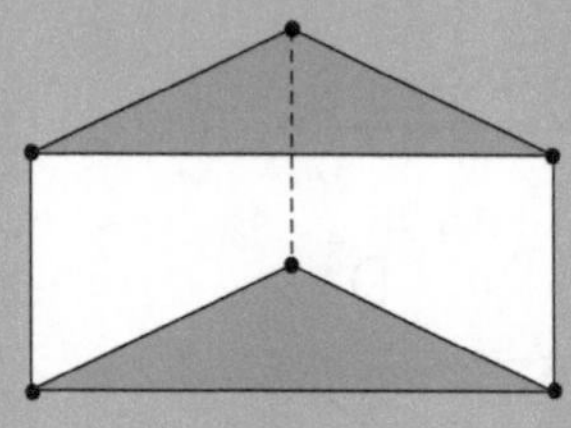

6 vertices

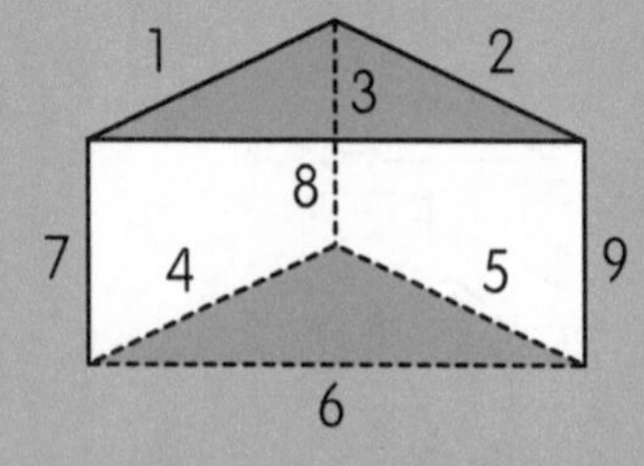

9 edges

The triangular prism has **5 faces**, **6 vertices**, and **9 edges**.

Worked Example 2

How many faces, vertices, and edges does the square pyramid have?

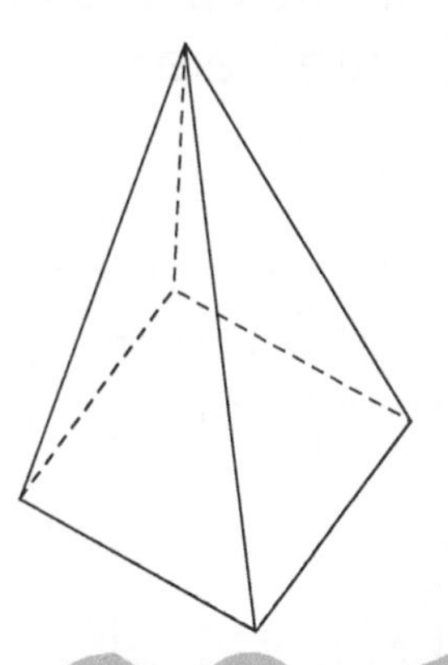

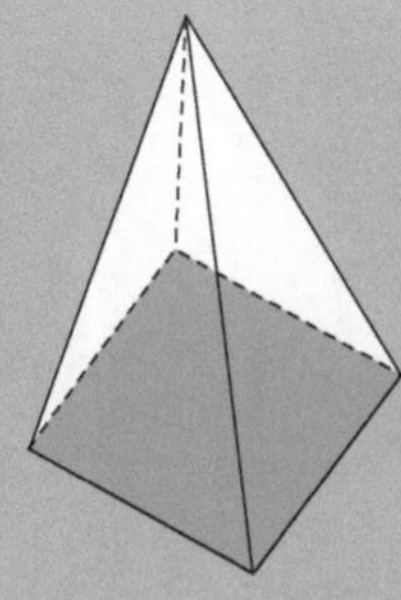

4 triangular faces + 1 square base = 5 faces

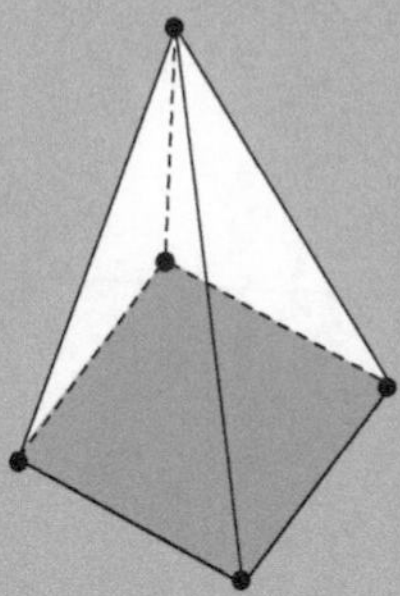

5 vertices

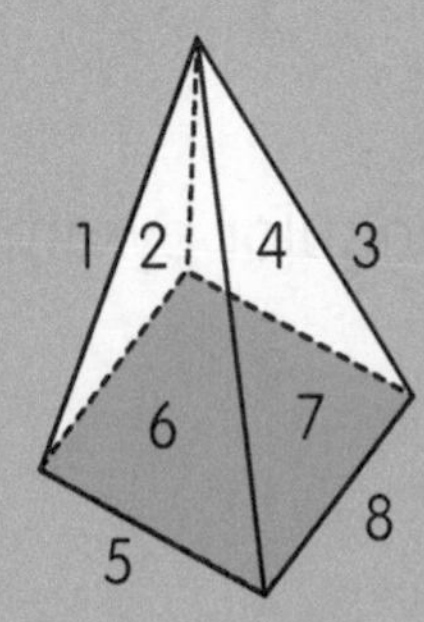

8 edges

The square pyramid has **5 faces**, **5 vertices**, and **8 edges**.

Answer all questions. Show your work and write your statements clearly.

1. The solid figure below is made up of a number of identical blocks. How many blocks are there?

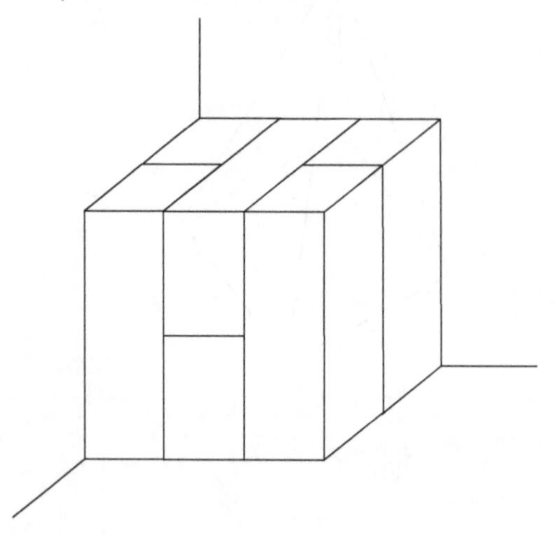

2. How many faces does the solid figure below have?

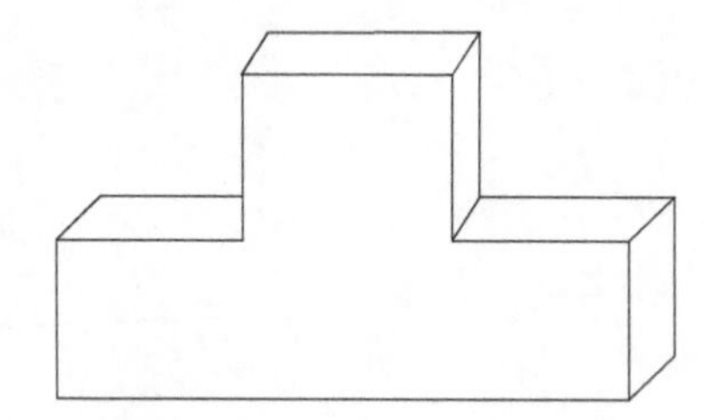

3. How many faces, vertices, and edges does a triangular pyramid have?

13 Review Questions 1

Worked Example

Reuben is 8 years old.
His father is 25 years older than him.
In how many years' time will Reuben be half his father's age?

Now

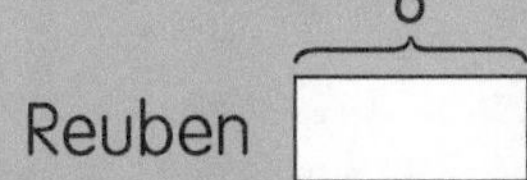

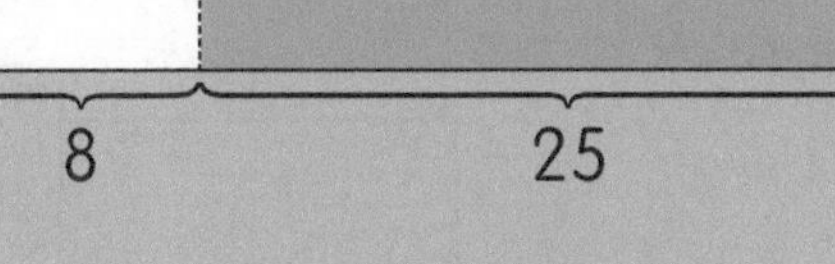

Later

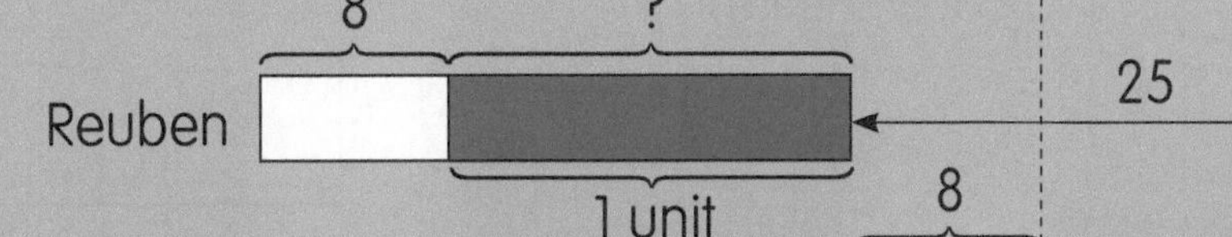

1 unit ⟶ 25 − 8
= 17

Reuben will be half his father's age in **17** years' time.

Check:
Reuben: 8 + 17 = 25
Reuben's father:
33 + 17 = 50
= 2 × 25

Observe: The age difference between the father and his son is always 25 at any point of time.

Answer all questions. Show your work and write your statements clearly.

1. The figure is made up of 2 cm squares. Find its
   (a) area,
   (b) perimeter.

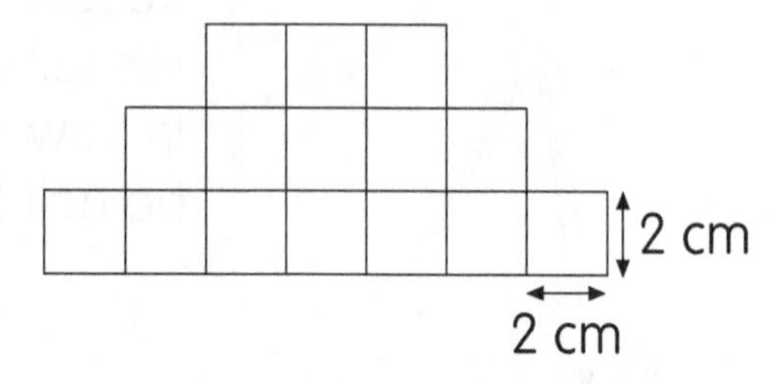

2. The figure below is made up of two squares. What is the perimeter of the figure?

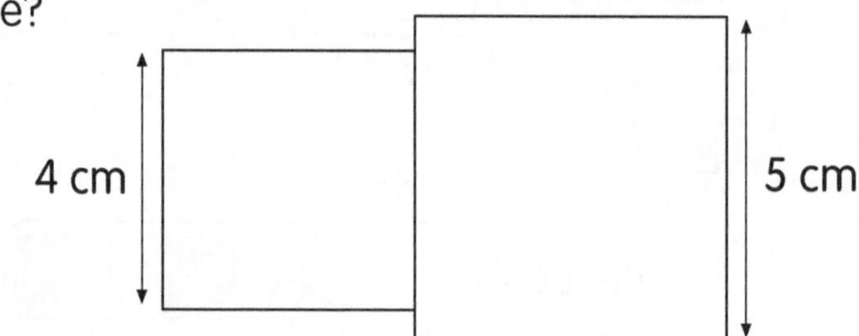

3. What is the missing number in the box?

$$\frac{2}{6} = \frac{\square}{9}$$

4. Find the sum of all the factors of 15.

5. The perimeter of a square hall is 60 m. Find its area.

6. A rectangular cardboard is 12 cm wide and has an area of 156 cm^2. What is its perimeter?

7. The perimeter of a rectangular corridor is 34 m and its width is 2 m. How much would it cost to carpet the corridor if it cost $68 per square meter?

8. The figure shows a picture mounted on a cardboard. What is the area of the shaded region?

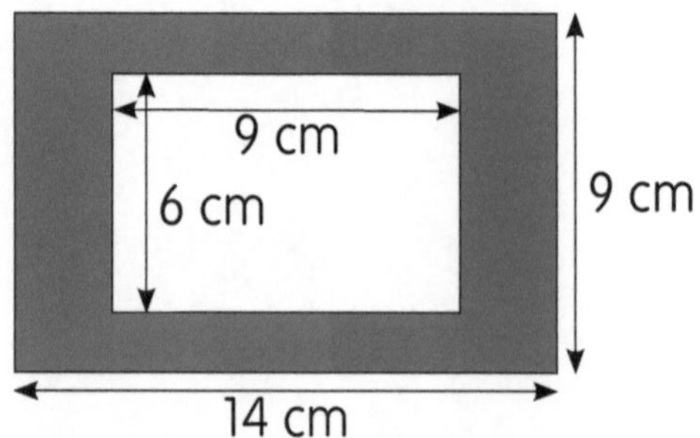

9. After spending $\frac{3}{10}$ of his savings to buy a radio, Mr. Frost had $294 left. How much did he have at first?

10. Farmer Paules planted some saplings along the length of his field. Each sapling was planted 12 m apart. If the distance between the first sapling and the last sapling was 120 m, how many saplings were planted?

11. There are 156 men at a sports event. There are 2 times as many children as women and there are 3 times as many women as men. If the seats are arranged in rows of 8, how many rows are required to seat all the people?

    Hint: Use a model drawing.

Challenging Problems

Worked Example

If $\blacktriangledown + \blacktriangledown + \square = 330$
and $\square + \square + \blacktriangledown = 210$,
find the value of $\blacktriangledown + \square$.

Method 1

$$\begin{aligned} \blacktriangledown + \blacktriangledown + \square &= 330 \text{ (given)} \\ \square + \square + \blacktriangledown &= 210 \text{ (given)} \\ \blacktriangledown + \blacktriangledown + \blacktriangledown + \square + \square + \square &= 330 + 210 \\ &= 540 \end{aligned}$$

$$\begin{aligned} (\blacktriangledown + \square) + (\blacktriangledown + \square) + (\blacktriangledown + \square) &= 540 \\ \blacktriangledown + \square &= 540 \div 3 \\ &= 180 \end{aligned}$$

The value of $\blacktriangledown + \square$ is **180**.

Method 2

$$\begin{aligned} \square + \square + \blacktriangledown &= 210 \text{ (given)} \\ 2\square + \blacktriangledown &= 210 \\ 2\square &= 210 - \blacktriangledown \end{aligned}$$

$$\begin{aligned} \blacktriangledown + \blacktriangledown + \square &= 330 \text{ (given)} \\ 2\blacktriangledown + \square &= 330 \\ 4\blacktriangledown + 2\square &= 2 \times 330 \\ &= 660 \end{aligned}$$

$$4\blacktriangledown + 210 - \blacktriangledown = 660$$
$$3\blacktriangledown + 210 = 660$$
$$3\blacktriangledown = 660 - 210$$
$$= 450$$
$$\blacktriangledown = 450 \div 3$$
$$= 150$$

$$\blacktriangledown + \blacktriangledown + \square = 330$$
$$150 + \blacktriangledown + \square = 330$$
$$\blacktriangledown + \square = 330 - 150$$
$$= 180$$

The value of $\blacktriangledown + \square$ is **180**.

Answer all questions. Show your work and write your statements clearly.

1. Forty-five stickers are to be arranged in albums so that each album has the same number of stickers. What are the possible numbers of albums needed?

   Hint: What are the factors of 45?

2. Jane had $100. She bought a handbag for $69.00 and 2 pairs of socks at $7.50 per pair. What was the greatest possible number of handkerchiefs she could buy with the remaining money if each handkerchief cost $2.50?

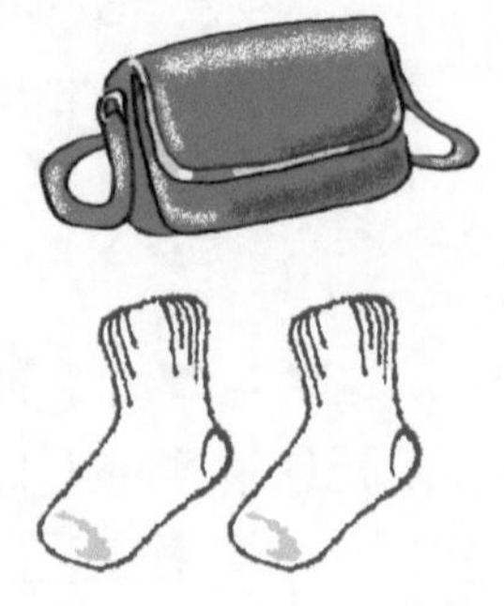

3. Peter's age is a multiple of 3. Last year, his age was a multiple of 4. In 2 years' time, his age will be a multiple of 5. How old is Peter now?

4. If ◆◆◆ + □□□ = 42, what is the value of ◆ + □?

5. If ■ + ● + ▲ = 45,

■ + ● = 20,

and ● + ▲ = 33,

what is the value of ■ + ▲?

6. Bob has 15 more marbles than Joe. Andy has 25 more marbles than the number of marbles that Bob and Joe have together. The three boys have 535 marbles altogether. How many marbles does Bob have?

7. Ai Ling had 137 stamps. If Li Yan gave away 33 stamps, she would have 3 times as many stamps as Ai Ling. How many stamps did Li Yan have?

8. Jack had 5 times as much money as Kelvin. After giving $18.60 to Kelvin, Jack had twice as much money as Kelvin and $12.90 more than Sam. How much did Sam have?

9. Farmer Tim has a total of 28 ducks and sheep on his farm. The total number of legs that the ducks and sheep have is 94. How many sheep are there on Farmer Tim's farm?

Hint: Use guess and check, or make a supposition.

10. Look at the number line below. What decimal number represents the point *X*?

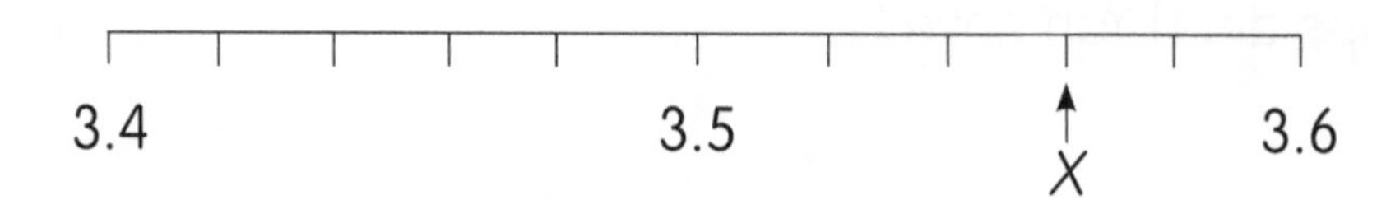

14 Review Question 2

Worked Example 1

Two-thirds of Sam's salary is equal to four-fifths of Tara's salary. Sam earns \$350 more than Tara. How much does Tara earn?

Method 1

\$350

Sam

Tara

1 unit

1 unit ⟶ \$350
5 units ⟶ 5 × \$350 = \$1,750
Tara earns **\$1,750**.

Method 2

$\frac{2}{3}$ of Sam's salary = $\frac{4}{5}$ of Tara's salary

$\frac{3}{2}$ of $\frac{2}{3}$ of Sam's salary = $\frac{3}{2} \times \frac{4}{5}$ of Tara's salary

Sam's salary = $\frac{6}{5}$ of Tara's salary

= Tara's salary + $\frac{1}{5}$ of Tara's salary

$\frac{1}{5}$ of Tara's salary = \$350

Tara's salary = 5 × \$ 350 = \$1,750

Tara earns **\$1,750**.

Worked Example 2

A group of tourists visited the Museum of Natural History last Sunday. $\frac{1}{3}$ of them were boys, $\frac{2}{9}$ were girls and the rest were adults. What fraction of the tourists were adults?

Method 1

$\frac{1}{3} + \frac{2}{9} = \frac{3}{9} + \frac{2}{9} = \frac{5}{9}$

$\frac{5}{9}$ of the tourists were children.

$1 - \frac{5}{9} = \frac{4}{9}$

$\mathbf{\frac{4}{9}}$ of the tourists were adults.

Method 2

$\frac{1}{3} = \frac{1 \times 3}{3 \times 3} = \frac{3}{9}$

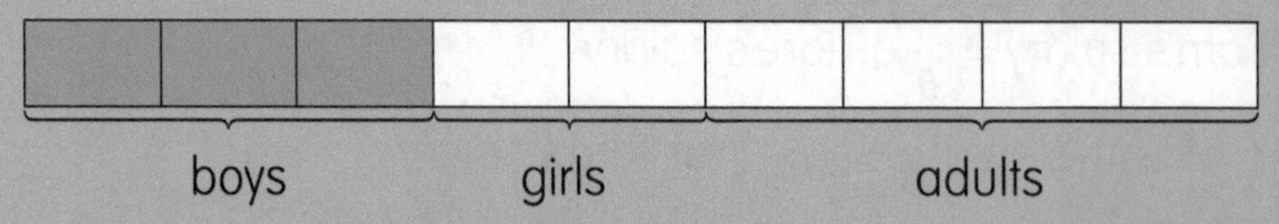

From the model, 4 out of 9 equal parts represent the adults.
So, $\mathbf{\frac{4}{9}}$ of the tourists were adults.

Answer all questions. Show your work and write your statements clearly.

1. Edward's monthly salary is $17,600 when rounded off to the nearest $100. Find his
   (a) greatest possible monthly salary,
   (b) smallest possible monthly salary.

2. Alison turned 135° counterclockwise and then made a $\frac{3}{4}$-turn clockwise. She is now facing West. Where was she facing at first?

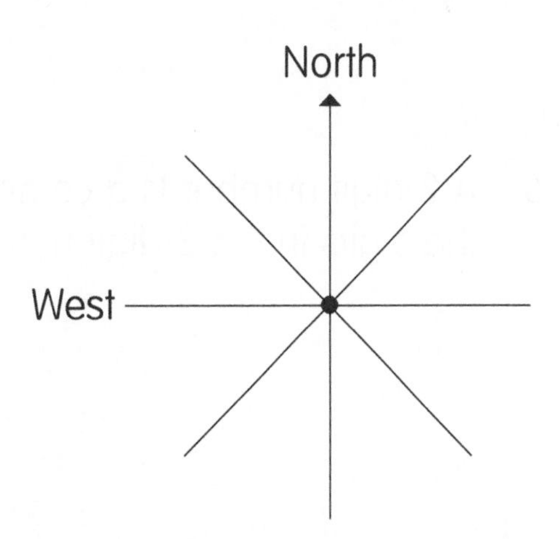

Hint: Label the directions first. Then work backwards.

3. What fraction of the figure below is shaded?

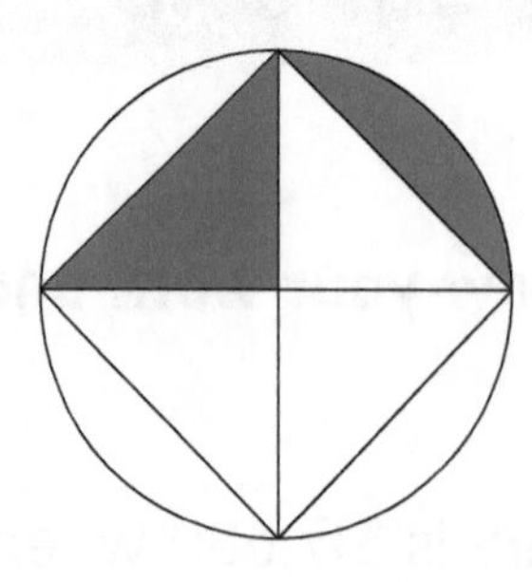

4. Pail A contains 4.8 L of water. Pail B contains 1.95 L less water. Water from both pails is poured into a container. How many liters of water are there in the container?

5. A 2-digit number is a common multiple of 5 and 6. The sum of the digits in the 2-digit number is 9. What is the 2-digit number?

6. Jerry wants to make a rectangle using a 20-cm long wire. If the width of the rectangle is 3 cm, what is the area of the rectangle?

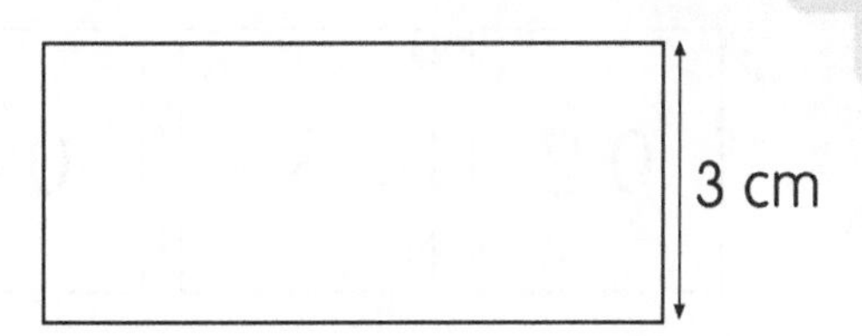

7. The figure below is made up of 8 identical squares. The area of the figure is 200 cm^2. What is the perimeter of the figure?

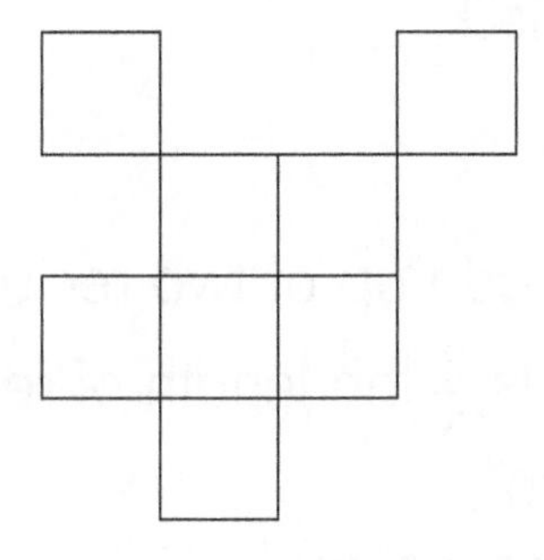

8. Alan has $48, Ben has $41, and Cary has $25. How much must Alan and Ben each give to Cary so that all of them will have an equal amount of money?

9. Use the numbers below to complete the following mathematical sentences.

0.2	3	0.4	0.6	6	8

(a) ☐ × ☐ = 0.6

(b) ☐ × ☐ = 2.4

(c) ☐ × ☐ = 3.2

Hint: Use guess and check.

10. The figure below is made up of two rectangles, A and B. The length of rectangle A is $\frac{2}{3}$ the length of rectangle B. Rectangle A has an area of 192 cm^2.
(a) What is the area of rectangle B?
(b) What is the perimeter of the figure?

12 cm | A | B

Challenging Problems

Worked Example

Leon and Joel had the same number of stamps. After Joel gave away 28 stamps and Leon sold 150 stamps, Joel had 3 times as many stamps as Leon. How many stamps did Leon have at first?

Before

Joel [| | | 28]

Leon [| | |] 150

After

Joel [| |] 1 unit

Leon [ ]

2 units ⟶ $150 - 28 = 122$

1 unit ⟶ $122 \div 2 = 61$

3 units ⟶ $3 \times 61 = 183$

$183 + 28 = 211$

Leon had **211** stamps at first.

Check:
Leon: $211 - 150 = 61$
Joel: $211 - 28 = 183$
$= 3 \times 61$

Answer all questions. Show your work and write your statements clearly.

1. How many squares are there in the figure below?

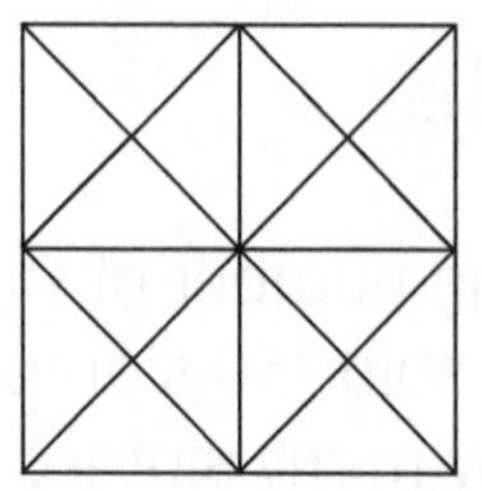

2. The figure is made up of 8 identical squares. What fraction of the figure is shaded?

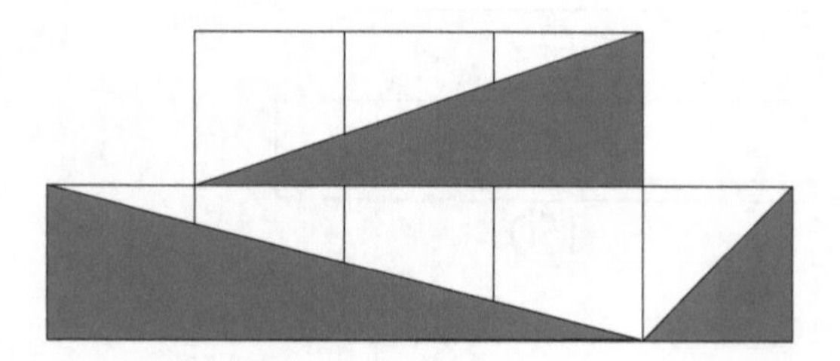

Hint: Think of the figure to be made up of 2 rectangles and 1 square.

3. In the figure below, the shaded region is a square. Find the area of the shaded region.

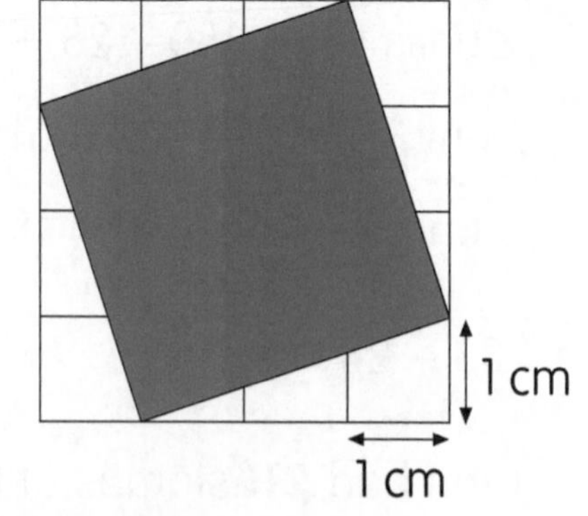

Hint: Area of shaded region = Area of larger square – Area of unshaded parts

4. Some oranges are to be shared among a group of children. If each child gets 3 oranges, there will be 2 oranges left. If each child gets 4 oranges, there will be a shortage of 2 oranges. How many children are there in the group?

5. The area of square *PQRS* is 169 cm^2. What is the length of *TR*?

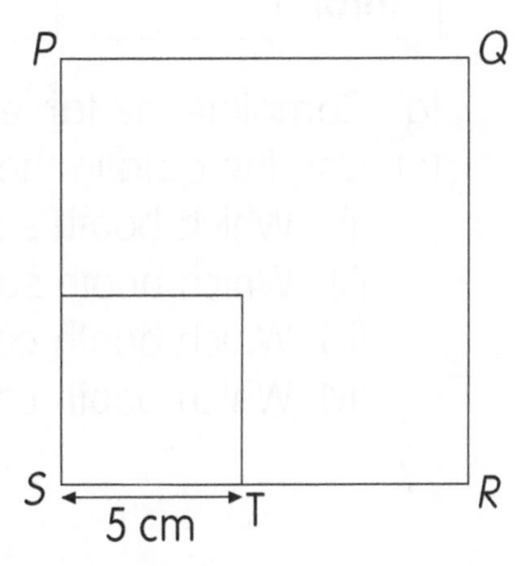

6. The area of square *ABCD* is 121 cm^2. The area of the shaded square is 16 cm^2. What is the length of *AE*?

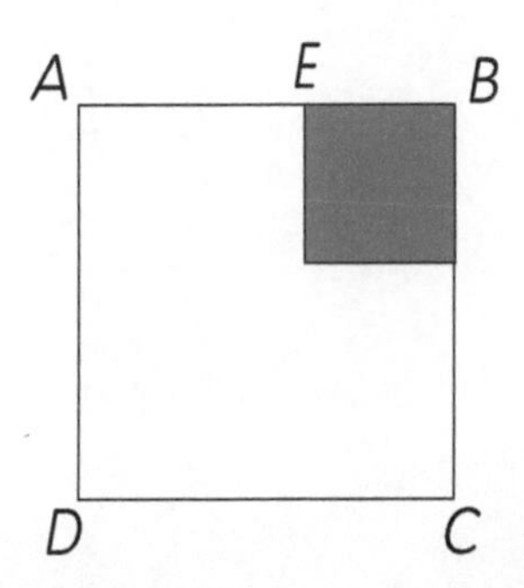

7. The table shows the number of muffins sold at some booths during a fair.

Booth	Chocolate muffin (80¢)		Strawberry muffin (70¢)		Total amount
	Number sold	Amount collected	Number sold	Amount collected	
A	12	$9.60	20	$14.00	$23.60
B	18		12		
C	25		15		
D	30		14		
E	18		16		
Total					

(a) Complete the table.

(b) Use the data in the table to answer the following questions.

(i) Which booth sold the least number of chocolate muffins?

(ii) Which booth sold the most number of strawberry muffins?

(iii) Which booth collected the least amount of money?

(iv) Which booth collected the most amount of money?

8. Marcel and Robin had some money. After Marcel loaned $17.60 to Robin, both of them had the same amount of money. If Robin had $38.40 at first, how much did Marcel have in the beginning?

9. Veronica bought 15 pencils and pens for $4.65. A pencil cost 25¢ and a pen cost 40¢.
   (a) How many pencils did she buy?
   (b) What was the total cost of the pens?

10. A number of identical cubes of sides greater than 1 cm are joined together to form a rectangular prism of sides 60 cm by 72 cm by 48 cm. What is the smallest possible number of cubes that are used to form the rectangular prism?

15 Review Questions 3

Worked Example 1

Carl, Dennis and Esther had $820 in all. Dennis paid $55 to attend a computer class. Carl used one-third of his money to buy a pair of track shoes. Esther used twice as much money as Carl to buy some books. If they each had the same amount of money left, how much did Esther have at first?

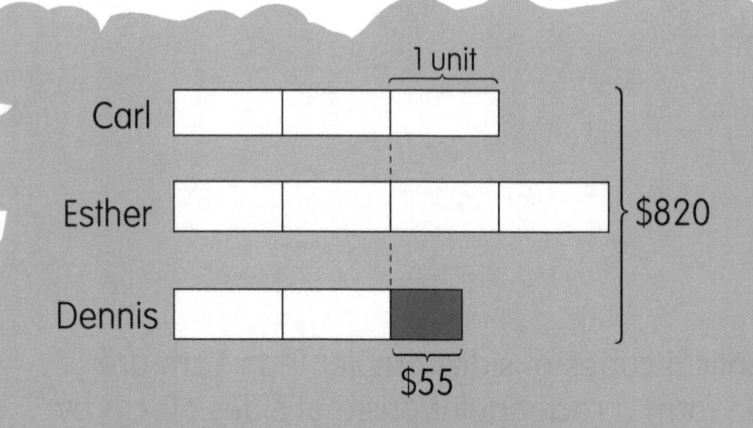

9 units ⟶ $820 – $55 = $765

1 unit ⟶ $765 ÷ 9 = $85

4 units ⟶ 4 × $85 = $340

Esther had **$340** at first.

Practice Questions

Answer all questions. Show your work and write your statements clearly.

1. Peter's height is 1.7 m when rounded off to the nearest tenth of a meter. Find to 2 decimal places,
   (a) his greatest possible height,
   (b) his least possible height.

2. How many unit cubes are used to form each of the following solid figures?
   (a)

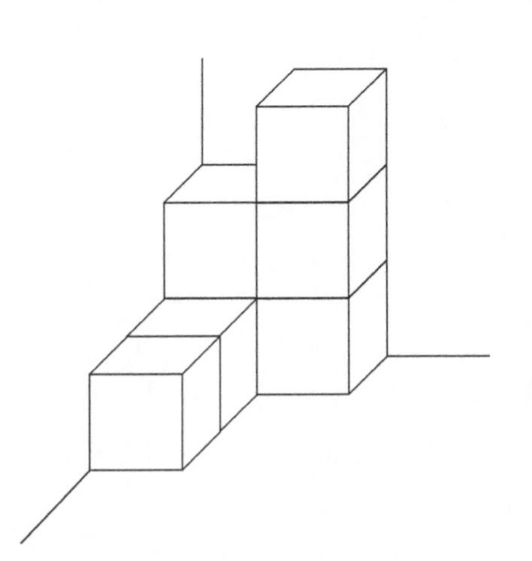

   (b)

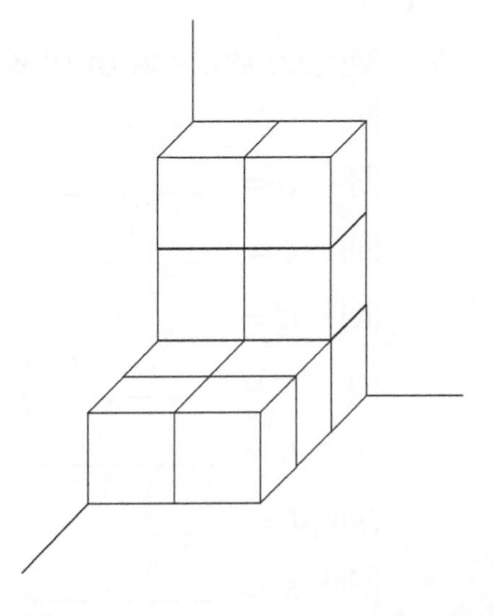

3. Draw 3 straight lines to divide the figure into two identical shapes. The first line has been done for you.

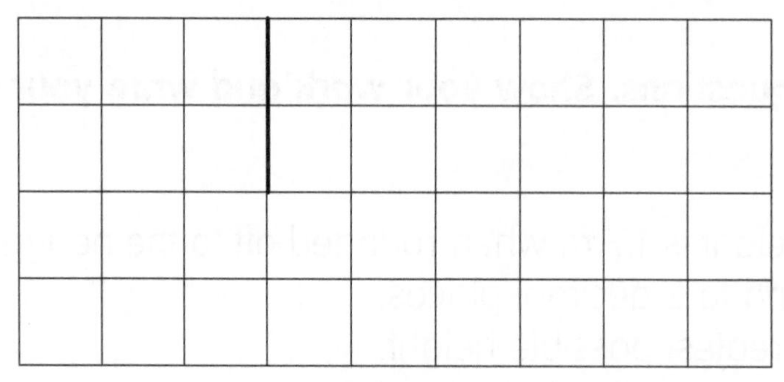

Figure

4. Study the diagram below.

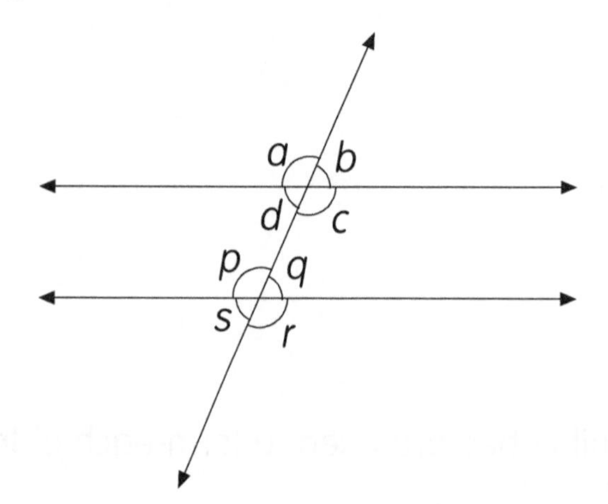

(a) Measure these angles.

(i) $a =$ ____________

(ii) $b =$ ____________

(iii) $c =$ ____________

(iv) $d =$ ____________

(v) $p =$ ____________

(vi) $q =$ ____________

(vii) $r =$ ____________

(viii) $s =$ ____________

(b) Name the angles that have the same measure as angle a.

5. Henry is 1.54 m tall. He is 8 cm shorter than Abraham. What is Abraham's height in meters?

6. Mr. Tan paid $72 for a wallet and 2 pairs of sandals. The wallet cost $27.60. How much did 1 pair of sandals cost?

7. In the figure below, *O* is the center of the square. Find the area of the shaded region.

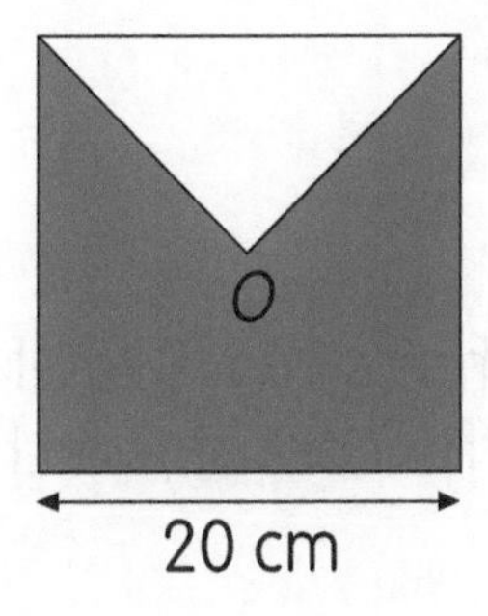

8. Reuben cut out 4 smaller squares from a piece of square cardboard as shown on the right. Each small square had an area of 6 cm^2. What was the area of the remaining cardboard?

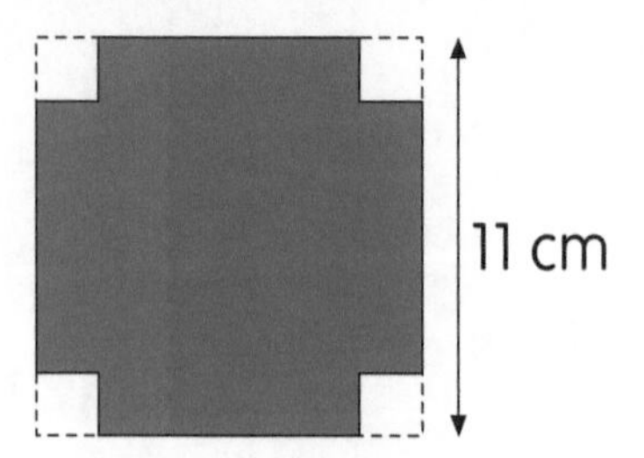

9. Use the numbers below to complete the following mathematical sentences.

1.5	2.4	3.2	2	4	5

(a) $\square \div \square = 0.3$ (b) $\square \div \square = 0.8$

(c) $\square \div \square = 1.2$ (d) $\square \div \square = 1.6$

10. Two tables and three chairs cost \$96. If three chairs cost as much as two tables, what is the cost of five chairs?

Challenging Problems

Worked Example

Each of the following figures is made up of △s.

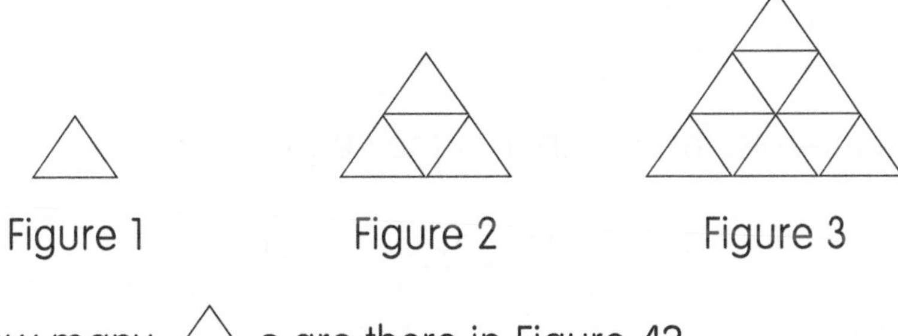

Figure 1　　Figure 2　　Figure 3

(a) How many △s are there in Figure 4?

(b) How many △s are there in Figure 10?

Figure	1	2	3
Number of △s	1	4	9
	↓	↓	↓
	1×1	2×2	3×3

(a) There are $4 \times 4 =$ **16** △s in Figure 4.

(b) There are $10 \times 10 =$ **100** △s in Figure 10.

Answer all questions. Show your work and write your statements clearly.

1. Without working out the answer, how could you determine which one of the following has a greater value?

56×9 $\qquad$ 57×8

2. What is the missing number in the sequence?

4, 7, 13, 22, ______, 49

3. What is the missing number in the sequence?

2, 4, 8, 32, ______, 8,192

4. In the multiplication below, letter P stands for a particular digit and letter Q stands for another digit. What digit does the letter Q stand for?

$$\begin{array}{r} P\ P\ P \\ \times \quad\ \ 3 \\ \hline 1\ Q\ Q\ P \\ \hline \end{array}$$

Hint: What digit multiplied by 3 has a product whose ones digit is the same digit?

5. Fill each box with the digits 1, 2, 3, or 4 only. The sum of the numbers in each row or column is shown at the sides. No numbers are to be repeated in each row or column.

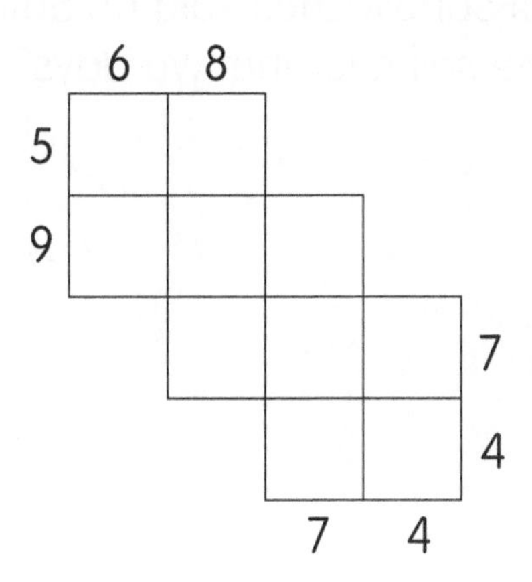

6. The shaded figure is made into rectangle *ABHG*. What is the length of *BH*? All angles are right angles.

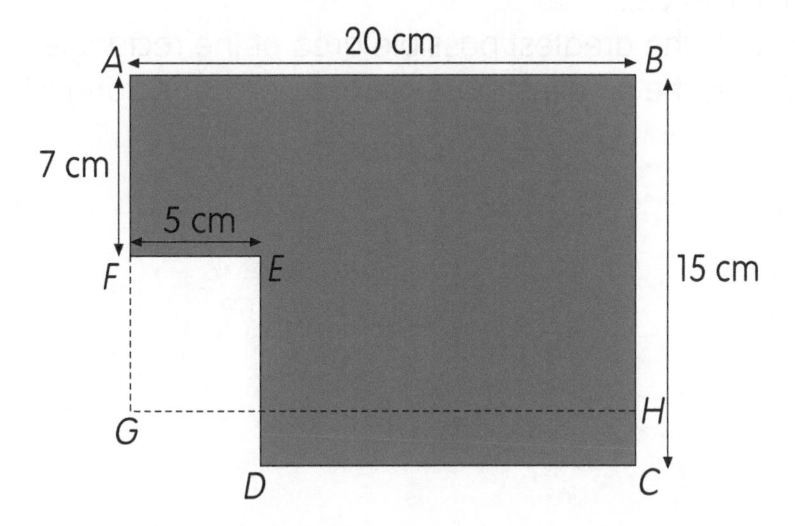

7. Mrs. Aziz sold 136 potato sandwiches on Saturday. This was 78 more than the tuna sandwiches she sold on the same day. On Sunday, the number of sandwiches that she sold was half the total number of sandwiches sold on Saturday. How many sandwiches did she sell over the two days?

8. A number of 1 cm squares can be used to form a rectangle of perimeter 18 cm.
   (a) What is the greatest possible area of the rectangle?
   (b) What is the smallest possible area of the rectangle?

9. In the figure, *PQRS* is a square. *T* and *U* are the midpoints of *PS* and *SR* respectively. What fraction of square *PQRS* is triangle *QTU*?

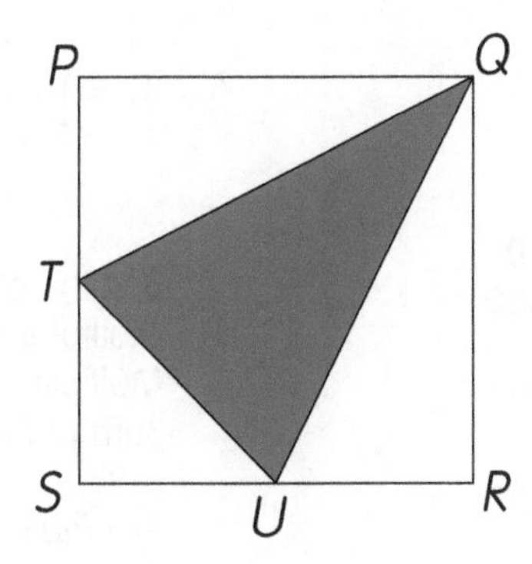

10. Thirteen coins made up of quarters and half-dollars have a total value of $4.50. How many coins of each kind are there?

Answers

1 Whole Numbers

Practice Questions (pp. 4–7)

1. (a) **5,078** (b) **8,750**
2. (a) **20,479** (b) **97,420**

   Extension:
   Smallest even number = 20,794
   Smallest odd number = 20,479
   Greatest even number = 97,420
   Greatest odd number = 94,207
3. (a) **7,403** (b) **3,074**
4. (a) **23,500**

   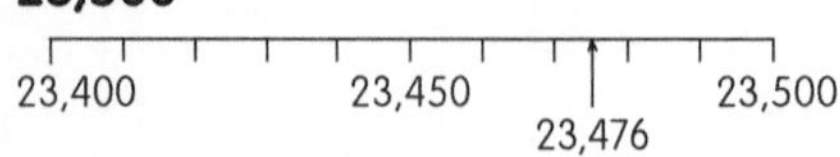

   23,476 is nearer to 23,500 than to 23,400.
   So, 23,476 is 23,500, when rounded to the nearest 100.

   (b) **75,700**

   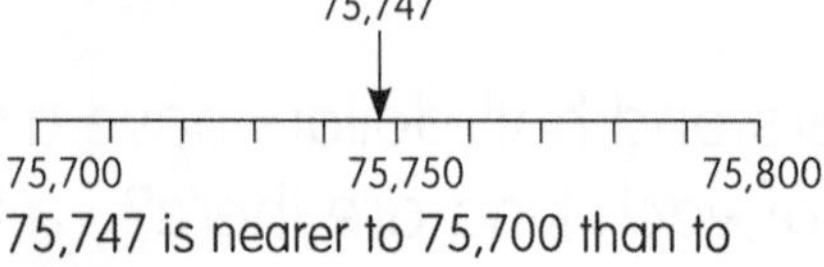

   75,747 is nearer to 75,700 than to 75,800.
   So, 75,747 is 75,700, when rounded to the nearest 100.

   (c) **49,100**
   (d) **50,500**
5. (a) **19,000**

   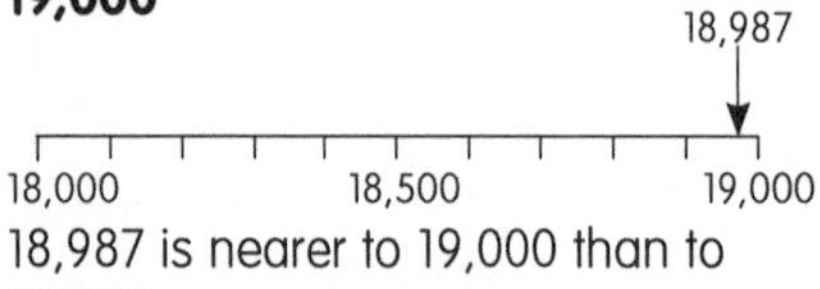

   18,987 is nearer to 19,000 than to 18,000.
   So, 18,987 is 19,000, when rounded to the nearest 1,000.

   (b) **120,000**

   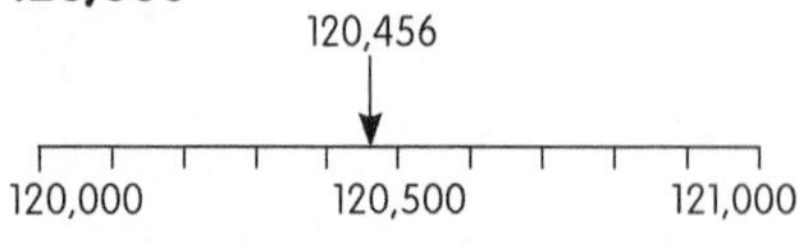

   120,456 is nearer to 120,000 than to 121,000.
   So, 120,456 is 120,000, when rounded to the nearest 1,000.

   (c) **487,000**
   (d) **200,000**
6. $39 = 1 \times 39$
   $= 3 \times 13$

   $54 = 1 \times 54$
   $= 2 \times 27$
   $= 3 \times 18$
   $= 6 \times 9$

   3 is the common factor of 39 and 54.
7. Multiples of 9: 9, 18, 27, …
   Multiples of 6: 6, 12, 18, 24, …
   Sum of the first 2 multiples of 9 = 9 + 18 = 27
   3rd multiple of 6 = 18
   27 – 18 = 9
   The required difference is **9**.
8. Multiples of 4: 4, 8, 12, 16, …
   Multiples of 3: 3, 6, 9, 12, 15, …
   4 + 8 + 12 + 3 + 6 + 9 + 12 = 54
   The required sum is **54**.
9. Multiples of 4: 4, 8, 12, … , 80, 84, (88), 92
   Multiples of 8: 8, 16, 24, 32, … , 80, (88), 96
   Multiples of 11: 11, 22, 33, … , 77, (88), 99
   The smallest whole number that is divisible by 4, 8, and 11 is **88**.
10. The 13th multiple of 3 is 13 × 3 = 39.

    P —(× 7)→ [?] —(+ 4)→ 39

    5 ←(÷ 7)— 35 ←— 39

    So, the value of P is **5**.
11. Multiples of 6: …, 30, 36, 42, (48), 54, 60, …
    Multiples of 7: …, 35, 42, (49), 56, …
    This year, Isaac's age is a multiple of 6. If he is 48 years old, he will be 49 next year. 49 is a multiple of 7. Both numbers satisfy the conditions in the question.
    He is **48** years old now.

12. *Method 1*
The number is
(i) (a multiple of 5) + 3 and
(ii) (a multiple of 4) + 1.
Starting with the number 40,
(i) 40 + 3 = 43
(ii) 40 + 1 = 41

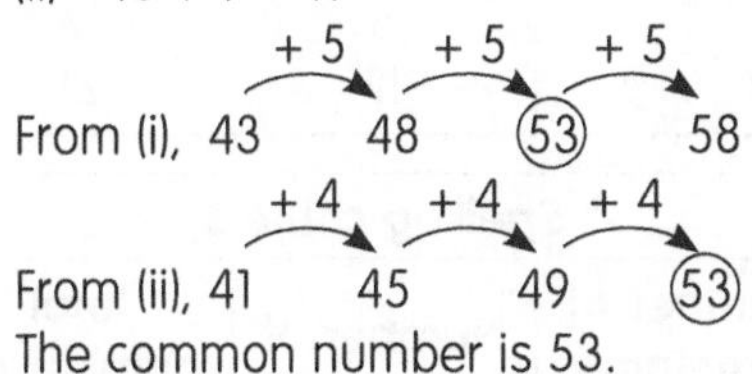

The common number is 53.

Method 2
Multiples of 5: ..., 40, 45, 50, 55, 60, ...
Numbers that leave a remainder of 3 when divided by 5: ..., 43, 48, 53, 58, ...
Multiples of 4: ..., 40, 44, 48, 52, 56, 60. ...
Numbers that leave a remainder of 1 when divided by 4: ..., 41, 45, 49, 53, 57, ...
The common number in both lists is **53**.

So, the number I am thinking of is **53**.

Challenging Problems (pp. 9–13)

1. (a) Greatest possible monthly expense = **$38,149**

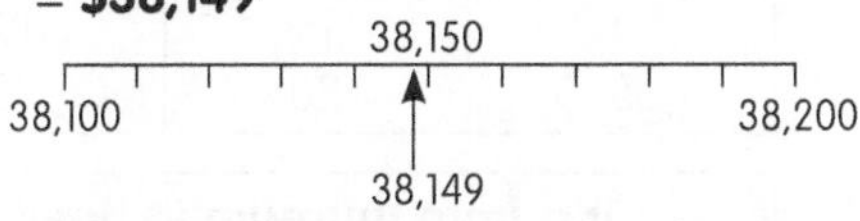

38,149 is the largest number less than 38,150, which is closer to 38,100 than to 38,200.
So, the greatest possible monthly expense is $38,149.

(b) Smallest possible monthly expense = **$38,050**

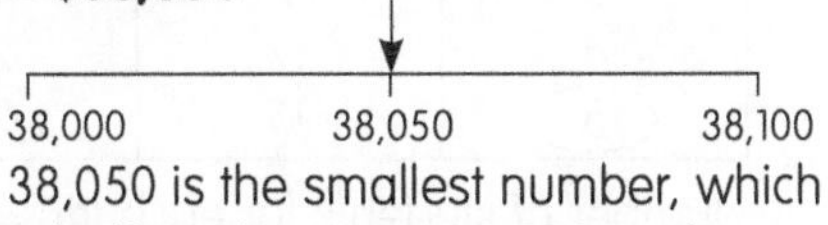

38,050 is the smallest number, which is halfway between 38,000 and 38,100.
So, the smallest possible monthly expense is $38,050.

2. Twelve sandwiches are to be arranged in plates, each containing the same number of sandwiches.

Number of plates	Number of sandwiches on each plate
1	12
2	6
3	4
4	3
6	2
12	1

From the table, 6 possible numbers of plates could be needed: **1**, **2**, **3**, **4**, **6**, **12**.

3. (a)

Pens	Possible numbers of boxes needed
Red	1, 3, 5, (15)
Blue	1, 3, 5, (15)
Black	1, 3, 5, (15)

(b) **15 boxes**
Note: In (b), each box will then have 2 red, 3 blue, and 5 black pens.

4. Multiples of 10: 10, 20, 30, (40), 50, ...
Multiples of 8: 8, 16, 24, 32, (40), ...
Number of plates of fried noodles = 40 ÷ 10
= 4
Number of plates of salad = 40 ÷ 8
= 5
Total number of plates = 4 + 5
= 9
Number of students = **40**

5. (a) **A** (b) **B**
(c) **C**
Observe that
- the numbers in circle A all divide 96;
- the numbers in circle B all divide 90;
- the numbers in the overlapping region C all divide 96 and 90.

Since 6 divides both 96 and 90, it belongs to group C.

6. **126 cubes**
Factors of 175 are 1, 5, 7, 25, 35, and 175.
Factors of 150 are 1, 2, 3, 5, 6, 10, 15, 25, 30, 50, 75, and 150.
Factors of 75 are 1, 3, 5, 15, 25, and 75.
Since each cube must be of the greatest

possible size, each side of the cube must have a dimension equal to the greatest common factor of 175, 150, and 75.
Highest common factor of 175, 150, and 75 = 25
Length of cube = 25 cm

$$\text{Number of cubes} = \frac{175}{25} \times \frac{150}{25} \times \frac{75}{25} = 7 \times 6 \times 3 = 126$$

7. **42 erasers**
The number of erasers must be a multiple of 6 which leaves a remainder of 2 when divided by 4 or 5.

Multiple of 6	Remainder when divided by 4	Remainder when divided by 5
6	2	1
12	0	2
18	2	3
24	0	4
30	2	0
36	0	1
(42)	2	2

Least number of erasers = 42

8. **$18**

Number of students	Amount paid	Cost of gift
1	$2	$6
2	$4	$8
3	$6	$10
4	$8	$12
5	$10	$14
6	$12	$16
7	$14	($18)

Number of students	Amount paid	Cost of gift
1	$3	$0
2	$6	$3
3	$9	$6
4	$12	$9
5	$15	$12
6	$18	$15
7	$21	($18)

Cost of gift = $18

9. **4 classes**

Science contest		
Number of remaining classes	Number of students	Total number of students
1	4	13
2	8	17
(3)	12	21

Spelling contest		
Number of remaining classes	Number of students	Total number of students
1	6	9
2	12	15
(3)	18	21

Total number of classes = 3 + 1 = 4

10. **23 students; 5 taxis**

Trip from hotel to museum		
Number of taxis	Number of students in taxis	Total number of students
1	4	7
2	8	11
3	12	15
4	16	19
(5)	20	(23)

Trip from museum to hotel		
Number of taxis	Numbers of students in taxis	Total number of students
1	3	11
2	6	14
3	9	17
4	12	20
(5)	15	(23)

Number of students for each trip = 23
Number of taxis for each trip = 5

11. **1,156**
The numbers 3, 5, 7, and 11 each have only 2 factors, 1 and itself.

$$\text{Smallest value} = 3 \times 5 \times 7 \times 11 + 1 = 1{,}156$$

12. **18**
Use a systematic list.

2,069	6,029	9,026
2,096	6,092	9,062
2,609	6,209	9,206
2,690	6,290	9,260
2,906	6,902	9,602
2,960	6,920	9,620

There are 18 such 4-digit numbers.

2 The Four Operations of Whole Numbers

Practice Questions (pp. 17–20)

1. 873 thousands + 178 thousands
= 1,051 thousands
There are **1,051** thousands speakers of Mandarin Chinese.
Note: 1,051 thousands = 1,051 × 1000
= 1,051,000

2. 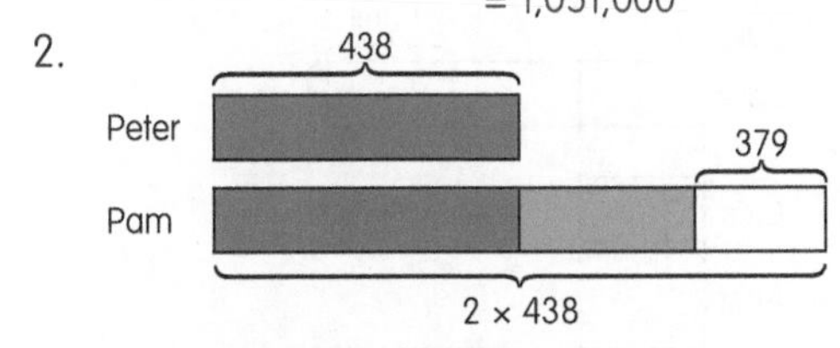

2 × 438 – 379 = 497
Pam has **497** stamps.

3. 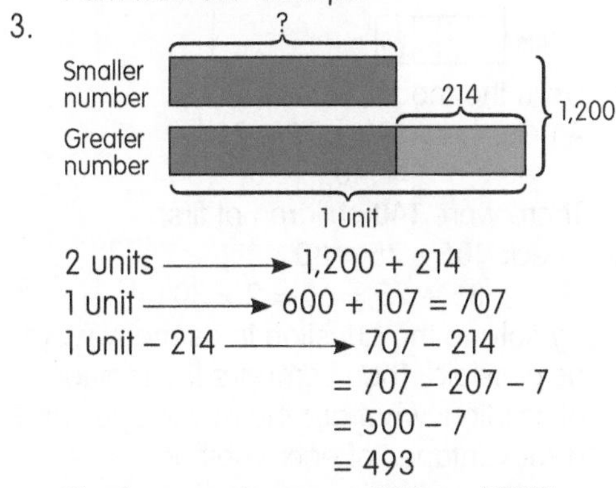

2 units ⟶ 1,200 + 214
1 unit ⟶ 600 + 107 = 707
1 unit – 214 ⟶ 707 – 214
= 707 – 207 – 7
= 500 – 7
= 493
The two numbers are **493** and **707**.

4. *Method 1*
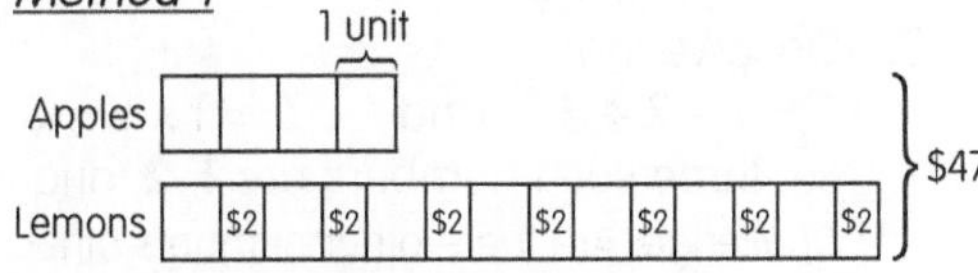

From the model,
$2 × 7 = $14
11 units ⟶ $47 – $14 = $33
1 unit ⟶ $33 ÷ 11 = $3
Cost of 1 lemon = $3 + $2 = $5
Cost of 3 lemons = 3 × $5 = **$15**

Method 2
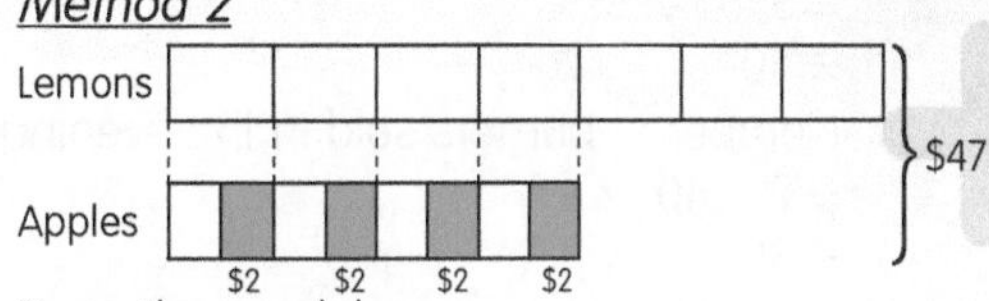

From the model,
11 units ⟶ $47 + 4 × $2 = $55
1 unit ⟶ $55 ÷ 11 = $5
Cost of 1 lemon is $5.
Cost of 3 lemons is 3 × $5 = **$15**.

5. 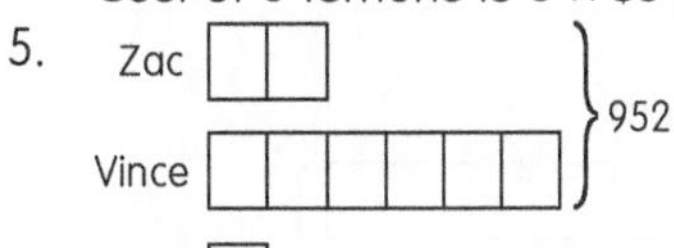

8 units ⟶ 952
1 unit ⟶ 952 ÷ 8 = 119
2 units ⟶ 2 × 119 = 238
6 units ⟶ 6 × 119 = 714
Jason collected **119** stickers.
Zac collected **238** stickers.
Vince collected **714** stickers.

6.

Tripods	Bipods
1 × 3 = (3)	1 × 2 = 2
2 × 3 = 6	2 × 2 = 4
3 × 3 = [9]	3 × 2 = [6]
4 × 3 = 12	4 × 2 = 8
	5 × 2 = 10
	6 × 2 = (12)

From the table, there are two possible answers.
3 bipods and **3 tripods**
6 bipods and **1 tripod**
Note: The number of tripods must be an odd number for the total to be 15.

7. 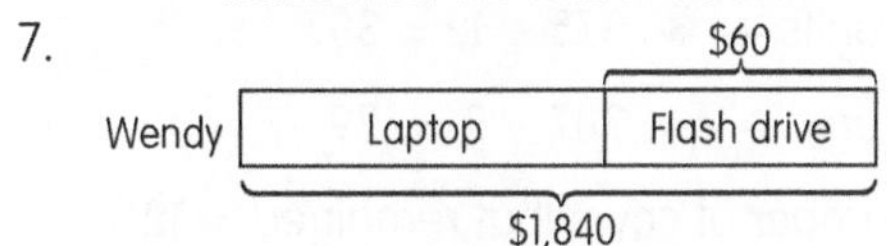

Cost of the laptop = $1,840 – $60
= $1,780

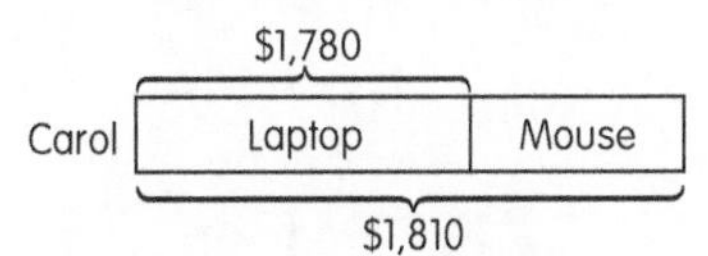

Cost of the infrared mouse
= $1,810 – $1,780 = **$30**

8. Number of burgers sold in the morning
= $120 ÷ $3
= 40
Number of burgers sold in the evening
= 2 × 40
= 80
Amount made in the evening
= 80 × $2.50
= $200
Total amount made
= $120 + $200
= **$320**

9. 3 m = 300 cm

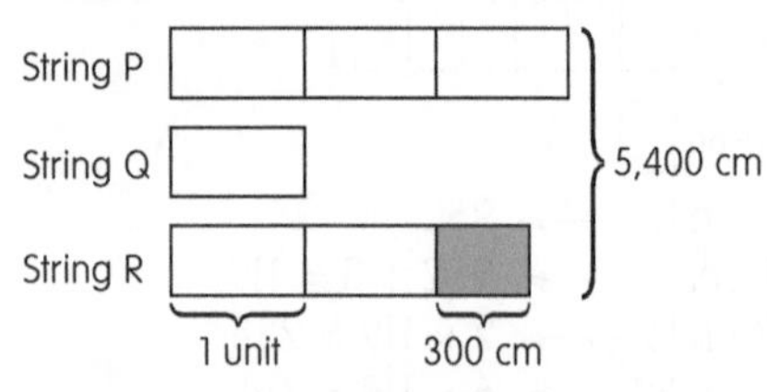

6 units ⟶ 5,400 cm − 300 cm
= 5,100 cm
1 unit ⟶ 5,100 cm ÷ 6 = 850 cm
2 units ⟶ 2 × 850 cm = 1,700 cm
Length of string R = 1,700 cm + 300 cm
= **2,000 cm** = **20 m**

10.

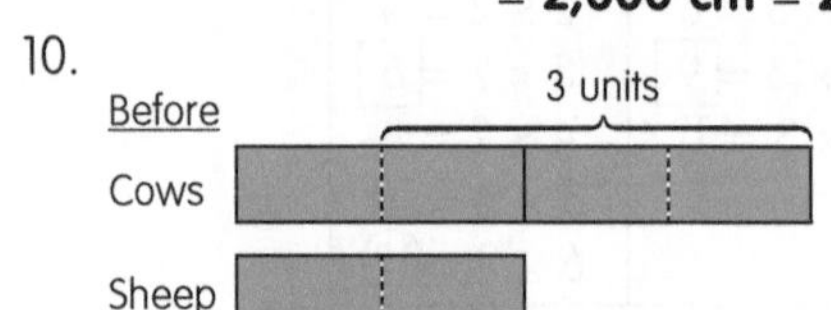

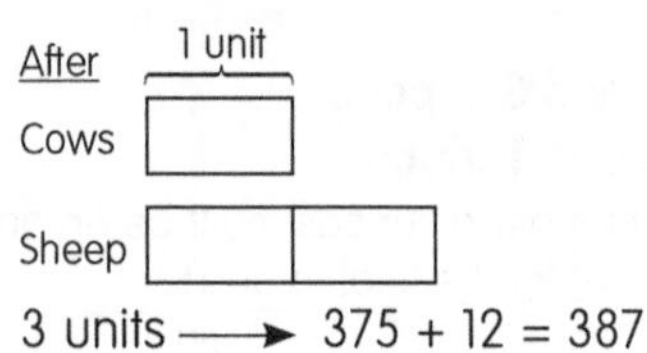

3 units ⟶ 375 + 12 = 387
1 unit ⟶ 387 ÷ 3 = 129
Number of cows that remained = **129**

Challenging Problems (pp. 23–26)

1. *Method 1*

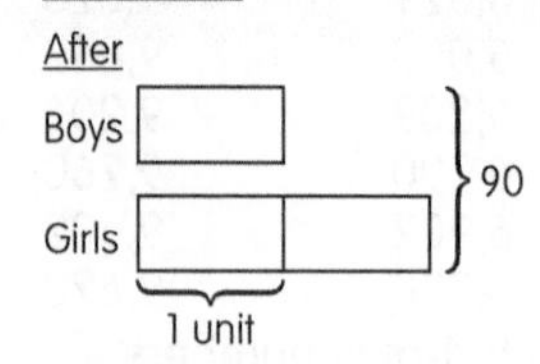

3 units ⟶ 90
1 unit ⟶ 90 ÷ 3 = 30
Number of boys at first = 30 + 75
= 105
Number of girls at first = 60 − 25
= 35
Number of children at first = 105 + 35
= **140**

Note: The '3 times as many boys as girls' is a redundant piece of information.

Method 2

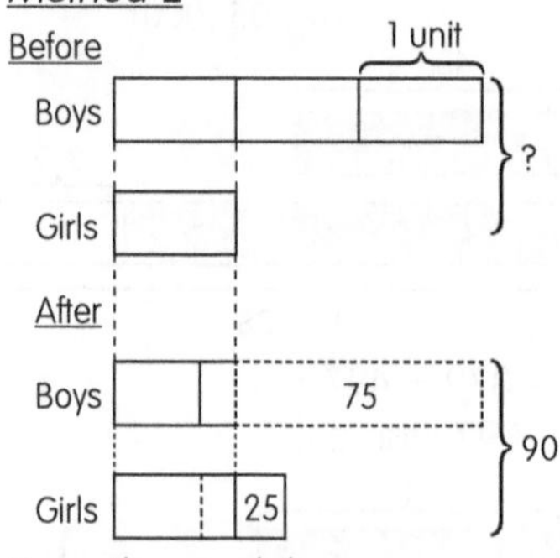

From the model,
4 units ⟶ 90 + 75 − 25
= 140
There were **140** children at first.
Check: 105 − 75 = 30
35 + 25 = 60 = 2 × 30
Try solving the question in as many ways as possible. Then compare the methods of solution: what are the advantages and disadvantages of each method?

Note: 'There were 2 times as many girls as boys' seems like a redundant piece of information.

2. Observe that
6 = 1 + 2 + 3 and 6 = 1 × 2 × 3
So, three such numbers are **1**, **2**, and **3**.
Challenge: Are there other numbers other than the number 6, which exhibit this numerical behavior?

3. **16** and **625**
10,000 = 10 × 10 × 10 × 10
= 2 × 5 × 2 × 5 × 2 × 5 × 2 × 5
= 2 × 2 × 2 × 2 × 5 × 5 × 5 × 5
= 16 × 625

4. Observe that at any time, Belinda is always 7 years older than her brother.

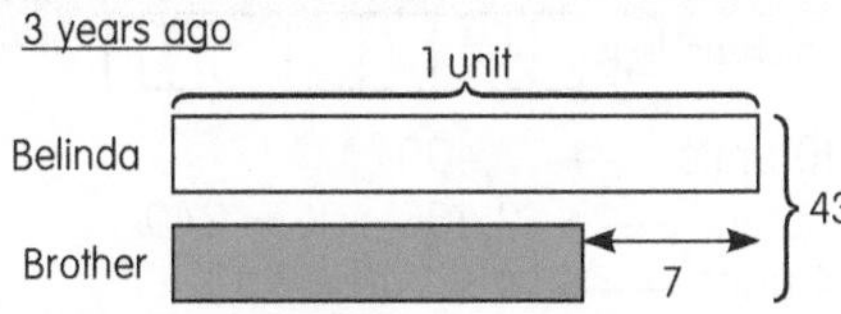

From the model,
2 units ⟶ 43 + 7 = 50
1 unit ⟶ 50 ÷ 2 = 25
So, Belinda was 25 years old 3 years ago.
She is 25 + 3 = 28 years old now.
And she will be 28 + 12 = **40 years old** in 12 years' time.

5.

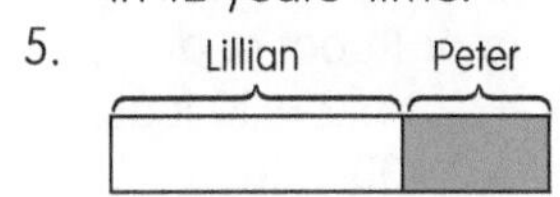

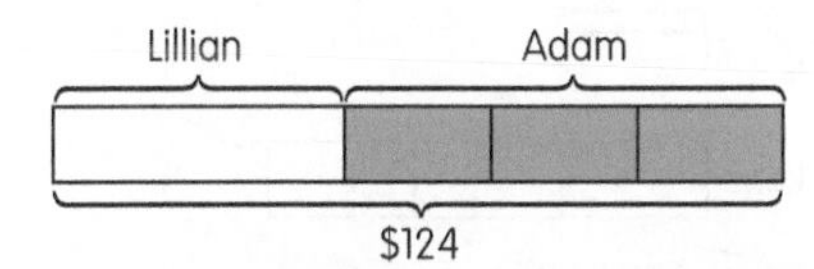

(a) 2 units ⟶ $124 – $78 = $46

Amount that Adam spent more than Peter = **$46**

(b) 1 unit ⟶ $46 ÷ 2 = $23
Amount that Lillian spent
= $78 – $23
= **$55**

6.

Glass: 750 cm³ (1 unit)
Bottle: 2 units
Jug: 8 units

1 unit ⟶ 750 cm^3
2 units ⟶ $2 \times 750 \text{ cm}^3 = 1{,}500 \text{ cm}^3$
8 units ⟶ $8 \times 750 \text{ cm}^3 = 6{,}000 \text{ cm}^3$
Capacity of 3 bottles = $3 \times 1{,}500 \text{ cm}^3$
= $4{,}500 \text{ cm}^3$
Capacity of 4 jugs = $4 \times 6{,}000 \text{ cm}^3$
= $24{,}000 \text{ cm}^3$
Total capacity = $4{,}500 \text{ cm}^3 + 24{,}000 \text{ cm}^3$
= **$28{,}500 \text{ cm}^3$**

7. *Method 1*

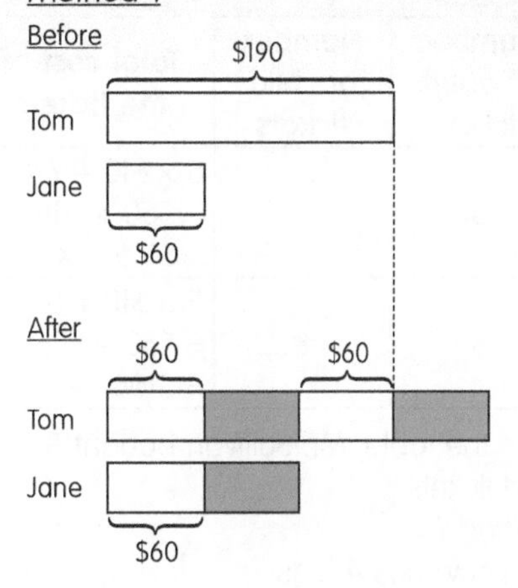

1 unit ⟶ $190 – $60 – $60
= $70
Their father gave each of them **$70**.

Method 2

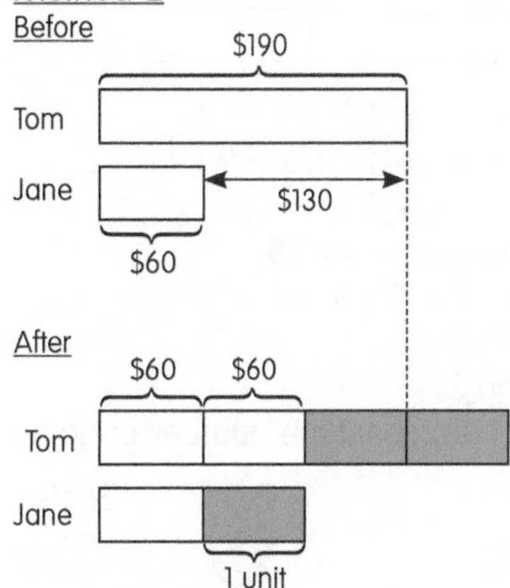

From the model,
1 unit = $130 – $60 = $70
Their father gave each of them **$70**.

8. *Method 1*
If all 13 tickets were child tickets, the total cost would be 13 × $7 = $91.
$106 – $91 = $15
The difference of $15 must have come from the adult tickets.
Each adult ticket cost $10 – $7 = $3 more than a child ticket.
Number of adult tickets
= $15 ÷ $3 = 5
Number of child tickets = 13 – 5 = **8**
Check: 5 × $10 + 8 × $7 = $106

Method 2

Number of adult tickets	Number of child tickets	Total cost of the tickets
6	7	$6 \times \$10 + 7 \times \$7$ $= \$60 + \$49$ $= \$109$ ✗
5	8	$5 \times \$10 + 8 \times \$7$ $= \$50 + \$56$ $= \$106$ ✓

From the table, Mr. Sullivan bought **8** child tickets.

9. *Method 1*

Each cow has 4 legs.
Each goat has 4 legs.
Number of cows and goats
$= 108 \div 4 = 27$

Goats
Cows

3 units ⟶ 27
1 unit ⟶ $27 \div 3 = 9$
2 units ⟶ $2 \times 9 = 18$
Number of cows = **18**
Check: $18 \times 4 + 9 \times 4 = 108$

Method 2
Let ① represent the number of goats.

	Cows	Goats
	②	①
	× 4	× 4
Number of legs	⑧	④
	108	

⑧ + ④ = ⑫ = 108
① = $108 \div 12 = 9$
② = $2 \times 9 = 18$
There are **18** cows.

10. *Method 1*

Each goat has 4 legs.
Each chicken has 2 legs.
Number of goats' legs
$= 1 \text{ unit} \times 4 = 4 \text{ units}$
Number of chickens' legs
$= 3 \text{ units} \times 2 = 6 \text{ units}$

Goats' legs
Chickens' legs
2,400

10 units ⟶ 2,400
1 unit ⟶ $2,400 \div 10 = 240$
4 units ⟶ $4 \times 240 = 960$
6 units ⟶ $6 \times 240 = 1,440$
Number of goats $= 960 \div 4 = 240$
Number of chickens $= 1,440 \div 2 = 720$
Number of chickens more than goats
$= 720 - 240 =$ **480**

Method 2
There are 3 times as many chickens as goats. So, one group of 1 goat and 3 chickens has $1 \times 4 + 3 \times 2 = 10$ legs.
Number of groups $= 2,400 \div 10$
$= 240$

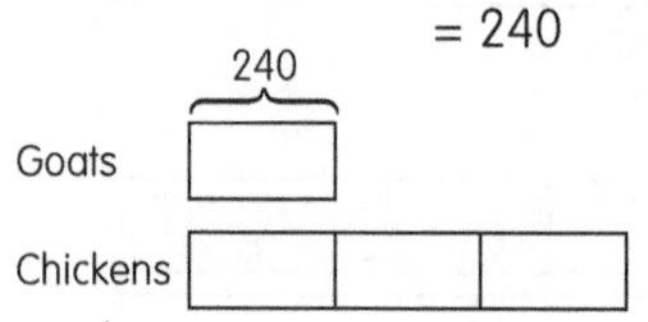

Number of chickens more than goats
$= 2 \times 240$
$=$ **480**

3 Mental Calculation

Practice Questions (pp. 29–30)

1. $556 + 67 - 56 = 556 - 56 + 67$
$= 500 + 67$
$=$ **567**
2. $255 + 364 + 145 + 636$
$= 255 + 145 + 364 + 636$
$= 400 + 1,000$
$=$ **1,400**
3. $752 + 62 + 38 - 252$
$= 752 - 252 + 62 + 38$
$= 500 + 100$
$=$ **600**
4. $604 + 1,796 = 600 + 4 + 1,796$
$= 600 + 1,800$
$=$ **2,400**
5. $60 \times 99 = 60 \times 100 - 60$
$= 6,000 - 60$
$=$ **5,940**
6. $36 \times 199 = 36 \times 200 - 36$
$= 7,200 - 36$
$=$ **7,164**

7. $25 \times 16 \times 125 = 25 \times 2 \times 8 \times 125$
$= 50 \times 1{,}000$
$= \mathbf{50{,}000}$

8. $125 \times 5 \times 32 = 125 \times 5 \times 8 \times 4$
$= 125 \times 8 \times 5 \times 4$
$= 1{,}000 \times 20$
$= \mathbf{20{,}000}$

9. $24 \times 25 \times 125$
$= 3 \times 8 \times 25 \times 125$
$= 3 \times 25 \times 8 \times 125$
$= 75 \times 1{,}000$
$= \mathbf{75{,}000}$

10. $4 \times 125 \times 25 \times 8$
$= 4 \times 25 \times 125 \times 8$
$= 100 \times 1{,}000$
$= \mathbf{100{,}000}$

Challenging Problems (pp. 33–36)

1. $98 + 999 \times 98 = 98 \times (999 + 1)$
$= 98 \times 1{,}000$
$= \mathbf{98{,}000}$

2. $56 \times 77 + 56 \times 23 = 56 \times 100$
$= \mathbf{5{,}600}$

3. $74 \times 13 + 13 \times 26 = 13 \times 100$
$= \mathbf{1{,}300}$

4. $23 \times 1{,}562 - 23 \times 562 = 23 \times 1{,}000$
$= \mathbf{23{,}000}$

5. $65 \times 3{,}142 - 2{,}142 \times 65$
$= 65 \times (3{,}142 - 2{,}142)$
$= 65 \times 1{,}000$
$= \mathbf{65{,}000}$

6. $3{,}568 \times 14 - 2{,}568 \times 14$
$= (3{,}568 - 2{,}568) \times 14$
$= 1{,}000 \times 14$
$= \mathbf{14{,}000}$

7. $62 \times 36 + 76 \times 18$
$= 62 \times 2 \times 18 + 76 \times 18$
$= 124 \times 18 + 76 \times 18$
$= 200 \times 18$
$= \mathbf{3{,}600}$
or
$62 \times 36 + 38 \times 2 \times 18$
$= 62 \times 36 + 38 \times 36$
$= (62 + 38) \times 36$
$= 100 \times 36$
$= \mathbf{3{,}600}$

8. $(2 + 4 + 6 + \cdots + 2{,}012) - (1 + 3 + 5 + \cdots + 2{,}011)$
$= (2 - 1) + (4 - 3) + (6 - 5) + \cdots + (2{,}012 - 2{,}011)$
$= \frac{2{,}012}{2} \times 1$
$= 1{,}006 \times 1$
$= \mathbf{1{,}006}$

9. $1 - \underbrace{2 + 3}_{1} - \underbrace{4 + 5}_{1} - \underbrace{6 + 7}_{1} - \cdots - \underbrace{2{,}008 + 2{,}009}_{1} - \underbrace{2{,}010 + 2{,}011}_{1}$
$= 1 + \frac{2{,}010}{2}$
$= 1 + 1{,}005$
$= \mathbf{1{,}006}$

10. (a)
```
  1 4
x 1 1
-----
1 5 4
```
4 × 1
1 × 1 + 4 × 1
1 × 1

(b)
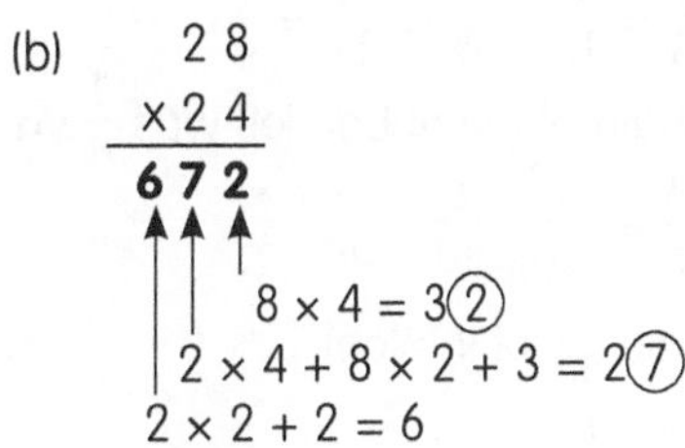

(c)
```
  1 6
x 3 4
-----
5 4 4
```
6 × 4 = 2④
1 × 4 + 3 × 6 + 2 = 2④
1 × 3 + 2 = 5

(d)
```
   5 3
 x 3 5
------
1 8 5 5
```
3 × 5 = 1⑤
5 × 5 + 3 × 3 + 1 = 3⑤
5 × 3 + 3 = 18

4 Operations on Fractions

Practice Questions (pp. 42–48)

1. Fraction of cake they ate together

$= \frac{1}{4} + \frac{3}{8}$

$= \frac{2}{8} + \frac{3}{8} = \mathbf{\frac{5}{8}}$

2. $\frac{1}{3} + \frac{4}{9} = \frac{3}{9} + \frac{4}{9} = \frac{7}{9}$

$\mathbf{\frac{7}{9}}$ of Michael's marbles are blue and green.

3. 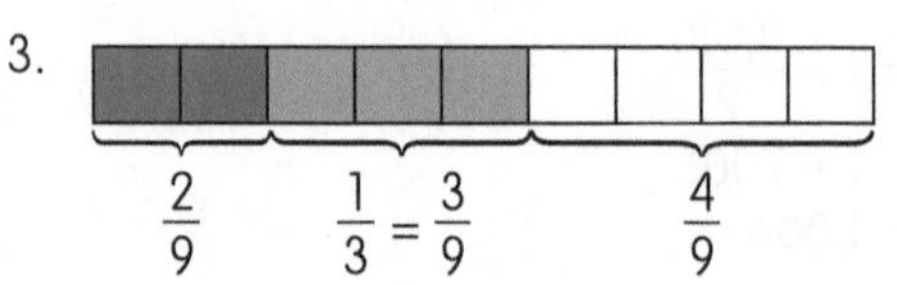

From the model, $\mathbf{\frac{4}{9}}$ of the melon was left.

4. $\frac{1}{2} + \frac{3}{8} = \frac{4}{8} + \frac{3}{8} = \frac{7}{8}$

$\mathbf{\frac{7}{8}}$ of Fred's paper clips are blue and yellow.

5. $\frac{7}{12} - \frac{1}{3} = \frac{7}{12} - \frac{4}{12} = \frac{3}{12} = \frac{1}{4}$

The length of the ribbon left was $\mathbf{\frac{1}{4}}$ **yd**.

6. $\frac{3}{10} + \frac{3}{5} = \frac{3}{10} + \frac{6}{10} = \frac{9}{10}$

Doug ate $\frac{9}{10}$ of the loaf.

$1 - \frac{9}{10} = \frac{1}{10}$

$\mathbf{\frac{1}{10}}$ of the loaf of bread was left.

7. *Method 1*

$\frac{7}{12} + \frac{1}{3} = \frac{7}{12} + \frac{4}{12} = \frac{11}{12}$

Freda had poured $\frac{11}{12}$ of the juice.

$1 - \frac{11}{12} = \frac{1}{12}$

$\mathbf{\frac{1}{12}}$ of the juice remained in the pitcher.

Method 2

$1 - \frac{7}{12} - \frac{1}{3} = \frac{12}{12} - \frac{7}{12} - \frac{4}{12}$

$= \frac{12 - 7 - 4}{12}$

$= \frac{1}{12}$

$\mathbf{\frac{1}{12}}$ of the juice was left.

8. $\frac{1}{2} + \frac{1}{4} + \frac{1}{8} = \frac{4}{8} + \frac{2}{8} + \frac{1}{8} = \frac{7}{8}$

$1 - \frac{7}{8} = \frac{1}{8}$

$\mathbf{\frac{1}{8}}$ of the fruits were strawberries.

9. (a) $\frac{6}{12}$, $\frac{1}{2}$, and $\frac{2}{4}$ are all equivalent to $\frac{1}{2}$

So, $\mathbf{\frac{3}{8}}$ is the odd one.

Since $\frac{1}{2} = \frac{4}{8}$, $\frac{3}{8}$ should be replaced by $\mathbf{\frac{4}{8}}$.

(b) $\frac{4}{6}$, $\frac{2}{3}$, and $\frac{8}{12}$ are all equivalent to $\frac{2}{3}$.

So, $\mathbf{\frac{7}{9}}$ is the odd one.

Since $\frac{2}{3} = \frac{6}{9}$, $\frac{7}{9}$ should be replaced by $\mathbf{\frac{6}{9}}$.

10. *Method 1*

Difference in time taken $= 5\frac{1}{4}\text{ h} - 4\frac{5}{8}\text{ h}$

$= 5\frac{2}{8}\text{ h} - 4\frac{5}{8}\text{ h}$

$= \frac{42}{8}\text{ h} - \frac{37}{8}\text{ h}$

$= \mathbf{\frac{5}{8}\text{ h}}$

Method 2

$4\frac{5}{8} \xrightarrow{+\frac{3}{8}} 5 \xrightarrow{+\frac{1}{4}} 5\frac{1}{4}$

$\frac{3}{8} + \frac{1}{4} = \frac{3}{8} + \frac{2}{8} = \frac{5}{8}$

The time difference is $\mathbf{\frac{5}{8}}$ **h**.

11. *Method 1*

40 – 25 = 15

There are 15 girls.

$\frac{15}{40} = \frac{5 \times 3}{5 \times 8} = \frac{3}{8}$

$\mathbf{\frac{3}{8}}$ of the class are girls.

Method 2

$\frac{25}{40} = \frac{5 \times 5}{5 \times 8} = \frac{5}{8}$

$\frac{5}{8}$ of the class are boys.

$1 - \frac{5}{8} = \frac{8}{8} - \frac{5}{8} = \frac{3}{8}$

$\mathbf{\frac{3}{8}}$ of the class are girls.

12. $1 - \frac{3}{5} = \frac{2}{5}$

$\frac{2}{5}$ of the rope remained.

$\frac{2}{5} \times 3 \text{ ft} = \frac{6}{5} \text{ ft} = 1\frac{1}{5} \text{ ft}$

The length of the remaining piece is **$1\frac{1}{5}$ ft**.

13. 1 minute = 60 seconds

$1\frac{3}{4}$ minutes = 1 minute + $\frac{3}{4}$ minute

= 60 seconds + $\frac{3}{4} \times 60$ seconds

= 60 seconds + 45 seconds

= **105 seconds**

14. *Method 1*

$\frac{3}{7} \times \square = 42$

$\frac{7}{3} \times \frac{3}{7} \times \square = \frac{7}{3} \times 42$

$1 \times \square = 98$

$\square = 98$

The number is **98**.

Method 2

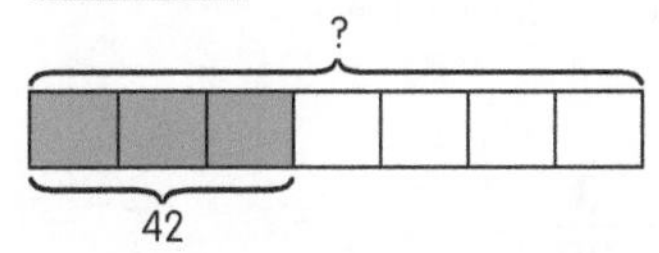

3 units ⟶ 42

1 unit ⟶ 42 ÷ 3 = 14

7 units ⟶ 7 × 14 = 98

The number is **98**.

15. $\frac{3}{5} \times 200 = 3 \times 40 = 120$

The owner sold 120 chairs.

120 × 42 = 5,040

He collected **$5,040**.

16. 26 × 12 = 312

The school hall has a total of 312 seats.

$1 - \frac{7}{8} = \frac{1}{8}$

$\frac{1}{8}$ of the seats are not occupied.

$\frac{1}{8} \times 312 = 39$

39 seats are unoccupied.

17. $\frac{2}{3} \times 36 = 2 \times 12 = 24$

Bag P has 24 red ribbons.

$\frac{5}{12} \times 60 = 5 \times 5 = 25$

Bag Q has 25 red ribbons.

So, **bag Q** has 1 more red ribbon than bag P.

18.

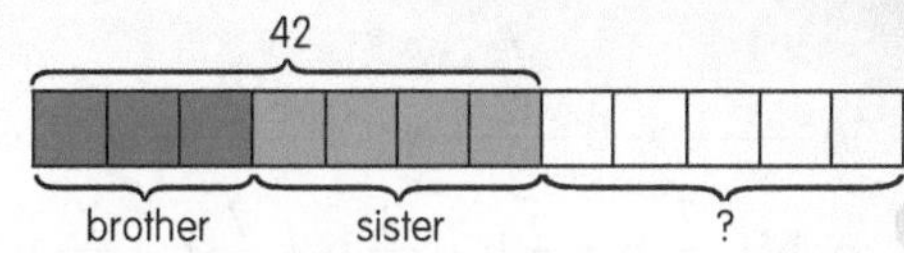

From the model,

7 units ⟶ 42

1 unit ⟶ 42 ÷ 7 = 6

5 units ⟶ 5 × 6 = 30

Andrew had **30** stamps left.

19. Joe: $\frac{1}{4} \times 24 \text{ h} = 6 \text{ h}$

Steve: $\frac{2}{3} \times 6 \text{ h} = 4 \text{ h}$

Difference in time taken = 6 h − 4 h = **2 h**

Challenging Problems (pp. 53–58)

1. $9 - \frac{1}{2} - \frac{5}{8}$

$= 8\frac{1}{2} - \frac{5}{8}$

$= 8\frac{4}{8} - \frac{5}{8}$

$= 7 + \frac{8}{8} + \frac{4}{8} - \frac{5}{8}$

$= 7 + \frac{7}{8}$

$= \mathbf{7\frac{7}{8}}$

2. In one whole, there are seven $\frac{1}{7}$s.

Number of $\frac{1}{7}$s in four wholes = 4 × 7

= 28

Number of $\frac{1}{7}$s in $\frac{3}{7}$ = 3

Number of $\frac{1}{7}$s in $4\frac{3}{7}$ = 28 + 3

= **31**

3. In one whole, there are nine $\frac{1}{9}$s.

Number of $\frac{1}{9}$s in three wholes

= 3 × 9

= 27

$\frac{1}{3} = \frac{3}{9} = \frac{1}{9} + \frac{1}{9} + \frac{1}{9}$

Number of $\frac{1}{9}$ s in $\frac{1}{3}$ = 3

Number of $\frac{1}{9}$ s in $3\frac{1}{3}$ = 27 + 3

= **30**

4. A $\xrightarrow{\frac{1}{4}\text{ h}}$ B $\xrightarrow{\frac{7}{12}\text{ h}}$ C $\xrightarrow{\frac{5}{6}\text{ h}}$ D

$$\frac{1}{4}\text{ h} + \frac{7}{12}\text{ h} + \frac{5}{6}\text{ h} = \frac{3}{12}\text{ h} + \frac{7}{12}\text{ h} + \frac{10}{12}\text{ h}$$
$$= \frac{20}{12}\text{ h}$$
$$= \frac{5}{3}\text{ h}$$
$$= \mathbf{1\frac{2}{3}\text{ h}}$$

5. $\frac{3}{5} + \frac{9}{10} = \frac{6}{10} + \frac{9}{10} = \frac{15}{10} = \frac{10}{10} + \frac{5}{10}$

$= 1 + \frac{1}{2} = 1\frac{1}{2}$

She used $1\frac{1}{2}$ m of cloth.

$7 - 1\frac{1}{2} = 5\frac{1}{2}$

$\mathbf{5\frac{1}{2}}$ m of cloth were left.

6. $\frac{3}{5} = \frac{6}{10}$

$\frac{4}{5} = \frac{8}{10}$

$\frac{6}{10}$ $\quad$ $\frac{7}{10}$ (circled) $\quad$ $\frac{8}{10}$

Fraction that is halfway between $\frac{3}{5}$ and $\frac{4}{5} = \mathbf{\frac{7}{10}}$

7.

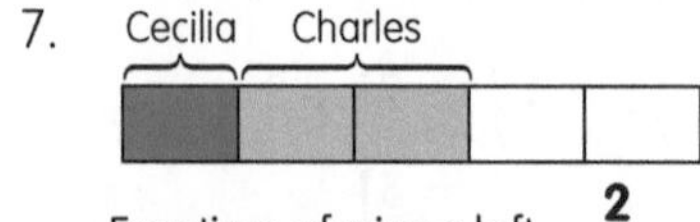

Fraction of pizza left = $\mathbf{\frac{2}{5}}$

8.

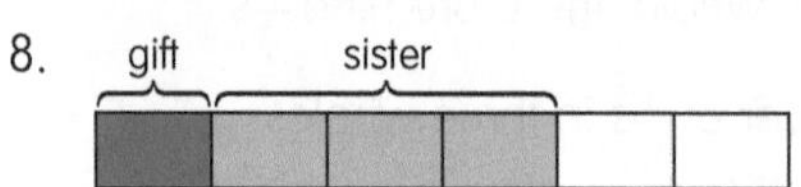

From the model, 2 out of 6 equal parts represent the amount of ribbon left.

$\frac{2}{6} = \frac{1}{3}$

Fraction of ribbon left = $\mathbf{\frac{1}{3}}$

9.

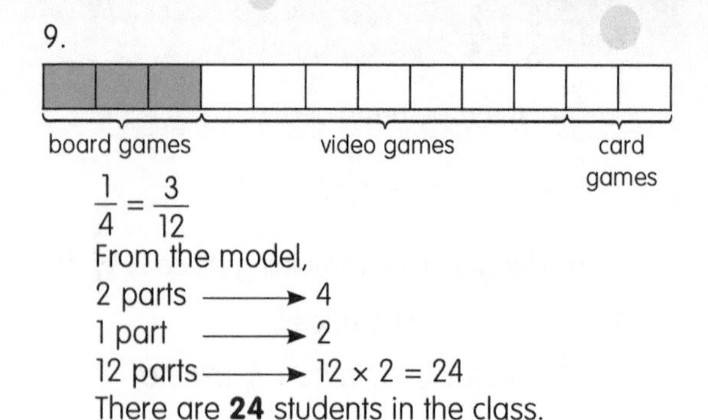

$\frac{1}{4} = \frac{3}{12}$

From the model,

2 parts ⟶ 4

1 part ⟶ 2

12 parts ⟶ 12 × 2 = 24

There are **24** students in the class.

10. *Method 1*

Boys: $\frac{1}{5} = \frac{4}{20}$

Girls: $\frac{7}{20}$

Men: $\frac{3}{10} = \frac{6}{20}$

Fraction of people that were women

$= 1 - \frac{4}{20} - \frac{7}{20} - \frac{6}{20}$

$= \frac{20}{20} - \frac{4}{20} - \frac{7}{20} - \frac{6}{20}$

$= \frac{3}{20}$

$\frac{6}{20} - \frac{3}{20} = \frac{3}{20}$

20 units ⟶ 960

1 unit ⟶ 960 ÷ 20 = 48

3 units ⟶ 3 × 48 = 144

Number of men more than women = **144**

Method 2

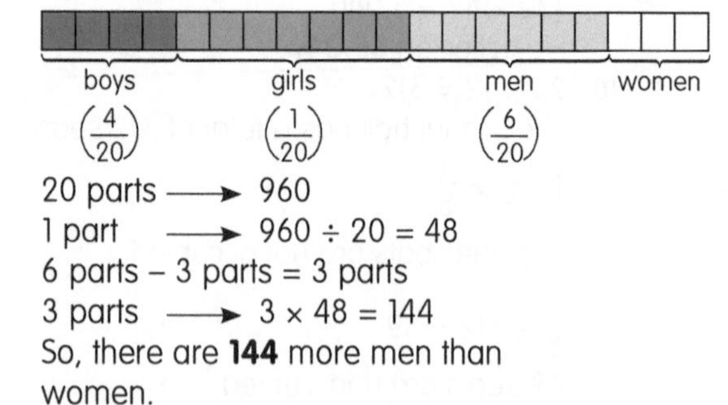

20 parts ⟶ 960

1 part ⟶ 960 ÷ 20 = 48

6 parts – 3 parts = 3 parts

3 parts ⟶ 3 × 48 = 144

So, there are **144** more men than women.

11. Number of triangles to be shaded

$= \frac{2}{3} \times 15$

$= 10$

Number of triangles that need to be shaded = 10 – 6

$= \mathbf{4}$

12.

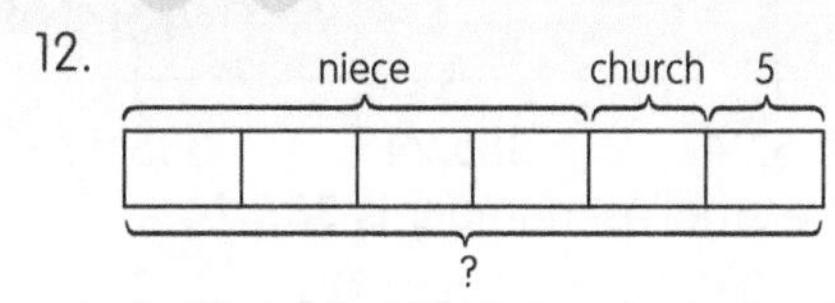

1 unit ⟶ 5
6 units ⟶ $6 \times 5 = 30$
Number of rare coins = **30**

13.

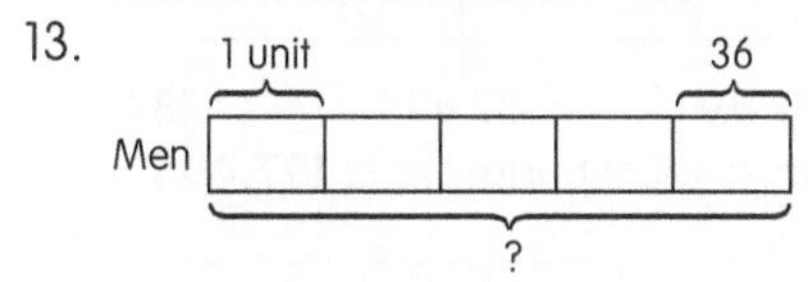

1 unit ⟶ 36
5 units ⟶ $5 \times 36 = 180$
Number of men who attended the party
= 180

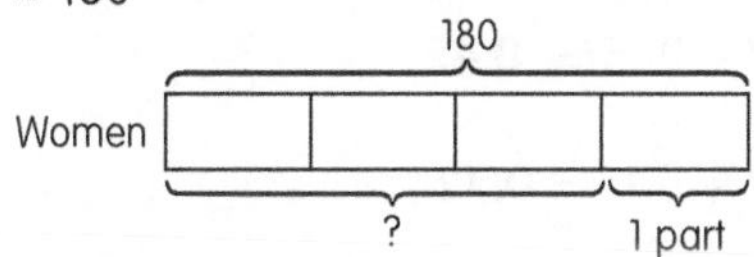

4 parts ⟶ 180
1 part ⟶ $180 \div 4 = 45$
3 parts ⟶ $3 \times 45 = 135$
Number of women who left the party
= **135**

14.

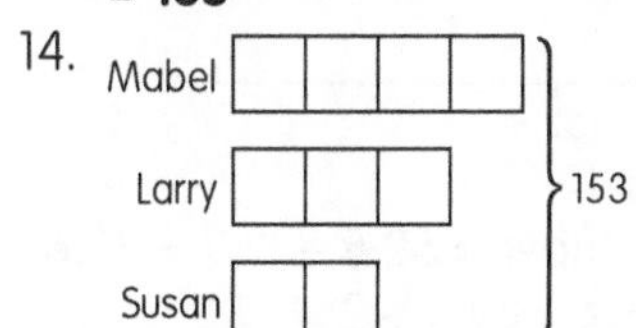

9 units ⟶ 153
1 unit ⟶ $153 \div 9 = 17$
3 units ⟶ $3 \times 17 = 51$
Number of badges Larry has = **51**

15.

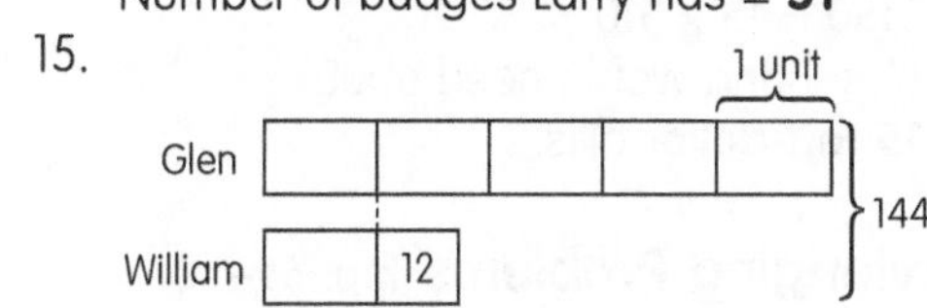

From the model,
6 units ⟶ $144 - 12 = 132$
1 unit ⟶ $132 \div 6 = 22$
1 unit + 12 ⟶ $22 + 12 = 34$
William has **34** candies.

16.

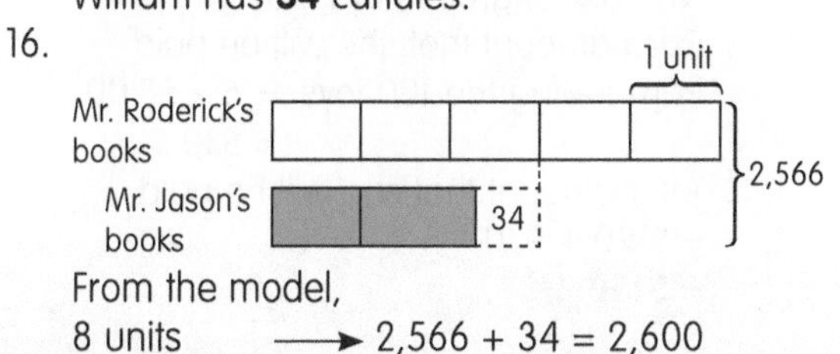

From the model,
8 units ⟶ $2{,}566 + 34 = 2{,}600$
1 unit ⟶ $2{,}600 \div 8 = 325$
3 units − 34 ⟶ $3 \times 325 - 34 = 941$
So, Mr. Jason has **941** books.

17.

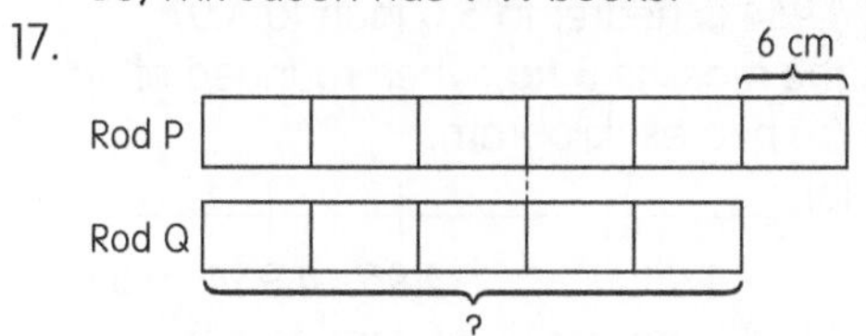

1 unit ⟶ 6 cm
5 units ⟶ 5×6 cm = 30 cm
Length of rod Q = **30 cm**
Check:
Rod P: $\frac{1}{2} \times 36$ cm = 18 cm
Rod Q: $\frac{3}{5} \times 30$ cm = 18 cm

18. $\frac{2}{3} = \frac{6}{9}$

$\frac{3}{7} = \frac{6}{14}$

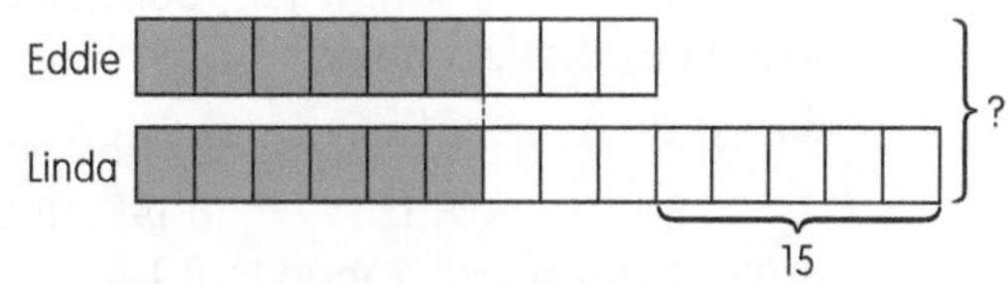

5 units ⟶ 15
1 unit ⟶ $15 \div 5 = 3$
23 units ⟶ $23 \times 3 = 69$
Number of books Eddie and Linda have
= **69**

5 Decimals

Practice Questions (pp. 62–65)

1. (a)

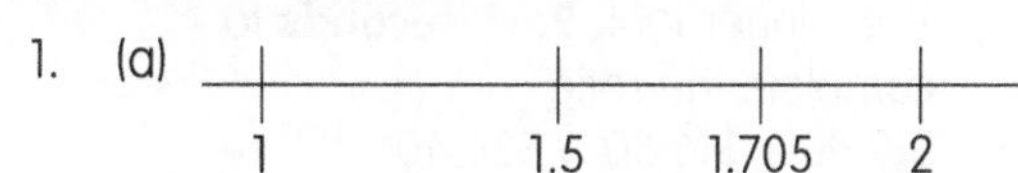

1.705 is nearer to 2 than to 1.
The thickness of the book is **2 cm**, when rounded off to the nearest centimeter.

(b)

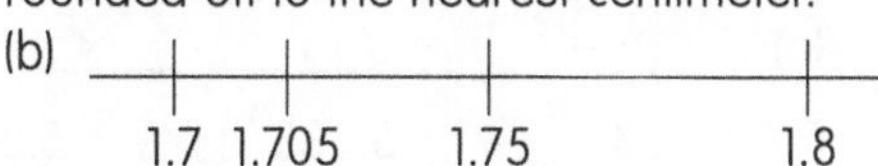

1.705 is nearer to 1.7 than to 1.8.
The thickness of the book is **1.7 cm**, when rounded off to one decimal place.

(c)

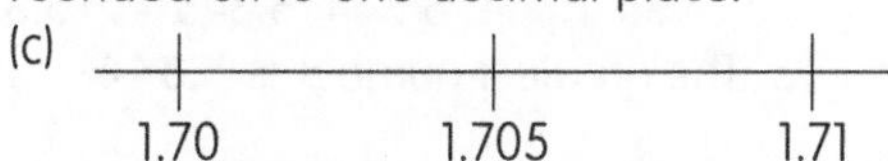

1.705 is halfway between 1.70 and 1.71.
The thickness is **1.71 cm**, when rounded off to two decimal places.

2. (a) 4 4.5 4.954 5

4.954 is nearer to 5.0 than to 4.0.
The mass is **5 kg**, when rounded off to the nearest kilogram.

(b) 4.9 4.95 4.954 5.0

4.954 is nearer to 5.0 than to 4.9.
The mass is **5.0 kg**, when rounded off to one decimal place.

(c) 4.95 4.954 4.955 4.96

4.954 is nearer to 4.95 than to 4.96.
The mass is **4.95 kg**, when rounded off to two decimal places.

3. (a)

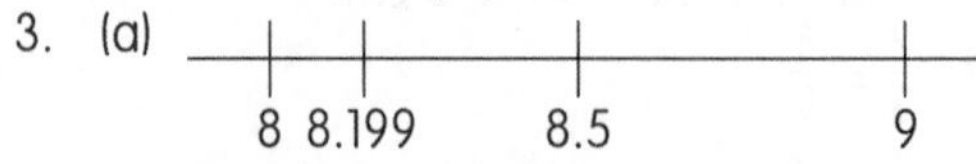

8.199 is closer to 8 than to 9.
The distance is **8 km**, when rounded off to the nearest kilometer.

(b)

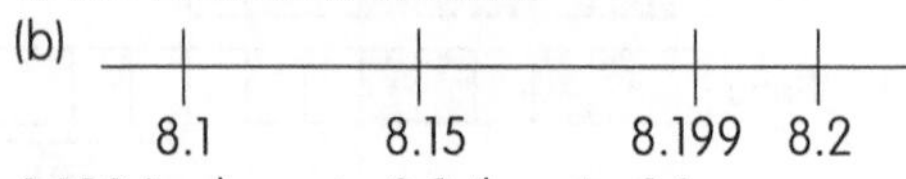

8.199 is closer to 8.2 than to 8.1.
The distance is **8.2 km**, when rounded off to the nearest tenth of a kilometer.

(c)

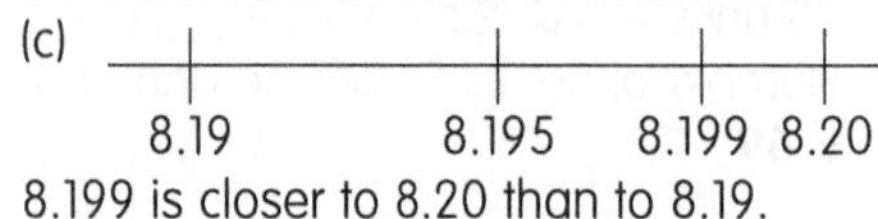

8.199 is closer to 8.20 than to 8.19.
The distance is **8.20 km**, when rounded to the nearest hundredth of a kilometer.

4. 10.56 – 1.09 = 9.47
The winner took **9.47 seconds** to complete the race.

5. \$19.90 + \$16.50 = \$36.40
2 × \$20 = \$40
\$40 – \$36.40 = \$3.60
He should get **\$3.60** change.

6. (a)

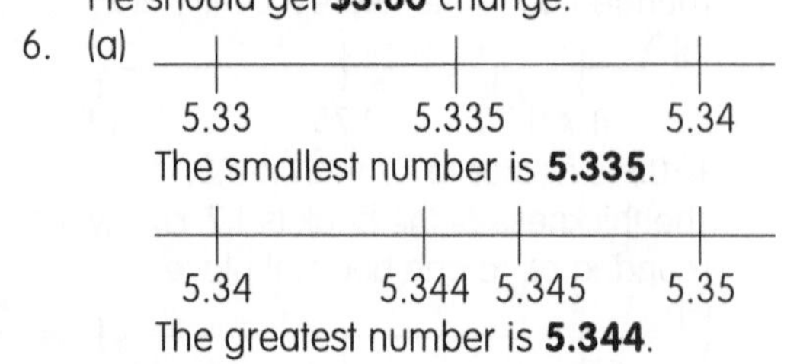

The smallest number is **5.335**.
The greatest number is **5.344**.

(b)

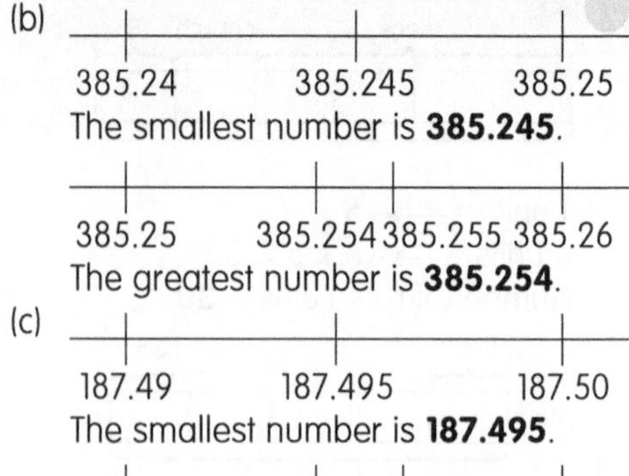

The smallest number is **385.245**.
The greatest number is **385.254**.

(c)

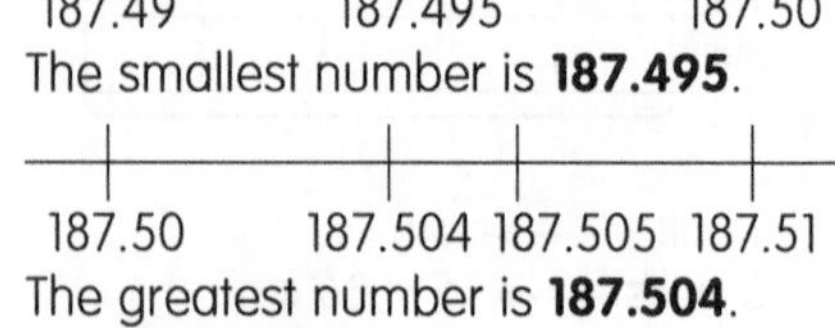

The smallest number is **187.495**.
The greatest number is **187.504**.

7. 0.27 + 0.15 = **0.42**
or
0.57 – 0.15 = **0.42**

0.57 + 0.15 = **0.72**
or
0.87 – 0.15 = **0.72**

8.

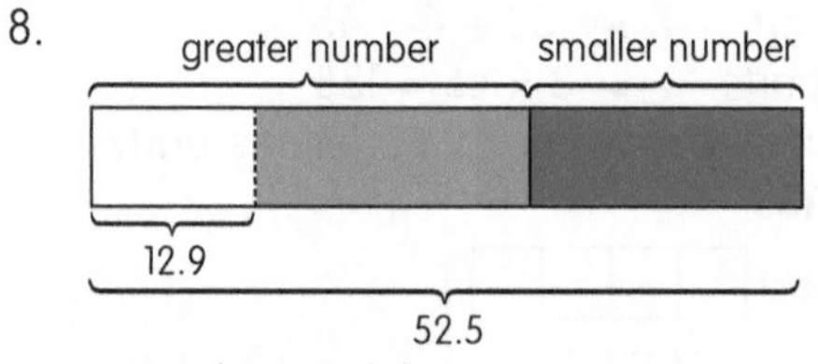

From the model,
2 × smaller number = 52.5 – 12.9 = 39.6
Smaller number = 39.6 ÷ 2 = 19.8
19.8 + 12.9 = 32.7 or 52.5 – 19.8 = 32.7
The two decimals are **19.8** and **32.7**.

9. \$49.85 is close to \$50.
3 × \$50 = \$150
\$150 = 15 × \$10
Mrs. Bond would need about **15 ten-dollar** bills.

Challenging Problems (pp. 69–71)

1. Amount of money that Candice will be paid from selling 100 toys = 100 × \$1.20
= \$120
100 = 15 × 6 + 10
Number of groups of 15 toys = 6
Extra amount that she will be paid from selling the 100 toys = 6 × \$5.00
= \$30
Total amount that she will be paid
= \$120 + \$30
= **\$150**

2. From 3:00 P.M. to 6:00 P.M., there are 3 hours.
   Amount that he had to pay
   = 3 × \$3.50
   = \$10.50
   From 6:00 P.M. to 7:45 P.M., there are 1 hour and 45 minutes.
   Amount that he had to pay
   = 2 × \$2.50
   = \$5
   Total amount that he had to pay
   = \$10.50 + \$5
   = **\$15.50**
3. ? —(÷ 6)→ ? —(+ 2.3)→ 4

   10.2 ←(× 6)— 1.7 ←(− 2.3)— 4

   Nelson is thinking of **10.2**.
4. Cost of 1 pear = \$140 ÷ 4 = \$0.35 = 35¢
   Cost of 1 orange = \$2.40 ÷ 6 = \$0.40 = 40¢
   If all 12 fruits were pears, then the total cost would be 12 × \$0.35 = \$4.20.
   So, the extra (\$4.45 − \$4.20) = \$0.25 = 25¢ must have come from the oranges.
   One orange costs 40¢ − 35¢ = 5¢ more than one pear.
   So, there are 25 ÷ 5 = **5 oranges** and 12 − 5 = **7 pears**.
5. 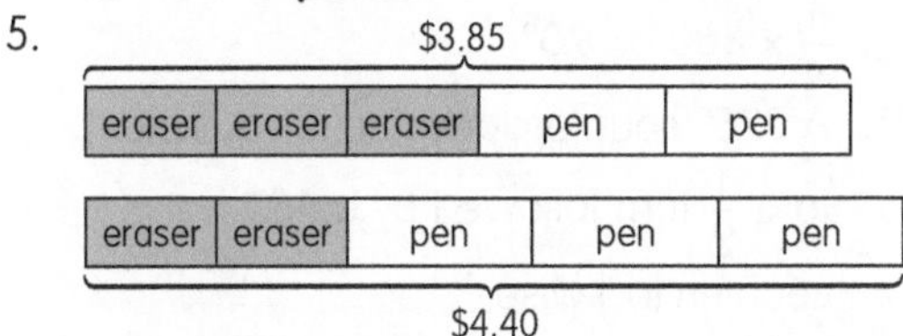

   Cost of 5 erasers and 5 pens
   = \$3.85 + \$4.40
   = \$8.25
   Cost of 1 eraser and 1 pen = \$8.25 ÷ 5
   = \$1.65
   Cost of 2 erasers and 2 pens = \$1.65 × 2
   = \$3.30
   Cost of 1 eraser = \$3.85 − \$3.30
   = \$0.55
   = **55¢**
6. Total cost of 10 watches and 8 bags
   = 2 × \$169.10
   = \$338.20
   Total cost of 9 watches and 8 bags
   = \$314.30
   Cost of 1 watch = \$338.20 − \$314.30
   = \$23.90
   Cost of 5 watches = 5 × \$23.90
   = \$119.50
   Cost of 4 bags = \$169.10 − \$119.50
   = \$49.60
   Cost of 1 bag = \$49.60 ÷ 4
   = \$12.40
   Difference between the cost of a watch and a bag = \$23.90 − \$12.40
   = **\$11.50**
7. If all 17 ribbons were blue, then the total length would be 17 × 1.7 m = 28.9 m.
   So, the extra (31.9 − 28.9) m = 3 m must have come from the green ribbon.
   A geen ribbon is (2.3 − 1.7) m = 0.6 m longer than a blue ribbon.
   So, there are 3 ÷ 0.6 = **5 green ribbons** and 17 − 5 = **12 blue ribbons**.
8. Suppose there were 15 nickels.
   Total value of the nickels
   = 15 × \$0.05
   = \$0.75
   One dime is 5¢ more than one nickel.
   \$1.05 − \$0.75 = \$0.30 or 30¢
   Number of dimes = 30¢ ÷ 5¢ = **6**
   Number of nickels = 15 − 6 = **9**
   Check: 6 × 10¢ + 9 × 5¢ = 105¢ = \$1.05
9. *Method 1*
   Suppose he sold 10 bags of red beans.
   Total mass of 10 bags of red beans
   = 10 × 1.5 kg
   = 15 kg
   One bag of green beans was 0.3 kg (or 300 g) heavier than one bag of red beans.
   16.2 kg − 15 kg = 1.2 kg
   = 1,200 g
   Number of bags of green beans sold
   = 1,200 g ÷ 300 g
   = **4**
   Number of bags of red beans sold
   = 10 − 4
   = **6**
   Check: 6 × 1.5 kg + 4 × 1.8 kg = 16.2 kg
   4 bags of green beans and **6** bags of red beans were sold.

Method 2

Use guess and check method.

Guess	1st	2nd
Number of bags of red beans	5	6
Total mass of red beans	5 × 1.5 kg = 7.5 kg	6 × 1.5 kg = 9.0 kg
Number of bags of green beans	5	4
Total mass of green beans	5 × 1.8 kg = 9.0 kg	4 × 1.8 kg = 7.2 kg
Total mass	7.5 kg + 9 kg = 16.5 kg	9.0 kg + 7.2 kg = 16.2 kg
Is the total mass 16.2 kg?	No	Yes

4 bags of green beans and **6** bags of red beans were sold.

6 Angles

Practice Questions (pp. 74–79)

1. A turn of 315° clockwise
   = An counterclockwise turn of 360° – 315°
   = 45° counterclockwise.
   A 45° counterclockwise from the museum is the **fitness center**.
2. 90° ⟶ 15 mins
   2:40 P.M. ⟶ 2:55 P.M
   15 mins
3. 

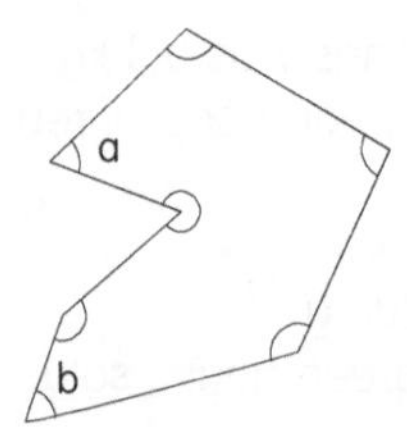

   Angles labeled a and b are each less than 90°.
   There are **2** marked angles less than 90°.
4. Half of a semicircle has an angle of
   $\frac{1}{2} \times 360° = 180°$.
   180° + 30° = 210°
   The measure of *p* is **210°**.
5. Angle at a point = 360°
   360° – 100° = 260°
   The measure of *r* is **260°**.
6. **28°**
7. Using a protractor, angle *b* is 90°.
   So, angle ***b*** is the right angle.
8. 2:30 A.M. ⟶ 3:00 A.M. ⟶ 4:00 A.M.
   In 1 hour, the minute hand makes 4 one-quarter-turns.
   In $\frac{1}{2}$ hour, the minute hand makes 2 one-quarter-turns.
   In $1\frac{1}{2}$ hours, the minute hand makes 4 + 2 = **6** one-quarter turns.
9. From North-West. A $\frac{1}{2}$-turn clockwise would lead Joseph to face South-East. Then, a 45° counterclockwise from South-East would lead him to face **East**.
10. *Method 1*
    From 1:05 P.M. to 1:20 P.M., there are 15 minutes.
    In 60 minutes, the minute hand moves 360°.
    In 15 minutes, the minute hand moves
    $\frac{1}{4} \times 360° = $ **90°**.
    Method 2
    1:05 P.M. —15 min⟶ 1:20 P.M.
    15 min = $\frac{1}{4}$ h
    In 1 hour, the minute hand moves 360°.
    In $\frac{1}{4}$ hour, the minute hand moves
    $\frac{1}{4} \times 360° = $ **90°**.
11. A 225° counterclockwise is equivalent to a $\frac{1}{2}$-turn followed by a 45° counterclockwise.
    A $\frac{1}{2}$-turn from the pet shop will bring Joan to face the fast-food restaurant. Then, a 45° counterclockwise from the fast-food restaurant will lead Joan to face the **bookshop**.
12. **Statement C**.
    A quick look based on the arc lengths used to represent the angle measures *p* and *q* seems to suggest that angle measure *q* is greater than angle measure *p*. However, using the protractor, it can be shown that angle measures *p* and *q* are both the same, although they do not appear to be so.

Challenging Problems (pp. 84–88)

1. (a) 3:00 P.M. $\xrightarrow{+\ 30\text{ mins}}$ 3:30 P.M.

   30 mins = $\frac{1}{2}$ h

   In 1 hour, the minute hand moves 360°.

   In $\frac{1}{2}$ hour, the minute hand moves

   $\frac{1}{2} \times 360° =$ **180°**

   (b) In 1 hour, the hour hand moves

   $\frac{1}{12} \times 360° = 30°$

   In $\frac{1}{2}$ hour, the hour hand moves

   $\frac{1}{2} \times 30° =$ **15°**

2. At 12:30, the hour hand is halfway between the numerals 12 and 1.
   The hour hand has since moved
   $\frac{1}{12} \times 30° = 15°$ (from 12:00) in half an hour.
   In the same half an hour, the minute hand has moved $\frac{1}{12} \times 360° = 180°$.
   $180° - 15° = 165°$
   So, the angle between the two hands is **165°**.

3. *Note*: A 180° counterclockwise is equivalent to a 180° clockwise, which is the same as a $\frac{1}{2}$-turn clockwise or counterclockwise.

   (a) **Shopping center** (b) **Museum**
   (c) **School** (d) **Shopping center**
   (e) **225°** (f) **135°**
   (g) **counterclockwise**
   (h) **counterclockwise**

4. (a) **North-East** (b) **West**
   (c) **West**

   South $\xrightarrow{270°\text{ counterclockwise}}$ West

   (d) **South-West**

   North-West $\xrightarrow{\frac{3}{4}\text{-turn clockwise}}$ South-West

5. The second hand sweeps through 360° in 60 seconds.
   The second hand sweeps through 90° in
   $\frac{60\text{ s}}{360°} \times 90° = 15\text{ s}$
   So, it takes **15 seconds** for the second hand on a watch to sweep through 90°.

6. **10** angles

Type of angle	Number of such angle measures
	4
	3
	2
	1
Total	10

7. Angle between two neighboring numerals on the clock $= \frac{1}{12} \times 360°$
   $= 30°$
   In 60 minutes, the hour hand moves 30°.
   Angle moved by hour hand in 40 minutes
   $= \frac{2}{3} \times 30° = 20°$

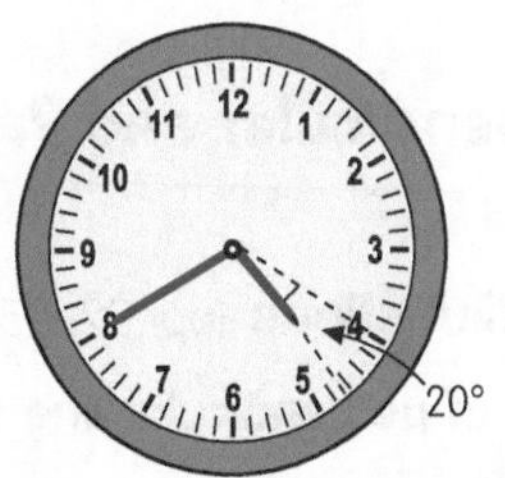

Angle between numeral 4 and numeral 8 on the clock = 30° × 4 = 120°
Angle formed by the hands of a clock at 4:40 = 120° − 20°
= **100°**

8. **A regular pentagon**

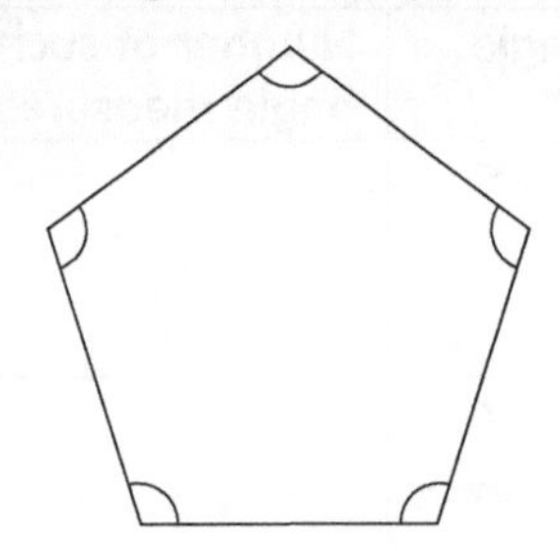

9. **A regular octagon**

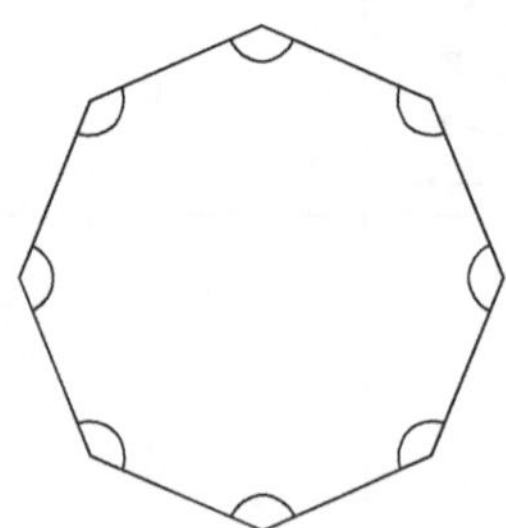

10.

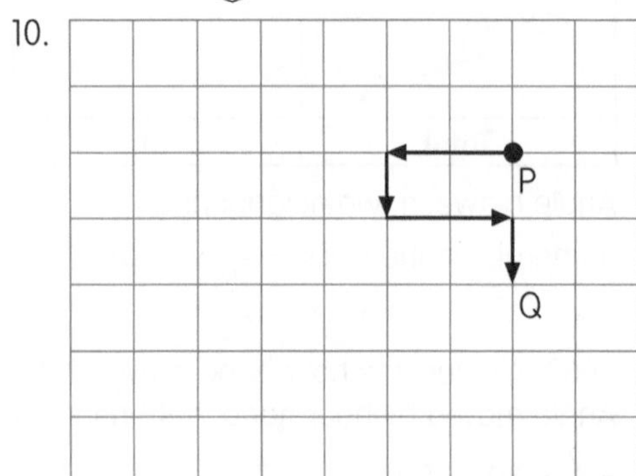

7 Perpendicular and Parallel Lines

Practice Questions (pp. 92–95)

1. **8 pairs of perpendicular line segments**
2. **$\overline{DF}$** or **$\overline{EB}$**
4. **Z** and **N**
5. **1 pair**
6. **$\overline{OC}$**
8. (a) **True** (b) **False** (c) **True** (d) **False**
   Statement (c) is based on the definition of two lines being parallel.
9. **3 pairs**
10. **2 pairs**
11. **3 pairs**
12. (a) **4 line segments** (b) **4 line segments**

Challenging Problems (pp. 98–102)

1. **Yes**
2. **2 pairs**
   Note: The figure is two-dimensional.
3. **7 line segments** ($\overline{WV}$ is parallel to $\overline{PQ}$, $\overline{QR}$, $\overline{RS}$, $\overline{UT}$, $\overline{PR}$, $\overline{QS}$, $\overline{PS}$.)
4. **3 pairs**
5. **8 pairs**
6. **3 pairs**
7. (a) **$\overline{CD}$** (b) **$\overline{AB}$** and **$\overline{LM}$**
   (c) **8 right angles**
8. (a) **$\overline{AD}$** and **$\overline{BC}$** (b) **$\overline{EC}$** and **$\overline{FB}$**
   (c) **$\overline{CF}$** and **$\overline{BA}$** (d) **$\overline{BE}$** and **$\overline{AF}$**
   (e) **$\overline{FE}$**, **$\overline{AD}$**, and **$\overline{BC}$**
9. **7 different line segments** ($\overline{VU}$ is parallel to $\overline{AB}$, $\overline{BC}$, $\overline{CD}$, $\overline{AC}$, $\overline{BD}$, $\overline{AD}$, and $\overline{XW}$.)
10. (a) **6** (b) **8**
11. **Yes**

8 Tiling Patterns and Symmetry

Practice Questions (pp. 105–108)

1. By counting the number of bricks that can fit in the empty space, **12** bricks have been removed from the wall.
2. **GH** is the line of symmetry, dividing the figure into two—the line acts as a mirror line.
3. **B**—4 lines of symmetry.
4. (a) Answers vary.
   Two examples are:

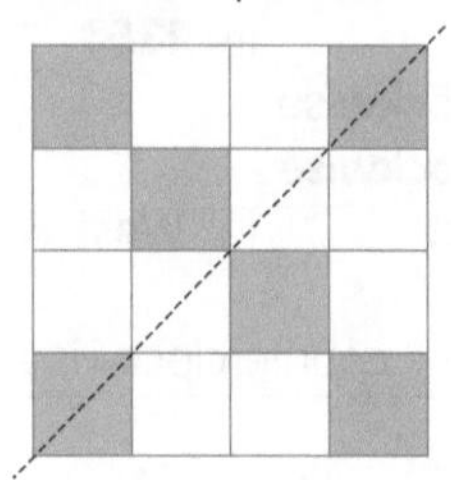

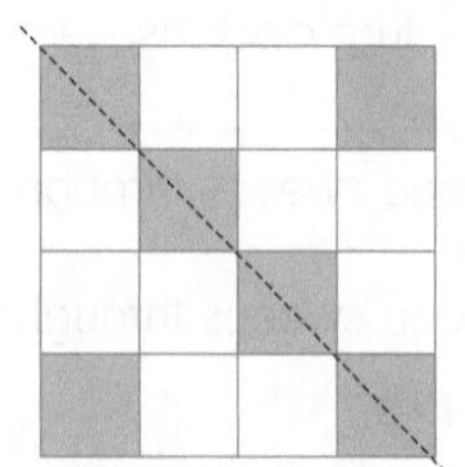

(b)

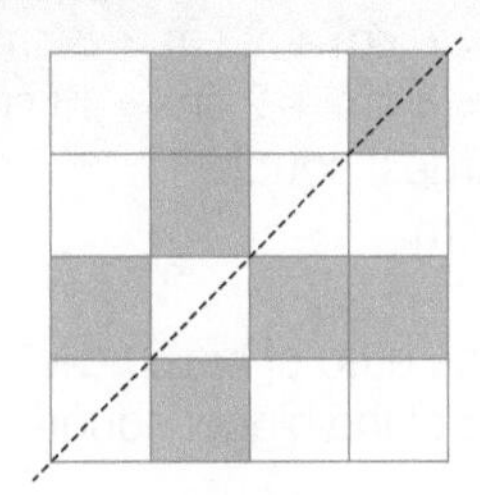

5. Answers vary.
   Some examples are:
   (a)

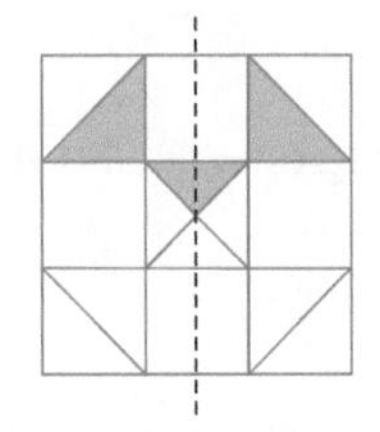

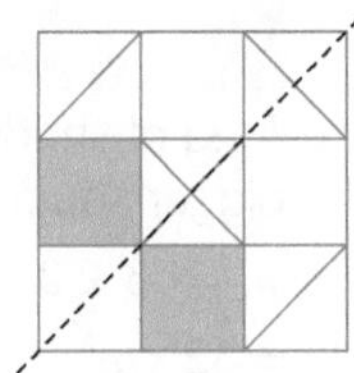

(b)

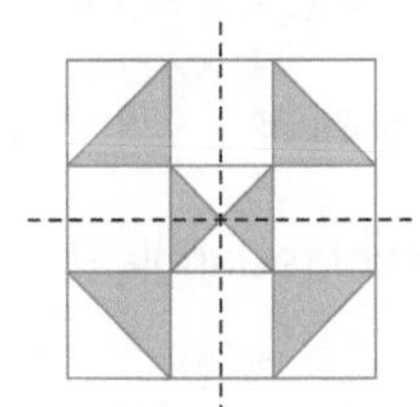

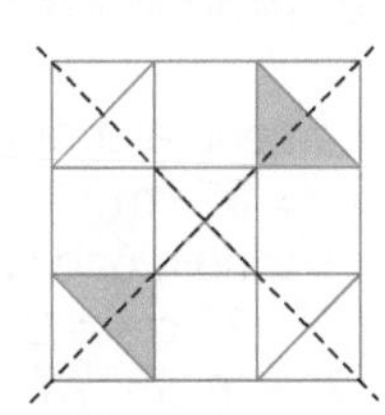

6. Act it out to verify your answer.

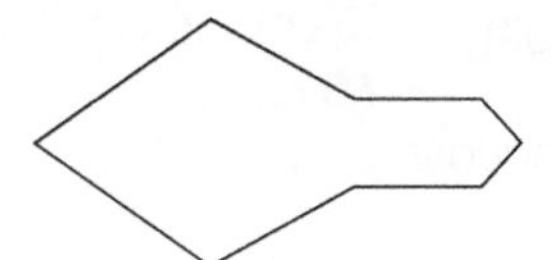

7.

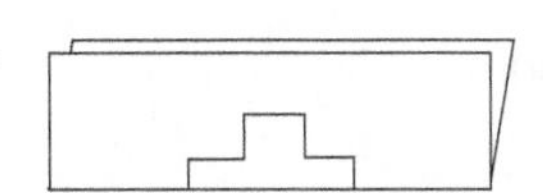

8.

9. Answers vary.
   One example is:
   (a)

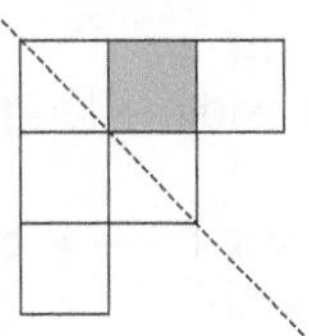

Answers vary.
One example is:
(b)

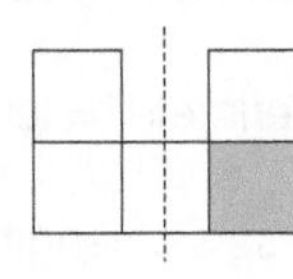

Challenging Problems (pp. 110-113)

1.

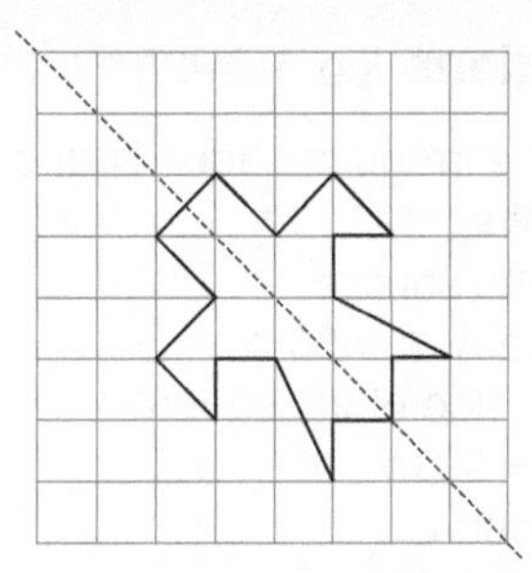

2. (a)

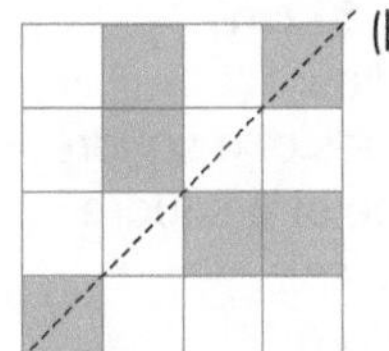

(b)

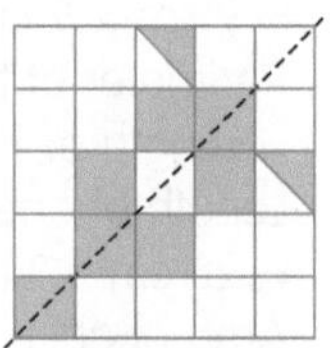

3. (a)

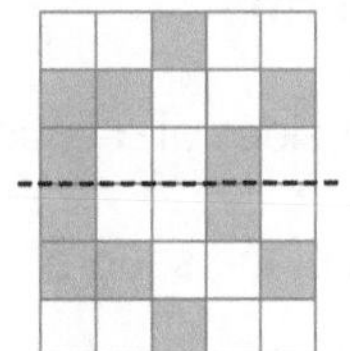

(b)

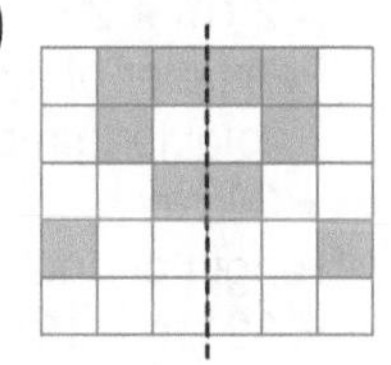

4. (a)

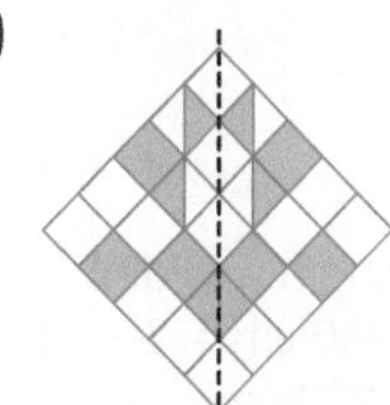

(b)

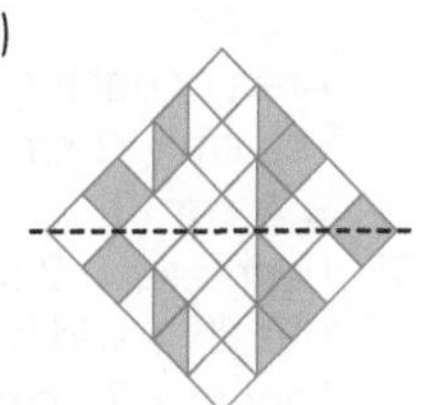

5.

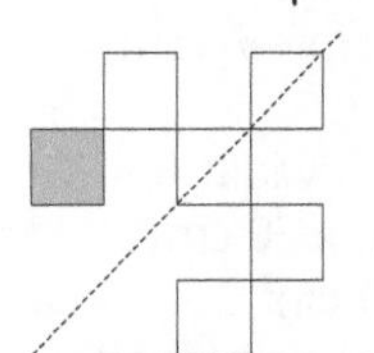

6. Answers vary.
   One example is:
   (a)

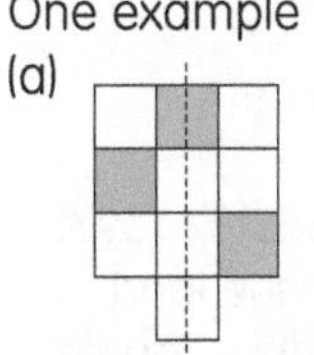

Answers vary.
One example is:
(b)

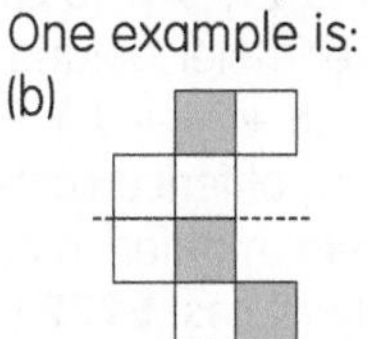

7. Answers vary.
   Some examples are:

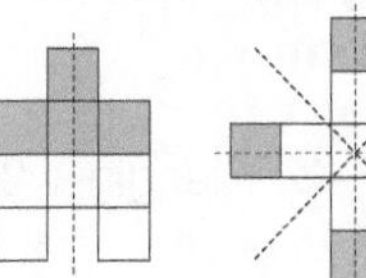

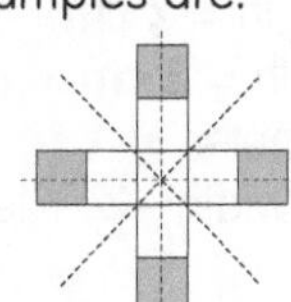

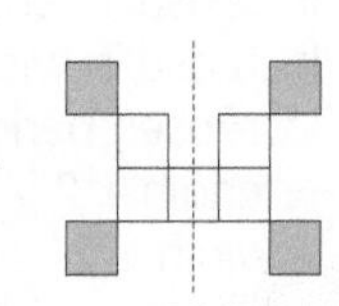

9 Area and Perimeter

Practice Questions (pp. 117–121)

1. The area of the irregular shape is about **12 square units**.
2. Perimeter of the square
   = length of the wire = 36 cm
   Length of one side of the square
   = 36 cm ÷ 4 = 9 cm
   Area of the square
   = 9 cm × 9 cm = **81 cm²**
3. Perimeter of the figure
   = Length of 14 sides of a square = 28 cm
   Length of one side of a square
   = 28 cm ÷ 14 = 2 cm
   Area of each square
   = 2 cm × 2 cm = **4 cm²**
4. Perimeter of figure
   = Total length of 16 sides of a square
   = 32 cm
   Length of one side of the square
   = 32 cm ÷ 16
   = 2 cm
   Area of each square
   = 2 cm × 2 cm
   = **4 cm²**
5. Perimeter = 2 × (length + width)
   Length + width = 440 cm ÷ 2 = 220 cm
   Length + 70 cm = 220 cm
   Length of table = 220 cm – 70 cm
   = 150 cm
   Area of table = length × width
   = 150 cm × 70 cm
   = **10,500 cm²**
6. Length of rectangular piece of land
   = 162 ÷ 9 = 18 cm
   Perimeter of land
   = 18 + 18 + 9 + 9 = 54 cm
   1 m of fence costs $18
   54 cm of fence cost 54 × $18 = $972
   It will cost **$972** to fence the land.
7. Perimeter = length + width + length + width
   Increase in length = **2 cm**
   Increase in width = **2 cm**
   Increased perimeter
   = length + 2 + width + 2 + length + 2 + width + 2
   = length + width + length + width + 2 + 2 + 2 + 2
   = **perimeter + 8 cm**
8. Length of DE = 6 cm + 2 cm = 8 cm
   Length of FG = 8 cm + 2 cm = 10 cm
   Area of the largest square
   = 10 cm × 10 cm
   = **100 cm²**
9. Observe that the area of the smaller square is half the area of the bigger square.

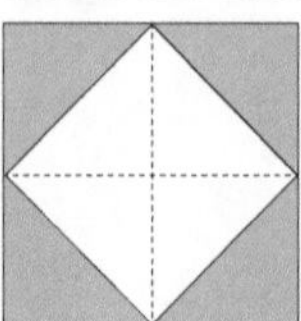

   Area of shaded region = Half area of bigger square
   $= \frac{1}{2} \times 8 \times 8$ cm²
   = **32 cm²**
10. Perimeter of square Q = 8 cm × 4
    = 32 cm
    Perimeter of rectangle P
    = 32 cm
    Length and width of rectangle P
    = 32 cm ÷ 2
    = 16 cm
    Length of rectangle P = 16 cm – 6 cm
    = 10 cm
    Area of rectangle P = 10 cm × 6 cm
    = **60 cm²**
11. Area of small square
    = 3 cm × 3 cm
    = 9 cm²
    Area of big square
    = 9 cm² × 9
    = 81 cm²
    Length of big square = 9 cm
    Perimeter of big square = 9 cm × 4
    = 36 cm
    Perimeter of small square
    = 3 cm × 4
    = 12 cm
    Length of wire = 36 cm + 12 cm
    = **48 cm**
12. Perimeter = length + width + length + width
    2 sets of length and width ⟶ 52 cm
    1 set of length and width
    ⟶ 52 cm ÷ 2 = 26 cm
    Use the guess and check method.
    Look for 2 numbers that add up to 26.

Guess	Length	Width	Area	Is the area 144 cm^2?
1st	16 cm	10 cm	160 cm^2	No
2nd	20 cm	6 cm	120 cm^2	No
3rd	18 cm	8 cm	144 cm^2	Yes

Length of retangle = **18 cm**
Width of retangle = **8 cm**

Challenging Problems (pp. 127–132)

1. Perimeter of the figure
   = 2 × (16 cm + 10 cm)
   = 2 × 26 cm
   = **52 cm**
2. Perimeter of the figure
   = 2 × (25 cm + 12 cm)
   = 2 × 37 cm
   = **74 cm**
   Note: The length 10 cm is redundant.
3. Total length of the bold lines
   = length + width
   = 12 cm + 8 cm
   = **20 cm**
   Note: The given lengths of 5 cm and 2 cm are redundant.
4. Area of unshaded region
   = Area of square A + Area of rectangle B – 2 × Area of shaded rectangle
   = 5 cm x 5 cm + 6 cm × 3 cm – 2 × 2 cm × 1 cm
   = 25 cm^2 + 18 cm^2 – 4 cm^2
   = 39 cm^2
   The area of the unshaded region of square A and rectangle B is **39 cm^2**.
5. $A = l \times w$
   $A' = 2l \times 2w = 4 \times l \times w = 4 \times A$
   The new surface area of the room will be 4 times the surface area of the first room.
   Cost of tiling the new room
   = 4 x $400 = $1,600
   He will charge **$1,600** to tile the other room.
6. The flat shape will look as follows:

   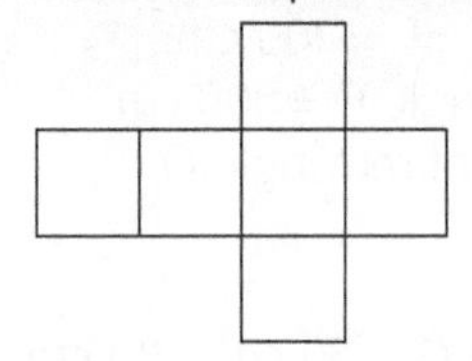

   Perimeter of the resulting shape
   = 14 × length of one side of a square
   = 14 × 1 cm
   = **14 cm**
7. Area of square *EFGH*
   = $\frac{1}{2}$ × square *ABCD*
   = $\frac{1}{2}$ × 2 cm × 2 cm
   = 2 cm^2
   Area of square *IJKL*
   = $\frac{1}{2}$ × square *EFGH*
   = $\frac{1}{2}$ × 2 cm^2
   = **1 cm^2**
8. Perimeter of square A = 12 cm × 4
   = 48 cm

   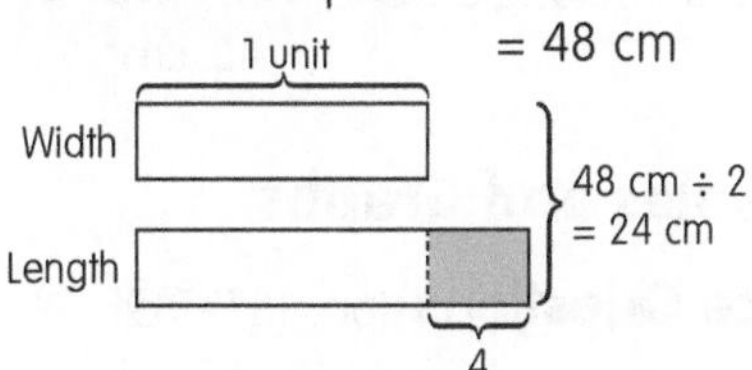

   2 units ⟶ 24 cm – 4 cm = 20 cm
   1 unit ⟶ 20 cm ÷ 2 = 10 cm
   Width of rectangle B = **10 cm**
9. (a) Answers vary. Two examples are:

   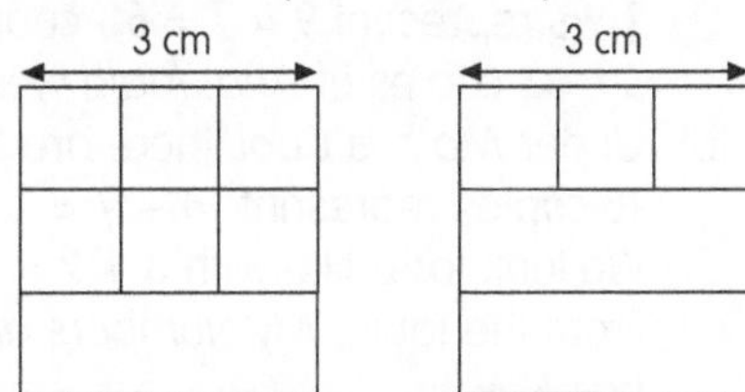

   6 squares, 1 rectangle;
   or **3 squares, 2 rectangles**

   (b) Answers vary. One example is:

   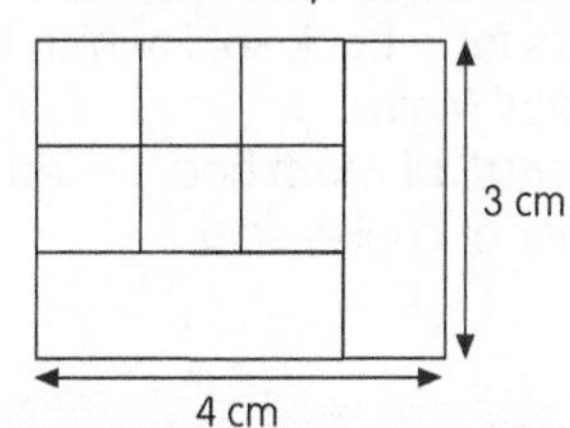

   6 squares, 2 rectangles

10. Perimeter of square P = 4 × 25 cm
= 100 cm
Perimeter of rectangle Q = 100 cm
Length and width of rectangle Q
= 100 cm ÷ 2
= 50 cm
Width of rectangle Q = 50 cm − 30 cm
= 20 cm
Area of rectangle Q = 30 cm × 20 cm
= **600 cm²**

11. Length of paper
= 15 cm + 50 cm + 12 cm
= 77 cm
Area of paper = 77 × 50
= **3,850 cm²**

12. 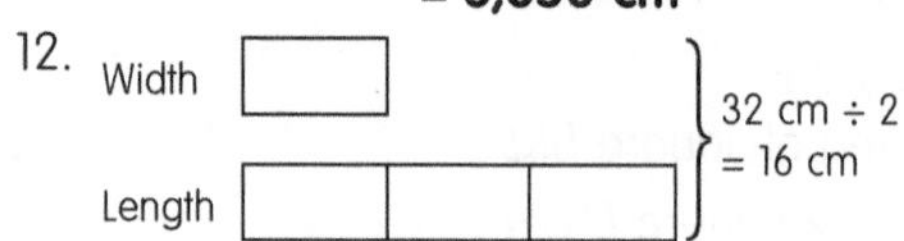

4 units ⟶ 16 cm
1 unit ⟶ 16 cm ÷ 4 = 4 cm
3 units ⟶ 3 × 4 cm = 12 cm
Area of rectangle *PQRS* = 12 cm × 4 cm
= **48 cm²**

10 Tables and Graphs

Practice Questions (pp. 137–139)

1. **Flight 80**
2. (a) **10** (b) **21**
   (c) **5** (d) **B** and **D**
3. (a) There are 7 ★'s under *Aha! Math.*
   1 ★ represents 9 copies.
   7 ★s represent 9 × 7 = 63 copies.
   So, **63** copies of *Aha! Math* were sold.
   (b) Under *Math Is Cool*, there are 3★.
   18 copies represent 18 ÷ 9 = 2 ★'s.
   We look for a title with 3 + 2 = 5 ★.
   From the table, *My Numbers and I* has 5 ★.
   So, the book sold was ***My Numbers and I.***
   (c) From the table, 2 is the least number of stars for a book sold, which is *Beautiful Math.*
   So, ***Beautiful Math*** had the least number of copies sold.
4. (a)

Mode of transport	Bicycle	Train	Bus	Walking	Car
Number of students	**320**	**140**	**470**	**40**	**380**

   (b) (i) **Bus** (ii) **Walking**
   (iii) **1,350** students (iv) **90** students
   (v) **280** students
   (vi) Bus: 470; Car: 380
   470 + 380 = 850
   850 ÷ 2 = 425
   470 − 425 = 45 or 425 − 380 = 45
   So, **45** students would need to travel by car instead of by bus.

Challenging Questions (pp. 143–146)

1. (a) 321 − 65 − 87 − 84 = 85
   85 students in Grade 3 attend English lessons.
   (b) 65 − 52 = 13
   13 more Grade 4 students attend English lessons than science lessons.
   (c) Students who attend math lessons
   = 123 + 131 + 97 + 136 = 487
   Students who attend science lessons
   = 82 + 52 + 64 + 60 = 258
   487 − 258 = 229
   229 more students attend math lessons than science lessons.
2. (a) **24** girls (b) **24** boys
   (c) **60** students (d) **20** boys
3. (a)

Activity	Number of boys	Number of girls	Total
Badminton	13	8	21
Tennis	**6**	6	12
Soccer	11	**5**	16
Basketball	9	4	**13**
Swimming	**7**	10	17
Total	**46**	**33**	**79**

   (b) (i) **Tennis** (ii) **Badminton**
   (iii) **3** girls (iv) **5** boys
   (v) **79** students

4. (a) **60** points
   (b) From the graph,
   22 students scored 80, and
   14 students scored 90.
   22 + 14 = 36
   So, **36** students obtained grade A.
   (c) 40 + 46 + 64 + 22 + 14 = 186
   So, **186** students passed the examination.
5. (a) 65 people, of which 24 are adults, chose computer games.
   65 − 24 = 41
   So, **41** children chose computer games.
   (b) 51 + 37 + 24 + 45 = 157
   The total number of adults was **157**.
   (c) Number of children who chose console games
   = 149 − 32 − 41
   = 76

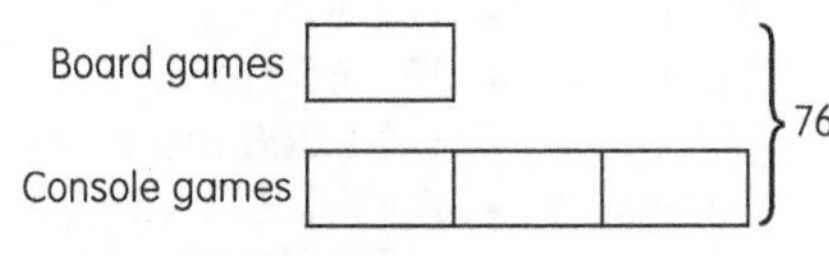

4 units ⟶ 76
1 unit ⟶ 76 ÷ 4 = 19
3 units ⟶ 3 × 19 = 57
Number of children who chose console games = **57**

11 Volume

Practice Questions (pp. 150–153)

1. The solid is made up of 12 cubes.
   Volume of the solid = 12 × Volume of 1 cube
   = 12 × 2 cm × 2 cm × 2 cm
   = **96 cm³**
2. Height of water needed = 20 cm − 9 cm
   = 11 cm
   Volume of water needed
   = 36 cm × 12 cm × 11 cm
   = 4,752 cm³
   = **4 L 752 mL**
3. Decrease in height of water
   = 15 cm − 12 cm
   = 3 cm
   Volume of water poured out
   = 40 cm × 25 cm × 3 cm
   = 3,000 cm³
   = **3 L**
4. Volume of water in container at first
   = 45 cm × 30 cm × 7 cm
   = 9450 cm³
   Volume of water in container now
   = 9,450 cm³ + 1,340 cm³
   = **10,790 cm³**
5. Volume of liquid in the first container
   = 26 cm × 21 cm × 15 cm
   = 8,190 cm³
   Volume of liquid in the second container
   = 30 cm × 25 cm × 18 cm
   = 13,500 cm³
   Volume of additional liquid that the second container can hold
   = 13,500 cm³ − 8,190 cm³
   = **5,310 cm³**
6. Volume of 1-cm cube
   = 1 cm × 1 cm × 1 cm
   = 1 cm³
   Volume of 6-cm cube
   = 6 cm × 6 cm × 6 cm
   = 216 cm³
   Volume of 8-cm cube
   = 8 cm × 8 cm × 8 cm
   = 512 cm³
   Volume of bigger cube
   = 1 cm³ + 216 cm³ + 512 cm³
   = 729 cm³
   729 = 9 × 9 × 9
   Length of new cube = **9 cm**
7. Volume of water in container
   = 32 cm × 18 cm × 12 cm
   = 6,912 cm³
   9 L 35 mL = 9,035 cm³
   Capacity of container
   = 6,912 cm³ + 9,035 cm³ − 4,247 cm³
   = **11,700 cm³**
8. (a) Fraction of tank that contains 5 L of water = $\frac{3}{4} - \frac{2}{3} = \frac{9}{12} - \frac{8}{12}$
   $= \frac{1}{12}$
   Capacity of tank = 12 × 5 L
   = **60 L**
   (b) Fraction of tank that is not filled with water = $1 - \frac{3}{4}$
   $= \frac{1}{4}$
   Volume of additional water needed
   $= \frac{1}{4} \times 60$ L
   = **15 L**

9. The dimensions of the tank are multiples of the dimensions of the rectangular container of oil.
   Number of rectangular containers of oil
   $= \frac{16 \times 18 \times 12}{8 \times 9 \times 3}$
   $= 2 \times 2 \times 4$
   = **16**

10. The dimensions of the block are multiples of 2.
    Maximum number of cubes $= \frac{18 \times 24 \times 6}{2 \times 2 \times 2}$
    $= 9 \times 12 \times 3$
    = **324**

Challenging Problems (pp. 155–159)

1. Length of aquarium = 36 cm
   Width of aquarium = 36 cm ÷ 2
   = 18 cm
   Height of aquarium = 18 cm ÷ 2
   = 9 cm
   Capacity of aquarium
   = 36 cm × 18 cm × 9 cm
   = **5,832 cm^3**

2. 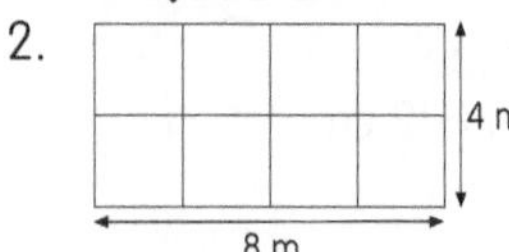

   Length of each cube = 8 m ÷ 4 = **2 m**

3. Not all dimensions of the wooden block are multiples of 3.
   Round down each dimension to the nearest multiple of 3.
   $19 \approx 18$
   $22 \approx 21$
   Maximum number of 3-cm cubes
   $= \frac{18 \times 21 \times 30}{3 \times 3 \times 3} = 6 \times 7 \times 10$
   = **420**

4. Not all dimensions of the rectangular prism are multiples of 3.
   Round down each dimension to the nearest multiple of 3.
   $23 \approx 21$
   $13 \approx 12$
   Maximum number of cubes
   $= \frac{21 \times 18 \times 12}{3 \times 3 \times 3} = 7 \times 6 \times 4$
   = **168**

5. Volume of water in 8 buckets
   = 34 L − 1.6 L
   = 32.4 L
   Capacity of 1 bucket = 32.4 L ÷ 8
   = 4.05 L
   = **4 L 50 mL**

6. Total number of 2-cm cubes required
   $= \frac{8 \times 8 \times 8}{2 \times 2 \times 2} = 4 \times 4 \times 4 = 64$
   Number of additional 2-cm cubes required
   = 64 − 6
   = **58**

7. Tank P
   Tank Q
   Tank R
   12 L 624 ml

   3 units ⟶ 12 L 624 mL
   1 unit ⟶ 12 L 624 mL ÷ 3
   = 4 L 208 mL
   2 units ⟶ 2 × 4 L 208 mL
   = 8 L 416 mL
   Capacity of tank P = **8 L 416 mL**

8. Multiples of 240: 240, 480, 720, 960, 1,200
   Multiples of 600: 600, 1,200, 1,800
   Least possible volume = 1,200 mL
   Least possible number of packs of detergent = **5**
   Least possible number of bottles of detergent = **2**

9. Volume of 1-cm cube
   = 1 cm × 1 cm × 1 cm
   = 1 cm^3
   Volume of 12-cm cube
   = 12 cm × 12 cm × 12 cm
   = 1,728 cm^3
   Volume of the two cubes
   = 1 cm^3 + 1,728 cm^3
   = 1,729 cm^3
   1,729 = 1,000 + 729
   $= 10 \times 10 \times 10 + 9 \times 9 \times 9$
   Lengths of the two new cubes: **9 cm** and **10 cm**

10. $2 \text{ L} = 2 \times 1{,}000 \text{ cm}^3$
Volume of water used to fill 16 bottles
$= 16 \times 2 \text{ L}$
$= 16 \times 2 \times 1{,}000 \text{ cm}^3$

Decrease in the height of water in the tank $= \frac{16 \times 2 \times 1{,}000}{100 \times 80}$ cm
$= 4$ cm
Height of water in the container after all the bottles were filled = 50 cm − 4 cm
= **46 cm**

11. Capacity of rectangular container
= 45 cm × 38 cm × 8 cm
Fraction of tank filled with $\frac{1}{3}$ of the water
$= \frac{1}{2} \times \frac{1}{3}$
$= \frac{1}{6}$
Fraction of tank filled with water after $\frac{1}{3}$ of the water has been poured out
$= \frac{1}{2} - \frac{1}{6}$
$= \frac{1}{3}$
Fraction of tank needed to be filled with water $= 1 - \frac{1}{3}$
$= \frac{2}{3}$
Volume of water that must be added
$= \frac{2}{3} \times 45 \text{ cm} \times 38 \text{ cm} \times 8 \text{ cm}$
$=$ **9,120 cm³**

12 Solid Figures

Practice Questions (pp. 162–167)

1. (a) **4** cubes (b) **4** cubes
2. (a) **7** cubes (b) **10** cubes
3. **9** cubes
4. (a) **10** cubes (b) **10** cubes

5.

Solid figure	Number of flat surfaces	Number of curved surfaces
Cube	6	0
Rectangular prism	**6**	**0**
Triangular pyramid	**4**	**0**
Square pyramid	**5**	**0**
Cone	**1**	**1**
Cylinder	**2**	**1**
Sphere	**0**	**1**

6.

Type of prism	Number of sides of the base	Number of rectangular faces
Triangular prism	3	3
Square prism	**4**	**4**
Rectangular prism	**4**	**6**
Pentagonal prism	**5**	**5**
Hexagonal prism	**6**	**6**

7.

Type of pyramid	Number of sides of the base	Number of triangular faces
Triangular pyramid	3	3
Square pyramid	**4**	**4**
Rectangular pyramid	**4**	**4**
Pentagonal pyramid	**5**	**5**
Hexagonal pyramid	**6**	**6**

8. **D** and **F**

Challenging Problems (pp. 170)

1. **6** blocks
2. **10** faces
3. **4 faces**, **4 vertices**, and **6 edges**

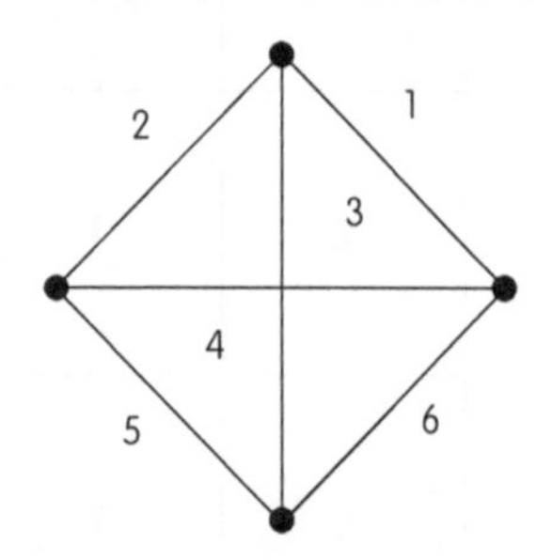

13 Review Questions 1

Practice Questions (pp. 172–175)

1. (a) Area of figure = area of 15 squares
= 15 × 2 cm × 2 cm
= **60 cm²**

(b) Perimeter of figure
= Length of 20 sides of a square
= 20 × 2 cm
= **40 cm**

2. Perimeter of figure
= 4 + 4 + 5 + 5 + 5 + 5
= **28 cm**

3. *Method 1*
$\frac{2}{6} = \frac{1}{3} = \frac{\boxed{3}}{9}$
Method 2
2 × 9 = 6 × *
* = 2 × 9 ÷ 6 = **3**

4. Factors of 15 are 1, 3, 5, and 15.
The sum = 1 + 3 + 5 + 15 = **24**

5. Perimeter of square hall = 60 m
Length of one side of the square
= 60 m ÷ 4 = 15 m
Area of square
= 15 m × 15 m
= **225 m²**

6. Length of rectangular cardboard
= Area ÷ width
= 156 cm² ÷ 12 cm
= 13 cm
Perimeter of rectangular cardboard
= 2 × (13 cm + 12 cm)
= 2 × 25 cm
= **50 cm**

7. Length + width = 34 ÷ 2 = 17 m
Length of corridor = 17 – 2 = 15 m
Area of corridor
= Length × width
= 15 m × 2 m
= **30 m²**
1 m² of carpeting costs $68
30 m² of carpeting cost 30 x $68
= $2,040
It would cost **$2,040** to carpet the corridor.

8. Area of big rectangle = 14 cm × 9 cm
= 126 cm²
Area of small rectangle = 9 cm × 6 cm
= 54 cm²
Area of shaded region
= 126 cm² – 54 cm²
= **72 cm²**

9. 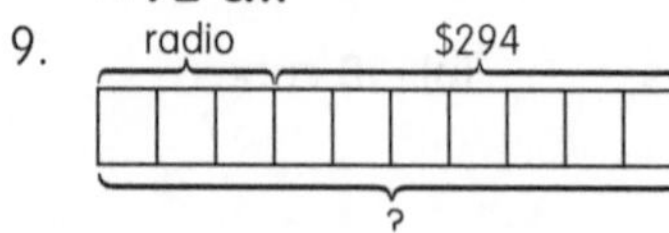

7 units ⟶ $294
1 unit ⟶ $294 ÷ 7 = $42
10 units ⟶ 10 × $42 = $420
Amount of money Mr. Frost had at first
= **$420**

10. Number of intervals = $120 \div 12 = 10$
Number of saplings
= Number of intervals + 1
= 10 + 1
= **11**

11.

Men: 1 unit (156)
Women: 3 units
Children: 6 units

1 unit ⟶ 156
10 units ⟶ $10 \times 156 = 1{,}560$
Number of rows required = $1{,}560 \div 8$
= **195**

Challenging Problems (pp. 177–180)

1. $45 = 1 \times 45$ (1 album of 45 stickers)
$= 3 \times 15$ (3 albums of 15 stickers each)
$= 5 \times 9$ (5 albums of 9 stickers each)
$= 9 \times 5$ (9 albums of 5 stickers each)
$= 15 \times 3$ (15 albums of 3 stickers each)
$= 45 \times 1$ (45 albums of 1 sticker each)
The possible numbers of albums are:
1, **3**, **5**, **9**, **15**, or **45**

2. $69 + 2 × $7.50 = $69 + $15
= $84
$100 – $84 = $16
Amount of money left = $16
16 = $2.50 × 6 + 1
Jane could buy **6** handkerchiefs with $1 left.

3. Multiples of 3: 3, 6, 9, 12, 15, 18, 21, 24, 27, 30, 33, 36, 39, ...
Multiples of 4: 4, 8, 12, 16, 20, 24, 28, 32, 36, 40, ...
Multiples of 5: 5, 10, 15, 20, 25, 30, 35, 40, ...
From the three lists, Peter is **33 years old**.

4. ◆◆◆ + □□□ = 42
(◆ + □) + (◆ + □) + (◆ + □) = 42
3 × (◆ + □) = 42
◆ + □ = $42 \div 3 = 14$
The total value of ◆ + □ is **14**.

5. ■ + ● + ▲ = 45 (■ + ● = 20)
▲ = 45 – 20
= 25

■ + ● + ▲ = 45 (● + ▲ = 33)
■ = 45 – 33
= 12
■ + ▲ = 12 + 25
= **37**

6.

Joe: 1 unit
Bob: 1 unit + 15
Andy: 2 units + 15 + 25
Total: 535

4 units ⟶ 535 – 15 – 15 – 25 = 480
1 unit ⟶ $480 \div 4 = 120$
Number of marbles Bob has = 120 + 15
= **135**

7.

Ai Ling: 137
Li Yan: 3 units + 33

$3 \times 137 + 33 = 444$
Li Yan had **444** stamps.

8. Before

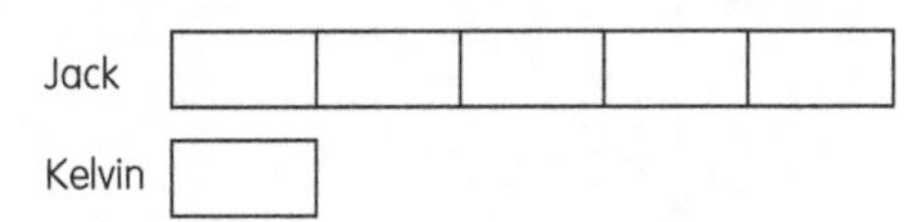

After

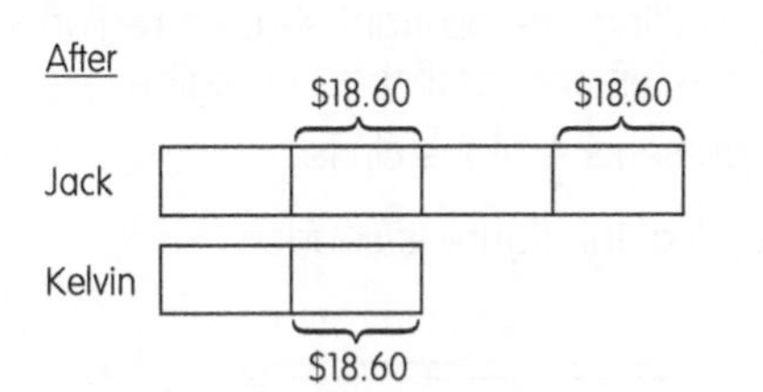

1 unit ⟶ $18.60
4 units ⟶ 4 × $18.60 = $74.40
Amount of money Sam had
= $74.40 – $12.90
= **$61.50**

9. If all 28 animals were ducks, then there would be $28 \times 2 = 56$ legs.
So, the extra $94 - 56 = 38$ legs must have come from the sheep.
1 sheep has 2 more legs than 1 duck.
There are $38 \div 2 =$ **19** sheep and $28 - 19 = 9$ ducks.
Check: $19 \times 4 + 9 \times 2 = 76 + 18 = 94$
10. **3.56**

14 Review Questions 2

Practice Questions (pp. 183–186)

1. (a) 17,649

17,600 17,650 17,700

Greatest possible monthly salary
= 1 unit below the midpoint figure
= **$17,649**

(b) 17,500 17,550 17,600

Smallest possible monthly salary
= Midpoint figure
= **$17,550**

2. West $\xrightarrow[\text{counterclockwise}]{\frac{3}{4}\text{-turn}}$ North $\xrightarrow[\text{clockwise}]{135^\circ}$ South-East

She was facing **South-East** at first.

3.

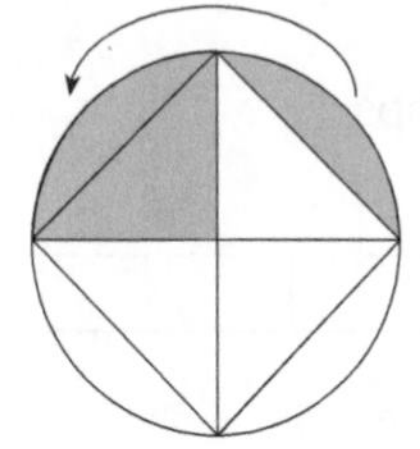

By shifting the top-right shaded region to the left, the total shaded region represents $\frac{1}{4}$ of the circle.
So, $\frac{\mathbf{1}}{\mathbf{4}}$ of the figure is shaded.

4.

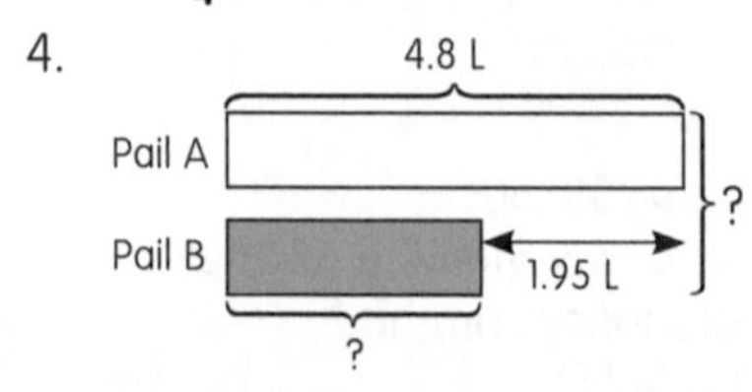

$4.8 \times 2 - 1.95 = 9.6 - 1.95 = 7.65$
7.65 L of water are in the container.

5. $5 \times 6 = 30$
Multiples of 30: 30, 60, 90, ...
$3 + 0 = 3$ ✗
$6 + 0 = 6$ ✗
$9 + 0 = 9$ ✓
The 2-digit number is **90**.

6. Perimeter of rectangle = 20 cm
Length + width = 20 m ÷ 2 = 10 cm
Length = 10 cm – 3 cm = 7 cm
Area of the rectangle = Length × width
= 7 cm × 3 cm
= **21 cm²**

7. Area of 8 squares = 200 cm²
Area of 1 square = 200 cm² ÷ 8 = 25 cm²
Length of each square = 5 cm
Perimeter of figure = 20 × 5 cm = **100 cm**

8. $48 + 41 + 25 = 114$
$114 \div 3 = 38$
Each will have $38.
$48 - 38 = 10$
Alan must give Cary **$10**.
$41 - 38 = 3$
Ben must give Cary **$3**.

9. (a) **0.2** × **3** (b) **0.4** × **6**
(c) **0.4** × **8**

10. (a) Length of rectangle A
= 192 ÷ 12 = 16 cm
Width of rectangle B
= Width of rectangle A
= 12 cm

16
Length of A
Length of B
?

2 units → 16
1 unit → 8
3 units → 3 × 8 = 24
Area of rectangle B
= 24 cm × 12 cm
= **288 cm²**

(b) Length of the figure = Length of rectangle A + Length of rectangle B
= 16 cm + 24 cm
= 40 cm
Width of the figure = 12 cm
Perimeter of the figure
= 40 + 12 + 40 + 12
= **104 cm**

Challenging Problems (pp. 188–191)

1.

Type of square	Number of such squares
	4
	4
	1
	1
Total	**10**

2. $\frac{1}{2}$

3. Area of shaded region
= Area of 16 squares – Area of 6 squares
= Area of 10 squares
= 10 x 1 cm x 1 cm
= **10 cm²**

4. One method of solution is as follows:
3 O's 3 O's 3 O's 3 O's (+ 2 O's)
+1 +1 +1 +1
4 O's 4 O's 4 O's 4 O's [– 2 O's]
The 2 extra oranges are given to 2 children, so that both of them have now 4 oranges each.
Since there are 2 oranges short, there must be another 2 more children, each with 3 oranges.
So, there are 2 + 2 = **4** children in the group.
There are 3 × 4 + 2 = 14 oranges in all.

5. 169 = 13 × 13
Length of one side of square *PQRS*
= 13 cm
Length of *TR*
= Length of *SR* – Length of *ST*
= 13 cm – 5 cm
= **8 cm**

6. 16 = 4 × 4
Length of one side of the shaded square
= 4 cm
121 = 11 × 11
Length of one side of the square *ABCD*
= 11 cm
Length of *AE*
= Length of *AB* – Length of *EB*
= 11 cm – 4 cm
= **7 cm**

7. (a)

Booth	Chocolate muffin (80¢)		Strawberry muffin (70¢)		Total amount
	Number sold	Amount collected	Number sold	Amount collected	
A	12	$9.60	20	$14.00	$23.60
B	18	**$14.40**	12	**$8.40**	**$22.80**
C	25	**$20.00**	15	**$10.50**	**$30.50**
D	30	**$24.00**	14	**$9.80**	**$33.80**
E	18	**$14.40**	16	**$11.20**	**$25.60**
Total	**103**	**$82.40**	**77**	**$53.90**	**$136.30**

(b) (i) Under the "Number sold" column for Chocolate muffin, the least number is **12**, which is for Booth A. So, Booth **A** sold the least number of chocolate muffins.

(ii) Under then "Number sold" column for Strawberry muffin, the highest number is 20, which is also for Booth A.
So, Booth **A** sold the most number of strawberry muffins.

(iii) Under the "Total amount" column, the least amount is $22.80, which is for Booth B.
So, Booth **B** collected the least amount of money.

(iv) Under the "Total amount" column, the highest amount is $33.80, which is for Booth D.
So, Booth **D** collected the most amount of money.

8.

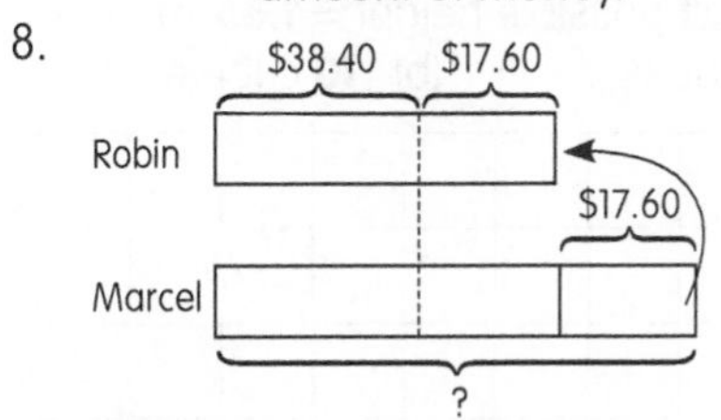

Amount of money Marcel had in the beginning = $38.40 + $17.60 + $17.60
= **$73.60**

9. (a) If Veronica bought all 15 pencils, the total cost would be 15 × 25¢ = 375¢ = \$3.75
This means that the extra \$4.65 – \$3.75 = \$0.90 = 90¢ must have come from the pens.
1 pen costs 40¢ – 25¢ = 15¢ more than 1 pencil.
So there are 90¢ ÷ 15¢ = 6 pens and 15 – 6 = 9 pencils.
She bought **9** pencils.
(b) 1 pen costs 40¢
6 pens cost 6 × 40¢ = 240¢ = **\$2.40**

10. To obtain the smallest possible number of cubes, the dimension of each cube must be as large as possible. The highest common factor of 60, 72, and 48 is required.
Highest common factor of 60, 72 and 48 = 12
Smallest possible number of cubes
$= \frac{60}{12} \times \frac{72}{12} \times \frac{48}{12} = 5 \times 6 \times 4$
$= \mathbf{120}$

15 Review Questions 3

Practice Questions (pp. 193–196)

1. (a) 1.7   1.74 1.75   1.8
Greatest possible height = **1.74 m**
(b) 1.6   1.65   1.7
Least possible height = **1.65 m**

2. (a) **7** cubes (b) **10** cubes

3.

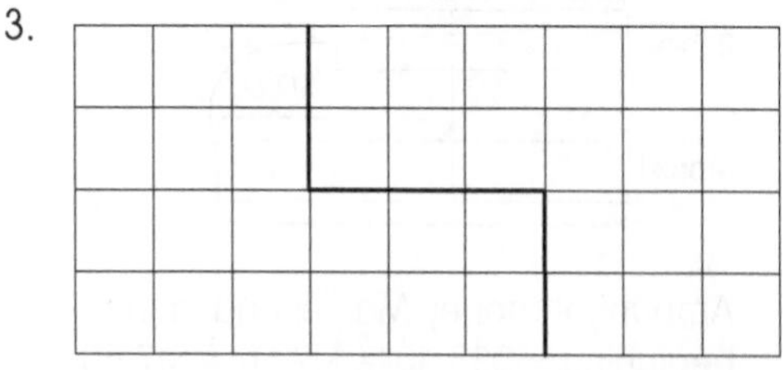

4. (a) (i) $m\angle a =$ **115°** (ii) $m\angle b =$ **65°**
(iii) $m\angle c =$ **115°** (iv) $m\angle d =$ **65°**
(v) $m\angle p =$ **115°** (vi) $m\angle q =$ **65°**
(vii) $m\angle r =$ **115°** (viii) $m\angle s =$ **65°**
(b) **c**, **p**, and **r**

5. Henry: 1.54 m
Abraham: 0.08 m more; ?

8 cm = 0.08 m
Height of Abraham = 1.54 m + 0.08 m
= **1.62 m**

6. Cost of 2 pairs of sandals
= \$72 – \$27.60
= \$44.40
Cost of 1 pair of sandals = \$44.40 ÷ 2
= **\$22.20**

7. Area of shaded region
$= \frac{3}{4} \times$ area of square
$= \frac{3}{4} \times 20\ \text{cm}^2$
$= \mathbf{300\ cm^2}$

8. Area of square cardboard
= 11 cm × 11 cm
= 121 cm^2
Area of 4 smaller squares
= 4 × 6 cm
= 24 cm^2
Area of remaining cardboard
= 121 cm^2 – 24 cm^2
= **97 cm^2**

9. (a) **1.5 ÷ 5** (b) **3.2 ÷ 4**
(c) **2.4 ÷ 2** (d) **3.2 ÷ 2**

10. \$96: Table | Table | Chair | Chair | Chair
\$96: Table | Table | Table | Table

Cost of 1 table = \$96 ÷ 4 = \$24
Cost of 2 tables = \$48
Cost of 3 chairs = \$48
Cost of 1 chair = \$48 ÷ 3
= \$16
Cost of 5 chairs = 5 × \$16
= **\$80**

Challenging Problems (pp. 198–201)

1. 56 × 9 = 56 × 8 + 56
57 × 8 = 56 × 8 + 8
Greater value: **56 × 9**

2. 4, 7, 13, 22, ___, 49
3 6 9 12 15

Method 1
Missing number = 22 + 12
= **34**

Method 2
Missing number = 49 − 15
= **34**

3. 2 = 2
$2 \times 2 = 4$
$2 \times 2 \times 2 = 8$
(or 2×4 – product of the previous 2 numbers)
$2 \times 2 \times 2 \times 2 \times 2 = 32$
(or 4×8 – product of the previous 2 numbers)
$2 \times 2 \times 2 \times 2 \times 2 \times 2 \times 2 \times 2 =$ **256**
(or 8×32 – product of the previous 2 numbers)
$\underbrace{2 \times 2 \times 2 \times \ldots \times 2}_{13\ 2\text{'s}} = 8{,}192$
(or 32×256 – product of the previous 2 numbers)

4. If P = 5, then $555 \times 3 = 1{,}665$
Q = **6**

5.
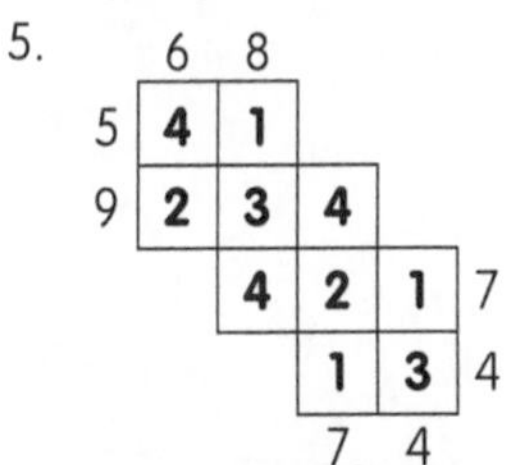

6. Length of *DE* = 15 − 7 = 8 cm
Area of shaded figure = $20 \times 15 - 5 \times 8$
= 260 cm^2
Area of rectangle *ABHG* = $20 \times BH$
$260 = 20 \times BH$
$BH = 260 \div 20 = 13$
Length of *BH* = **13 cm**

7.
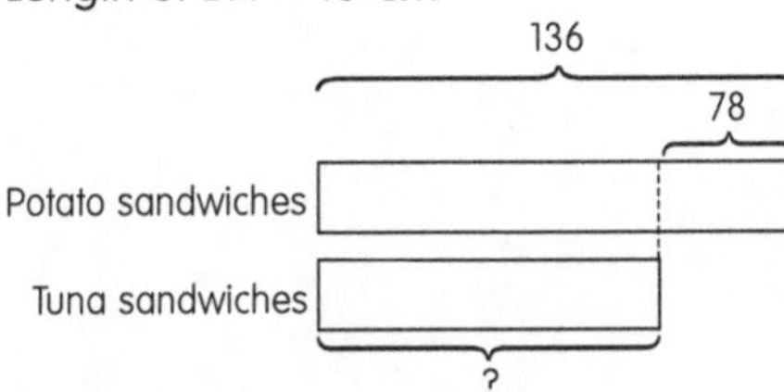

Number of tuna sandwiches sold on Saturday = 136 − 78
= 58
Total number of sandwiches sold on Saturday = 136 + 58
= 194
Total number of sandwiches sold on Sunday = $194 \div 2$
= 97
Number of sandwiches sold over two days = 194 + 97
= **291**

8. (a) Perimeter
= $2 \times$ (length + width) = 18 cm
Length + width = 18 cm $\div$ 2 = 9 cm

Length	Breadth	Area
5	4	20
6	3	18
7	2	14
8	1	8

Greatest possible area of rectangle
= 4 cm $\times$ 5 cm
= **20 cm²**

(b) Smallest possible area of rectangle
= 1 cm $\times$ 8 cm
= **8 cm²**

9.
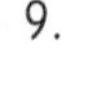
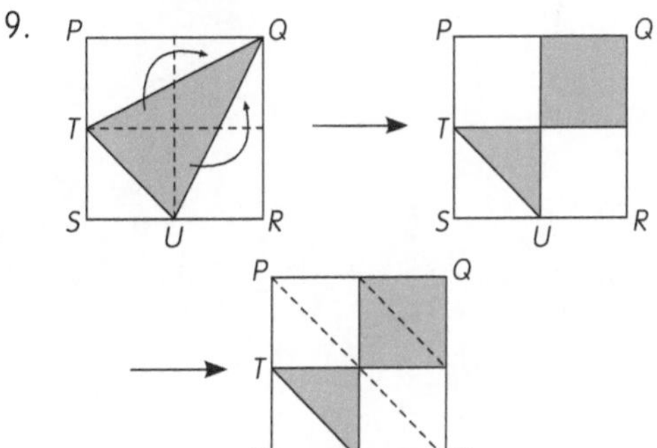

3 out of 8 parts are shaded.
Fraction = $\mathbf{\frac{3}{8}}$

10. Suppose there were 13 quarters.
Total value of the quarters = $13 \times \$0.25$
= \$3.25
One half-dollar is 25¢ more than one quarter.
\$4.50 − \$3.25 = \$1.25
\$1.25 = 125¢
\$0.25 = 25¢
Number of half-dollars = 125¢ $\div$ 25¢
= **5**
Number of quarters = 13 − 5
= **8**
Check: $5 \times \$0.50 + 8 \times \$0.25 = \$4.50$

Blank

Blank

Blank